D0209474

Aromatic Substitution Reactions

Prentice-Hall Foundations of Modern Organic Chemistry Series

KENNETH L. RINEHART, JR., Editor

Volumes published or in preparation

N. L. ALLINGER and J. ALLINGER	**STRUCTURES OF ORGANIC MOLECULES**
TRAHANOVSKY	**FUNCTIONAL GROUPS IN ORGANIC COMPOUNDS**
STEWART	**THE INVESTIGATION OF ORGANIC REACTIONS**
SAUNDERS	**IONIC ALIPHATIC REACTIONS**
GUTSCHE	**CHEMISTRY OF CARBONYL COMPOUNDS**
PRYOR	**INTRODUCTION TO FREE RADICAL CHEMISTRY**
STOCK	**AROMATIC SUBSTITUTION REACTIONS**
RINEHART	**OXIDATION AND REDUCTION OF ORGANIC COMPOUNDS**
DEPUY	**MOLECULAR REACTIONS AND PHOTOCHEMISTRY**
IRELAND	**ORGANIC SYNTHESIS**
DYER	**APPLICATIONS OF ABSORPTION SPECTROSCOPY OF ORGANIC COMPOUNDS**
BATES and SCHAEFER	**RESEARCH IN ORGANIC CHEMISTRY**
TAYLOR	**HETEROCYCLIC COMPOUNDS**
HILL	**COMPOUNDS OF NATURE**
BARKER	**ORGANIC CHEMISTRY OF BIOLOGICAL COMPOUNDS**
STILLE	**INDUSTRIAL ORGANIC CHEMISTRY**
SIM, RINEHART NORMAN, and GILBERT	**X-RAY CRYSTALLOGRAPHY, MASS SPECTROMETRY, AND ELECTRON SPIN RESONANCE OF ORGANIC COMPOUNDS**
BATTISTE	**NON-BENZENOID AROMATIC COMPOUNDS**

AROMATIC SUBSTITUTION REACTIONS

Leon M. Stock

Department of Chemistry
University of Chicago

PRENTICE-HALL, INC., ENGLEWOOD CLIFFS, N.J.

Library of Congress Catalog Card Number 68-13875
Printed in the United States of America

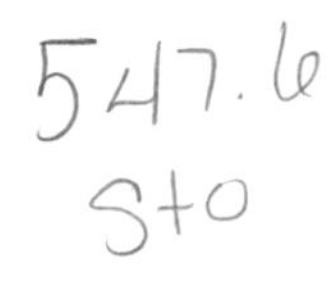

PRENTICE-HALL INTERNATIONAL, INC., London
PRENTICE-HALL OF AUSTRALIA, PTY. LTD., Sydney
PRENTICE-HALL OF CANADA, LTD., Toronto
PRENTICE-HALL OF INDIA PRIVATE LTD., New Delhi
PRENTICE-HALL OF JAPAN, INC., Tokyo

Current Printing (last digit):
10 9 8 7 6 5 4 3 2

To Mary, Katie, and Ann

Foreword

Organic chemistry today is a rapidly changing subject whose almost frenetic activity is attested by the countless research papers appearing in established and new journals and by the proliferation of monographs and reviews on all aspects of the field. This expansion of knowledge poses pedagogical problems; it is difficult for a single organic chemist to be cognizant of developments over the whole field and probably no one or pair of chemists can honestly claim expertise or even competence in all the important areas of the subject.

Yet the same rapid expansion of knowledge—in theoretical organic chemistry, in stereochemistry, in reaction mechanisms, in complex organic structures, in the application of physical methods—provides a remarkable opportunity for the teacher of organic chemistry to present the subject as it really is, an active field of research in which new answers are currently being sought and found.

To take advantage of recent developments in organic chemistry and to provide an authoritative treatment of the subject at an undergraduate level, the *Foundations of Modern Organic Chemistry Series* has been established. The series consists of a number of short, authoritative books, each written at an elementary level but in depth by an organic chemistry teacher active in research and familiar with the subject of the volume. Most of the authors have published research papers in the fields on which they are writing. The books will present the topics according to current knowledge of the field, and individual volumes will be revised as often as necessary to take account of subsequent developments.

The basic organization of the series is according to reaction type, rather than along the more classical lines of compound class. The first ten volumes in the series constitute a core of the material covered in nearly every one-year organic chemistry course. Of these ten, the first three are a general introduction to organic chemistry and provide a background for the next six, which deal with specific types of reactions and may be covered in any order. Each of the reaction types is presented from an elementary viewpoint, but in a depth not possible in conventional textbooks. The teacher can decide how much of a volume to cover. The tenth examines the problem of organic synthesis, employing and tying together the reactions previously studied.

The remaining volumes provide for the enormous flexibility of the series. These cover topics which are important to students of organic chemistry and are sometimes treated in the first organic course, sometimes in an intermediate course. Some teachers will wish to cover a number of these books in the one-year course; others will wish to assign some of them as outside reading; a complete intermediate organic course could be based on the eight "topics" texts taken together.

The series approach to undergraduate organic chemistry offers then the considerable advantage of an authoritative treatment by teachers active in research, of frequent revision of the most active areas, of a treatment in depth of the most fundamental material, and of nearly complete flexibility in choice of topics to be covered. Individually the volumes of the Foundations of Modern Organic Chemistry provide introductions in depth to basic areas of organic chemistry; together they comprise a contemporary survey of organic chemistry at an undergraduate level.

KENNETH L. RINEHART, JR.
University of Illinois

Preface

Several fundamental concepts appropriate in a first course in organic chemistry arise quite naturally in the discussion of the chemistry of benzene and its derivatives. In this monograph I have attempted to present some of the results that led to the development of these concepts prior to the introduction of the ideas themselves. With respect to aromaticity, it seemed reasonable to discuss the problem from a historical viewpoint to emphasize the power of simple symmetry arguments. Aromaticity and electron delocalization are subsequently discussed from the standpoint of both resonance theory and molecular orbital theory. The molecular orbital theory permits the rational discussion of the chemistry of other conjugated, unsaturated hydrocarbons and their ionic derivatives. The mechanisms of selected electrophilic, nucleophilic, and free radical substitution reactions, the elimination reaction leading to benzyne, and the remarkable rearrangement reactions of aromatic compounds are examined to illustrate the experimental approaches that are useful for the definition of the course of reactions.

Many quantitative relative rate data are now available for the electrophilic substitution reactions of monosubstituted benzenes. These results are discussed fully inasmuch as they offer a proving ground for the qualitative ideas of the polar, resonance, and steric effect theory of directive effects. In addition, these relative rate data are discussed quantitatively from the standpoint of the Brown $\rho^+\sigma^+$ relationship. A scheme for the prediction of the substitution pattern in the more highly substituted compounds based on this linear free energy approach is presented. The first six chapters of this monograph portray the chemistry of benzene and its derivations from the viewpoint of physical organic chemistry. However, the actual methods used in the laboratory and in the chemical industry for the preparation of compounds depend on many factors in addition to mechanistic considerations. Accordingly, the final chapter is devoted to a survey of preparative methods and descriptive chemistry of benzene derivatives to bridge the gap between theory and synthesis.

In conclusion, I wish to express my sincere appreciation to Professor K. L. Rinehart for his helpful and constructive criticism of the manuscript.

LEON M. STOCK

Contents

1

AROMATICITY 1

2

ELECTROPHILIC SUBSTITUTION REACTIONS 21

3

DIRECTIVE EFFECTS IN ELECTROPHILIC SUBSTITUTION REACTIONS 40

QUANTITATIVE TREATMENTS FOR BENZENE DERIVATIVES AND POLYNUCLEAR HYDROCARBONS 59

NUCLEOPHILIC SUBSTITUTION AND ELIMINATION REACTIONS 81

6

REARRANGEMENT REACTIONS 103

7

THE SYNTHETIC CHEMISTRY OF BENZENE DERIVATIVES 118

Aromatic Substitution Reactions

1
Aromaticity

1.1 INTRODUCTION

Benzene, first isolated and identified by Michael Faraday in 1825, is the parent hydrocarbon of a large class of organic molecules known as the *aromatic compounds.* The term *aromatic* was originally applied to these molecules because certain early examples such as vanillin and cinnamic acid had a pleasant fragrance. The designation has been retained, but the concept of aromaticity now has an important chemical significance. Benzene and the other aromatic molecules have high structural symmetry and are unusually stable, differing uniquely from the saturated and unsaturated molecules of the aliphatic series. The origin of the structural symmetry and stability are examined in this chapter as a prelude to the discussion of the reactions of benzene and its derivatives in subsequent chapters.

The molecular formula of benzene is C_6H_6. In 1864, Kekulé proposed that benzene be formulated as a monocyclic molecule with three double bonds. The inference of this proposal, in terms of the structural theory, is that there is a long carbon-carbon bond distance and a short carbon-carbon bond distance.

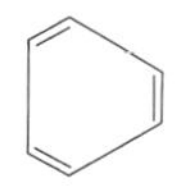

The structural theory serves a dual function. It is fundamentally a topological theory for the formulation of the arrangement of atoms in a molecule. These formulations assume an added importance in the sense that the lines connecting the nuclei are identified with the concept of the chemical bond. Ideally, the line structure of a molecule should portray the molecular topology and symbolize the chemistry of the compound. Kekulé's structure for benzene fails to accomplish these objectives. The chemistry of benzene is not accommodated by a structure with three double bonds, as discussed in Sec. 1.3. A second, even more serious problem exists. The Kekulé structure requires, according to the structural theory, that the five hydrogen atoms of a monosubstituted benzene be chemically distinct. To illustrate, the hydrogen atoms adjacent to the substituent Y are not equivalent.

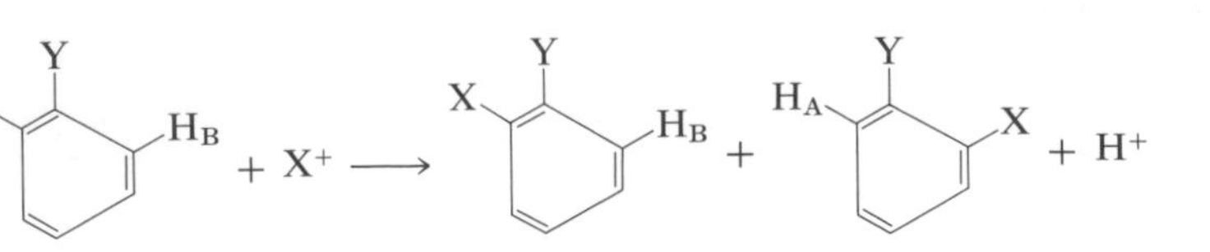

One, H_A, is separated from Y by a carbon-carbon double bond; the other H_B, is separated from Y by a carbon-carbon single bond. Thus, two 1,2-disubstituted benzenes, **A** and **B,** should form when H_A and H_B are replaced by X. Contrary to this expectation, only one 1,2-disubstituted benzene is produced. This failure of the Kekulé structure was recognized early and an extensive investigation of benzene and its derivatives was undertaken to establish the actual structure.

1.2 THE GEOMETRY OF BENZENE

In 1869–1874, Ladenburg proved that the six hydrogen atoms of benzene were equivalent. To simplify his argument, it will be assumed that the nuclei of 2-hydroxybenzoic acid are positioned as shown in **A.** The hydroxyl group of **A** was replaced by a hydrogen atom to yield benzoic acid with the carboxyl group in the 1-position (**B**). Ladenburg also decarboxylated **A** to yield hydroxybenzene (**C**). He then converted **C** to benzoic acid (**D**) with the carboxyl group in the 2-position.

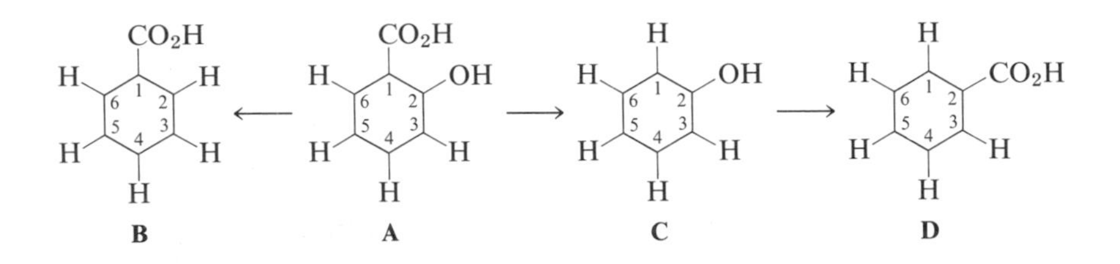

Ladenburg found that the acids, **B** and **D,** were identical. This finding indicates that the carboxyl groups occupy equivalent positions in **B** and **D** and that the hydrogen atoms replaced by the carboxyl group are also equivalent. Thus, the hydrogen atoms in the 1- and 2-positions of benzene are identical. Extension of the work revealed the equivalence of all six hydrogen atoms of benzene.

Another definitive contribution was Wroblewsky's synthesis of the "five possible" Kekulé bromobenzoic acids. The syntheses were accomplished by blocking various positions, introducing the bromo substituent at one desired site, and subsequently removing the blocking group.

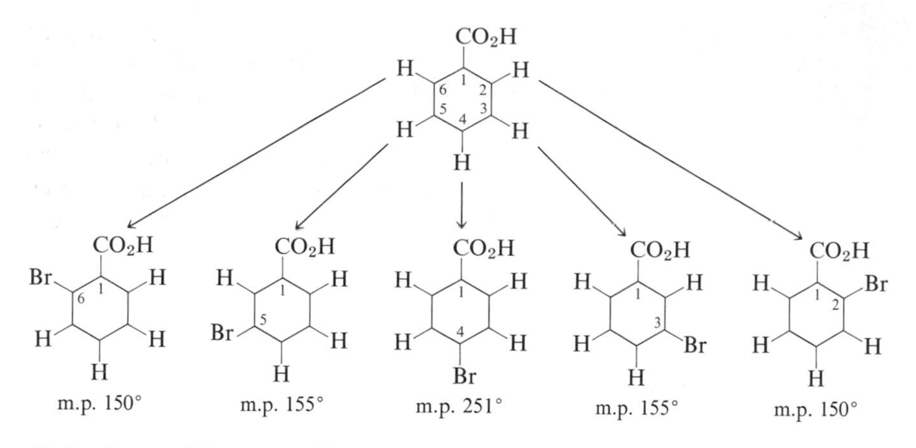

Only three different acids were obtained. The pair of acids with substituents in the 1- and 2- and in the 1- and 6-positions were identical. The pair substituted on carbon atoms 1 and 3 and 1 and 5 were also identical but different from the first pair. The acid with the substituents in the 1- and 4-positions provided the third isomer. This research unambiguously demonstrated that three isomeric disubstituted benzenes exist and that there are three, not five, nonequivalent hydrogen atoms in the monosubstituted benzenes.

Ladenburg and Wroblewsky established the symmetry properties of benzene. Any structure proposed for benzene must predict the formation of one monosubstituted compound and three disubstituted compounds. As discussed, the Kekulé structure does not. The two geometric arrangements that do have the requisite symmetry are the regular, planar hexagon and the prism.

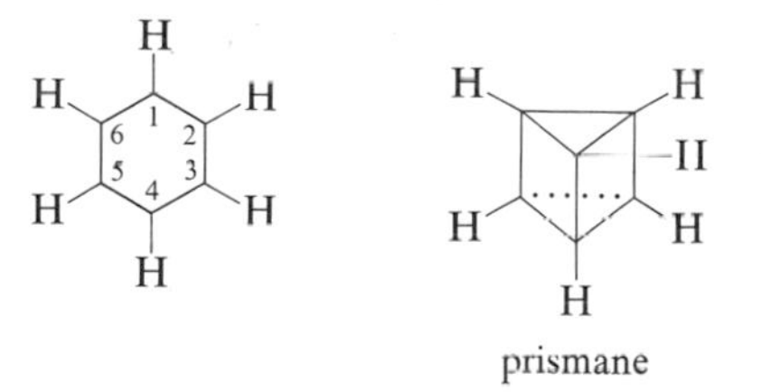

prismane

Ladenburg proposed, in fact, that benzene was prismane. The prismatic structure satisfies the requirements that the six hydrogen atoms of benzene be equivalent and that three nonequivalent disubstituted compounds exist. The three disubstituted compounds are shown:

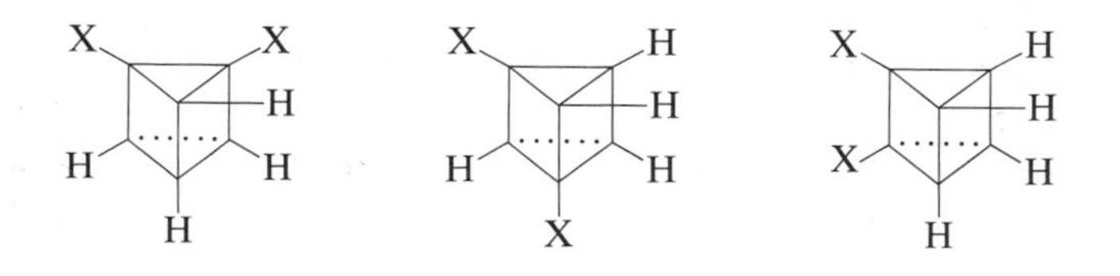

The structures of the three disubstituted planar representations may be assigned and related to the structures of the disubstituted prismanes. This analysis depends on the fact that a different number of compounds are formed when a third substituent is introduced into each of the isomeric disubstituted compounds. For the case of two identical substituents, the 1,2-disubstituted planar compound may yield two different trisubstituted compounds; whereas the 1,3- and 1,4-isomers yield three and one trisubstituted compounds, respectively.

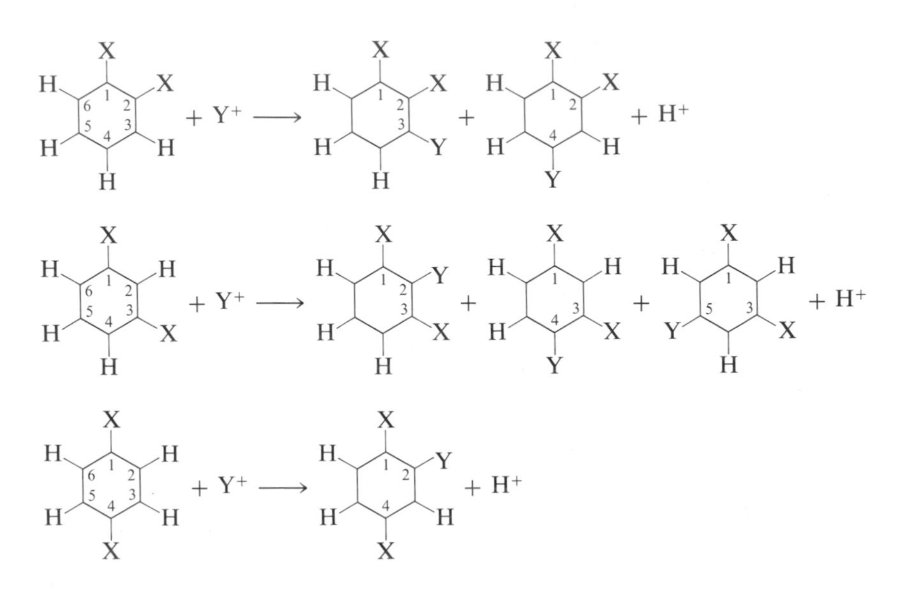

Each isomeric disubstituted prismane also would yield a different number (1, 2, or 3) of trisubstituted compounds (Prob. 1.2). The isomer that forms two trisubstituted compounds is shown.

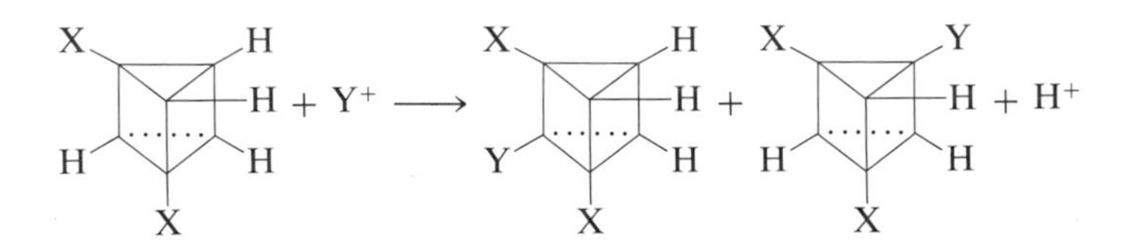

Accordingly, the structure of the disubstituted benzene that forms two trisubstituted compounds is either the prismane shown above or the 1,2-disubstituted planar compound. There is an important difference in these structures. The carbon atoms that are substituted in the planar representation are bonded; whereas the carbon atoms that are substituted in the related prismane are not bonded. Baeyer discovered that the disubstituted benzenes which form two trisubstituted compounds are reduced to 1,2-disubstituted cyclohexanes. This observation implies that carbon atom 1 and carbon atom 2 are bonded in the disubstituted benzene. The result is easily accommodated by the planar structure:

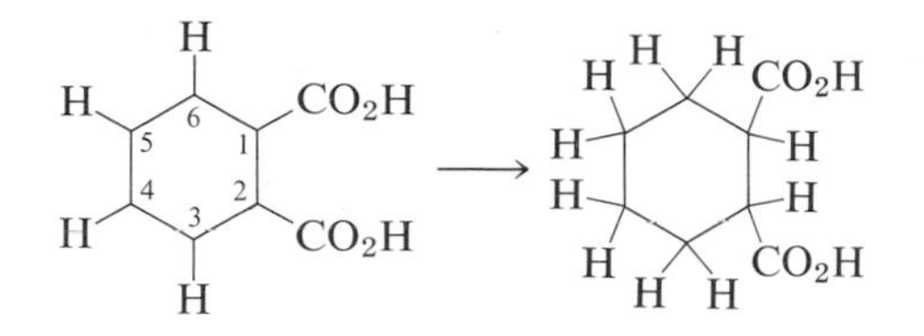

On the other hand, there is no simple path for the conversion of the related disubstituted prismane

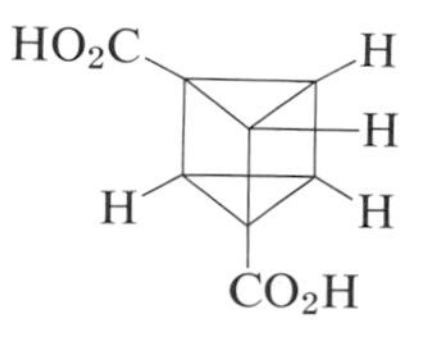

to a 1,2-disubstituted cyclohexane. Therefore, Baeyer concluded that benzene could not be prismane.

The early investigations of the chemistry of benzene revealed that the six carbon atoms of benzene were arranged in a planar, regular hexagon. This conclusion, based on careful experiment and inductive argument, was subsequently confirmed by the application of physical methods for the determination of structure. The six carbon nuclei are, indeed, located at the vertices of a planar, regular hexagon. The distance between adjacent carbon nuclei is 1.397 Å. The six hydrogen nuclei are symmetrically positioned 1.084 Å from the six carbon nuclei.

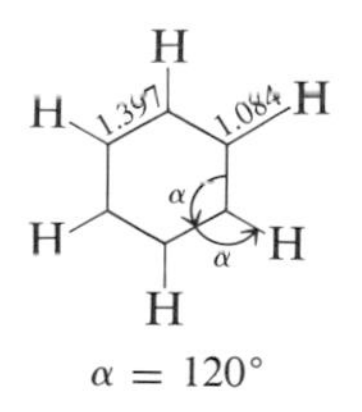

$\alpha = 120°$

The determination of structure secured the early conclusion that the six hydrogen atoms of benzene are geometrically and chemically equivalent. Consequently, only one product is formed when one hydrogen atom is replaced by another atom or group of atoms. Several of the more important monosubstituted benzenes are presented in Table 1-1. These compounds will be mentioned often in this text.

The six carbon nuclei in the monosubstituted compounds are also located at the vertices of regular hexagons. Inspection of the structure of benzoic acid reveals that one, two, or three carbon-carbon bond lengths separate the hydrogen atoms from the carboxyl group. The *ortho* hydro-

Table 1-1
COMMON MONOSUBSTITUTED BENZENE DERIVATIVES†

Toluene, methylbenzene, $C_6H_5CH_3$	Phenol, hydroxybenzene, C_6H_5OH
Chlorobenzene, C_6H_5Cl	Anisole, methoxybenzene, $C_6H_5OCH_3$
Bromobenzene, C_6H_5Br	Benzoic acid, $C_6H_5CO_2H$
Biphenyl, phenylbenzene, $C_6H_5C_6H_5$	Ethyl benzoate, $C_6H_5CO_2C_2H_5$
	Benzaldehyde, C_6H_5CHO
Aniline, aminobenzene, $C_6H_5NH_2$	Acetophenone, phenyl methyl ketone, $C_6H_5COCH_3$
Nitrobenzene, $C_6H_5NO_2$	

† The name in standard usage is presented first. The nomenclature of benzene and its derivatives is discussed in Chapters 11 and 12 of J. G. Traynham, *Organic Nomenclature: A Programmed Introduction,* Prentice-Hall, Inc., Englewood Cliffs, N.J., 1966.

gen atoms (2 and 6) are one bond length from the substituent and are identical. The *meta* hydrogen atoms (3 and 5) are two bond lengths from the carboxyl group and are also identical. The *para* hydrogen atom is three bond lengths away.

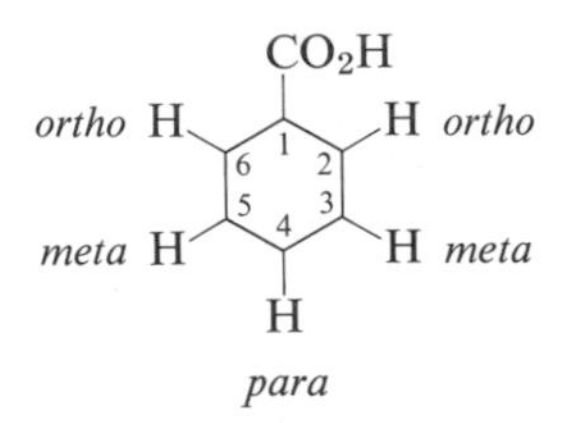

Only three bromobenzoic acids may be formed by the replacement of these hydrogen atoms.

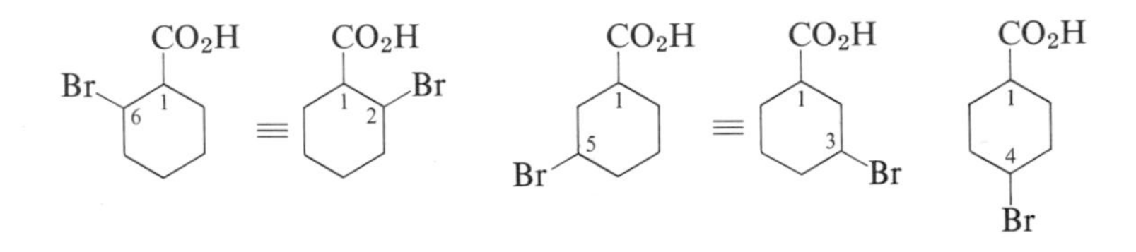

The definition of the structure of benzene, first by chemical inference and later by physical measurement, had important consequences. The fact that the carbon nuclei of benzene are located at the vertices of a regular hexagon revealed that the structural theory based on line representations of the chemical bonds was inadequate. It is impossible to devise a line structure for benzene that satisfies the symmetry requirements. As already discussed, the Kekulé structure is incorrect because, among other reasons, it predicts that there should be a long carbon-carbon bond distance and a short carbon-carbon bond distance associated, respectively, with the single and double bonds. Other possible line structures are equally unsatisfactory because they fail to portray the structural symmetry.

1.3 THE STABILITY OF BENZENE

The Kekulé structure is also unsatisfactory in the sense that it fails to predict the chemistry of benzene. The reaction chemistry of benzene and an olefin are contrasted in Table 1-2. Clearly, benzene does not react as a molecule with three olefinic double bonds.

Table 1-2

REACTIONS OF BENZENE AND AN OLEFIN

Benzene	Olefin
Br_2: Inert to the reagent	Br_2: Rapidly consumes reagent
$KMnO_4$: Inert to the reagent	$KMnO_4$: Oxidized rapidly
Typical reaction is substitution:	Typical reaction is addition:
$C_6H_6 + X_2 \longrightarrow C_6H_5X + HX$	$H_2C{=}CH_2 + X_2 \longrightarrow XCH_2CH_2X$

Since benzene is highly unsaturated, early investigators concluded that benzene was unusually stable. The term *stable* now has several connotations and its use without specific designation of the sense may be confusing. The two meanings most often implied are *kinetic* stability or *thermodynamic* stability. These two kinds of stability are not related. Kinetic stability means that a substance is unreactive and not easily transformed or decomposed. Kinetic stability has its origin in the large activation-free energy required for reaction. Thermodynamic stability means that a substance has less energy content than some other related reference substance. Thermodynamic stability has its origin in the greater attractive interactions between the nuclei and the electrons that constitute the chemical bonds. The reaction data, Table 1-2, are clearly kinetic phenomena, indicating that benzene is more stable than an olefin in a kinetic sense. Benzene is also unusually stable in a thermodynamic sense. The thermodynamic stability of an organic compound may be determined by combustion to carbon dioxide and water or by hydrogenation to another substance of known energy content. The thermodynamic heat change, ΔH, for such reactions may be measured with high accuracy. The enthalpy, H, of the products provides the reference energy for the comparison of different compounds.

The hydrogenation method illustrates the approach. The catalytic hydrogenation of benzene to cyclohexane yields 49.8 kcal $mole^{-1}$.

$$\underset{\text{benzene}}{C_6H_6} + 3H_2 = \underset{\text{cyclohexane}}{C_6H_{12}} + 49.8 \text{ kcal}$$

The enthalpy of benzene is, therefore, 49.8 kcal $mole^{-1}$ greater than that of the thermodynamically more stable cyclohexane. The catalytic hydrogenation of cyclohexene produces 28.8 kcal $mole^{-1}$.

$$\underset{\text{cyclohexene}}{C_6H_{10}} + H_2 = \underset{\text{cyclohexane}}{C_6H_{12}} + 28.8 \text{ kcal}$$

The enthalpy of cyclohexene is, therefore, 28.8 kcal mole^{-1} greater than that of cyclohexane. These results are summarized in Fig. 1-1.

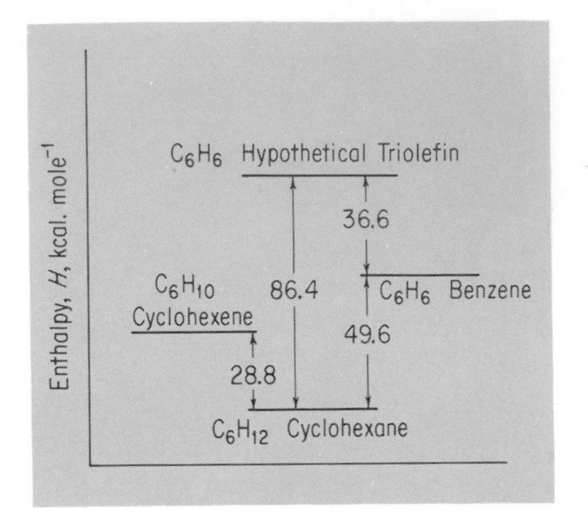

Fig. 1-1 Enthalpy relationship between cyclohexene, benzene, a hypothetical triolefin and cyclohexane. The thermodynamic energy differences, ΔH, are given in kcal. mole^{-1}.

The measured heat changes are secure experimental facts. The question of interest, however, is whether benzene is thermodynamically stable relative to a cyclic triolefin. An answer is possible only by an estimate of the expected heat change for the hydrogenation of a hypothetical cyclic triolefin. The usual approach, see Prob. 1.3, is to approximate this heat change as three times the heat of hydrogenation of cyclohexene (3 × 28.8).

$$\underset{\text{hypothetical triolefin}}{\text{(cyclohexatriene)}} + 3H_2 = \underset{\text{cyclohexane}}{C_6H_{12}} + 86.4 \text{ kcal}$$

The difference between the estimated value for the hydrogenation of the triolefin, 86.4 kcal, and the actual value for benzene, 49.8 kcal, is 36.6 kcal. This analysis suggests benzene is 36.6 kcal more stable than anticipated (Fig. 1-1). The excess thermodynamic stability deduced by such comparisons is called the *stabilization energy* (sometimes *resonance energy*). The inference of a large stabilization energy is that the binding interactions between the nuclei and the electrons are greater than anticipated and that the compound, in this case benzene, is unusually stable in a thermodynamic sense.

1.4 AROMATICITY

Compounds that exhibit the important distinguishing characteristics of high structural symmetry and a large thermodynamic stabilization energy are designated as aromatic compounds. Benzene is not unique in this respect. There are many other aromatic compounds. Typical examples are naphthalene; anthracene and other polyunsaturated, polycyclic hydrocarbons; and heterocyclic compounds such as pyridine, quinoline, and thiophene. Symmetrical structures with alternate single and double bonds are shown. These structures are known as Kekulé structures.

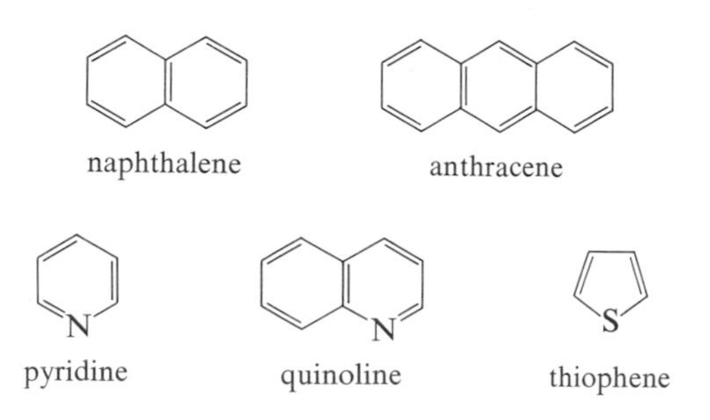

The designation of aromaticity implies that a compound is thermodynamically more stable than expected. Other properties may be inferred from this designation, but these properties are secondary to the fundamental idea that aromatic character has its origin in the forces which bind nuclei and that certain bonding situations lead to an important increase in thermodynamic stability. The enhanced thermodynamic stability of benzene originates in the enhanced mobility of the π electrons of this compound. The idea is intuitively apparent from an orbital model. Formally, benzene may be constructed from six trigonal sp^2 hybridized carbon-hydrogen fragments. Three of the four electrons of the carbon atom are associated with potential C—H or C—C σ bonds. The fourth electron resides in the *p* orbital. The molecule constructed from six such fragments has six carbon-hydrogen and six carbon-carbon σ bonds. The electrons in these σ bonds are constrained to a small volume element between the bonding nuclei and are said to be localized.

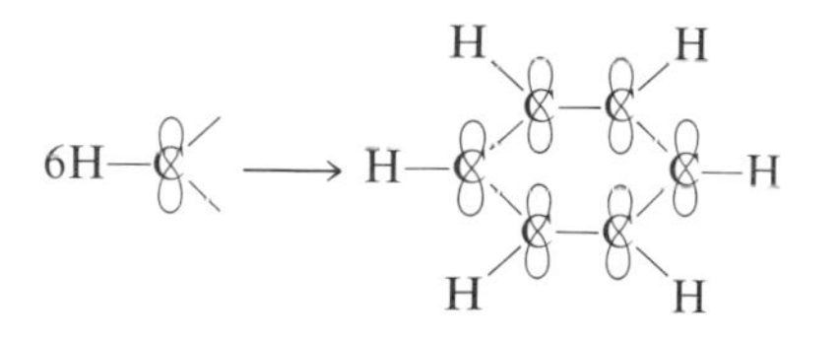

The σ bonding electrons are not mobile; therefore, they play only a minor role in the determination of the character of other bonds in the same molecule. The chemical bonds of aliphatic compounds are all localized in this sense. Benzene, however, has six *p* orbitals that are each occupied by one electron. When adjacent *p* orbitals overlap, a π bond is formed. In benzene, in contrast to a simple aliphatic olefin, each *p* orbital is flanked by two other equivalent *p* orbitals. Thus, bonding interactions occur between each *p* orbital and its two neighbors. In this situation the π electrons are not confined to the region between any pair of carbon atoms and are said to be delocalized. Delocalization has two important consequences. First, the bonding interactions between any two adjacent carbon nuclei become equivalent; second, the binding interactions increase relative to the binding energy of localized π bonds. The first factor accounts for the high symmetry of benzene and the second factor accounts for the greater thermodynamic stability of the molecule. The inadequacy of the Kekulé formulation originates in its portrayal of the π electrons in isolated, localized double bonds. Clearly, a different notation is necessary for the delocalized π electrons in benzene and other aromatic substances. G. W. Wheland's proposal that a circle be used for the π electrons in these substances has received widespread acceptance. The circle is reserved for the indication of delocalized π electrons that confer the property of aromaticity.

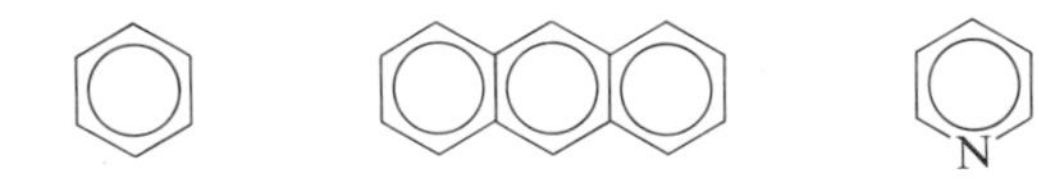

The mobility of the π electrons of benzene and other aromatic compounds has been confirmed by nuclear magnetic resonance (nmr) spectroscopy. Several factors determine the magnetic field strength required for resonance. These factors and the principles of magnetic resonance are discussed by N. L. Allinger and J. Allinger in *Structures of Organic Molecules,* p. 33, and by J. R. Dyer in *Applications of Absorption Spectroscopy of Organic Compounds,* Chapter 4 (both books in this series). A novel effect, known as the *ring current effect,* contributes to the determination of the field strength required for the resonance of hydrogen atoms in aromatic compounds. Its importance is illustrated by the large difference in the chemical shifts of the hydrogen atoms of benzene (τ2.7) and ethylene (τ4.6). The ring current effect, as the name implies, arises through the movement of the delocalized π electrons of benzene in the applied magnetic field H_1. The circulation of the π electrons produces a small secondary field H_2. The lines of force of this secondary field are shown in Fig. 1-2. This smaller secondary field reinforces the strong applied field at the positions of the hydrogen atoms. Consequently, when the π electrons are delocalized and capable of motion, the applied field needed for resonance need not be as strong, and the resonance signal is observed at lower fields. Because of this ring current effect, nmr spectroscopy provides a powerful method for the detection of delocalized electrons.

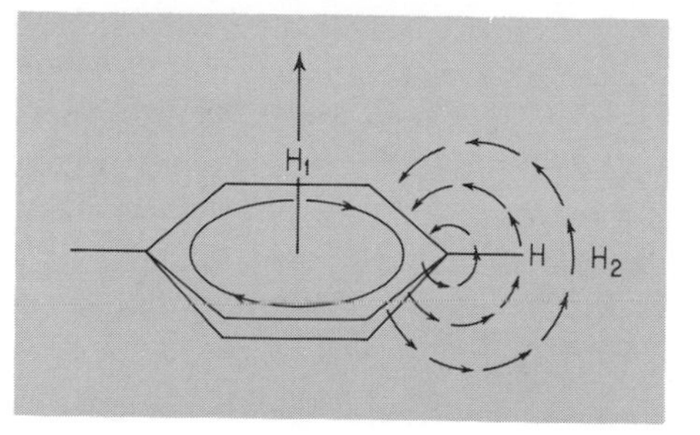

Fig. 1-2 Lines of force of small secondary field, H_2, that result from the motions of the π electrons in the strong applied field, H_1.

1.5 THEORETICAL DESCRIPTIONS OF DELOCALIZED BONDS

Two theories, the resonance theory and the molecular orbital theory, are used for the discussion of delocalized bonds. Resonance theory is largely based on intuitive chemical reasoning, and its successful use depends, in some measure, on the experience and knowledge of the chemist. However, this approach offers a powerful and extremely convenient chemical shorthand for the discussion of very complex problems involving delocalized bonds. Resonance theory treats benzene as a hybrid of two Kekulé structures. These two structures and the double-headed arrow portray the idea that the π electron distribution cannot be adequately presented in any conventional structure based on localized bonds. Rather, the real molecule is portrayed as a composite of two hypothetical structures with localized bonds. The mirror image relationship of the two structures infers the equivalence of the six carbon-carbon bonds. When two (or more) localized bond structures of equal (or nearly equal) energy may be drawn, the molecule is expected to possess added thermodynamic stability.

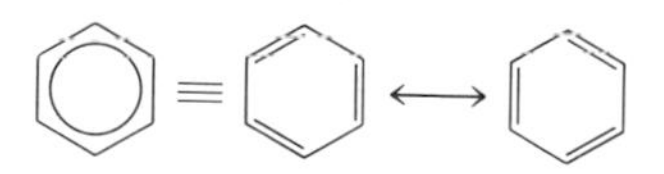

Molecular orbital theory offers a somewhat firmer basis for the description of delocalized bonds. The simplest version is known as the Hückel molecular orbital theory. This theory presumes that the π electrons occupy molecular orbitals (MO's) that extend over all the unsaturated, conjugated nuclei of the molecule. The application of precise quantum theory for the assessment of molecular properties is an incredibly difficult problem because the interactions between all the nuclei and all the electrons must be treated. Many approximations are necessary to simplify the problem. One realistic simplification is to factor the electrons into σ bond electrons and π bond electrons. The localized σ electrons are set aside and attention is focused on the π electrons. This approximation is justified because the variations in the chemistry of unsaturated substances are largely determined by variations in the energy content of the π electrons. The application of the Hückel theory to ethylene illustrates the approach. Formally, ethylene is constructed from two trigonal sp^2 hybridized CH_2 fragments. The electrons in the carbon-hydrogen and carbon-carbon

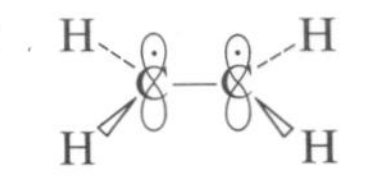

σ bonds are not considered further. The π bond is the consequence of the overlap of the sp^2 carbon atomic p orbitals. The electrons of the π bond do not remain in these atomic p orbitals. Rather, these electrons occupy a new molecular orbital specific for ethylene. The MO's for ethylene and other unsaturated molecules are mathematically synthesized, in the Hückel approach, from the atomic p orbitals. A rigorous development of the mathematical method used for the construction of these orbitals on the basis of fundamental considerations is beyond the scope off this monograph; only the important concepts and the resulting simple equations will be discussed.

The success of the Hückel method originates in its recognition of the fact that the energy content of a π electron is reduced as the opportunity for interactions with additional positively charged carbon nuclei increase. Thus, the energy content of the π electrons depends on their degree of delocalization. The relative energy levels of the MO's may be estimated from two simple equations that are applicable for many simple unsaturated molecules. Two energy quantities, designated α and β, become important in this analysis. The energy α is that of an electron in a p orbital of an isolated sp^2 carbon atom. This energy is used as a reference for the comparison of the energy levels of the MO's. The energy β is that of an electron in the vicinity of two sp^2 carbon atoms that are within bonding distance. When an electron interacts with two positively charged carbon nuclei, rather than one, its potential energy is reduced. Accordingly, β is a negative number. The value of β is about -18 kcal, as discussed on p. 15.

The first general solution of the Hückel treatment, Eq. (1.1), predicts the energy levels of the MO's of a planar chain of bonded sp^2 carbon atoms. This solution is applicable for ethylene, 1,3-butadiene, 1,3,5-hexatriene, etc.

$$\epsilon_j = \alpha + 2\beta \cos\left(\frac{j\pi}{n+1}\right) \qquad j = 1, 2, 3, \ldots, n \tag{1.1}$$

In Eq. (1.1), α and β have the significance noted; ϵ_j is the energy of the first ($j = 1$), second ($j = 2$), or nth ($j = n$) MO: j assumes all values from unity to the number n of sp^2 carbon atoms involved. There are as many MO's as there are sp^2 carbon atoms in the chain: 2 MO's for ethylene, 4 MO's for 1,3-butadiene, 6 MO's for 1,3,5-hexatriene.

Ethylene, with two carbon atoms, has $n = 2$, $j = 1$, and $j = 2$. The energy of the first MO, ϵ_1, is given by Eq. (1.2).

$$\epsilon_1 = \alpha + 2\beta \cos\left(\frac{\pi}{3}\right) = \alpha + \beta \tag{1.2}$$

The energy of the second MO, ϵ_2, is given by Eq. (1.3). The energy levels and shapes of the MO's are shown in Fig. 1-3.

$$\epsilon_2 = \alpha + 2\beta \cos\left(\frac{2\pi}{3}\right) = \alpha - \beta \tag{1.3}$$

The same concepts that are used in the atomic orbital approach for atoms and ions are used in the molecular orbital treatment. Each orbital may accommodate two electrons. The Pauli–Aufbau principle and Hund's rule of maximum multiplicity dictate the order in which the MO's are filled. Hence, the two π electrons are placed in the first MO of ethylene. If the energy of the MO is less than α, as is the first MO of ethylene, the orbital is said to be bonding. The shape of the first MO for ethylene, Fig. 1-3, indicates that the electron density is concentrated between the two carbon nuclei in accord with the idea that electron density is responsible for the chemical bond. If the energy of the MO is greater than α, as is the second MO of ethylene, the orbital is said to be antibonding. The shape of the second MO reflects this antibonding character with the electron density displaced from the region between the two carbon nuclei. The Hückel theory also permits an estimate of the total energy of the

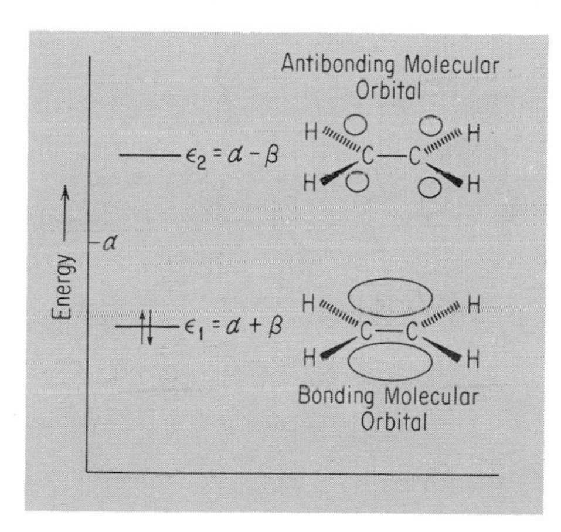

Fig. 1-3 Energy levels and shapes of the bonding and antibonding molecular orbitals of ethylene.

π electrons, E_π. It is the sum of the energies of the π electrons in the occupied orbitals. For ethylene, with two π electrons in the first MO,

$$E_\pi = 2\epsilon_1 = 2(\alpha + \beta) = 2\alpha + 2\beta \quad (1.4)$$

A second general solution of the Hückel theory is applicable for the assessment of the energies of the MO's occupied by the π electrons of cyclic molecules composed entirely of sp^2 hybridized carbon atoms.

$$\epsilon_k = \alpha + 2\beta \cos\left(\frac{2k\pi}{n}\right) \quad (1.5)$$

$$k = 0, \pm 1, \pm 2, \ldots, \pm\left(\frac{n-1}{2}\right)$$ (for n an odd number of carbon atoms in the ring)

$$k = 0, \pm 1, \pm 2, \pm 3, \ldots, +\frac{n}{2}$$ (for n an even number of carbon atoms in the ring)

The energy ϵ_k of the kth MO is given by Eq. (1.5), where k assumes the values shown under Eq. (1.5). There are as many MO's, n, as there are carbon atoms in the ring. The energies of the MO's of benzene may be obtained from this equation with $n = 6$, $k = 0, \pm 1, \pm 2, +3$. These energy levels are shown in Fig. 1-4.

The six π electrons of benzene occupy the first three bonding MO's. The total energy of the π electrons is given by Eq. (1.6).

$$E_\pi = 2\epsilon_0 + 2\epsilon_1 + 2\epsilon_{-1} = 2(\alpha + 2\beta) + 4(\alpha + \beta) = 6\alpha + 8\beta \quad (1.6)$$

Frequently, it is desirable to compare the values of E_π deduced by the Hückel method with E_π for the classical structure. The difference between the two values is called the delocalization energy, *DE;* it is a theoretical estimate of the stabilization energy obtained by the delocalization of the

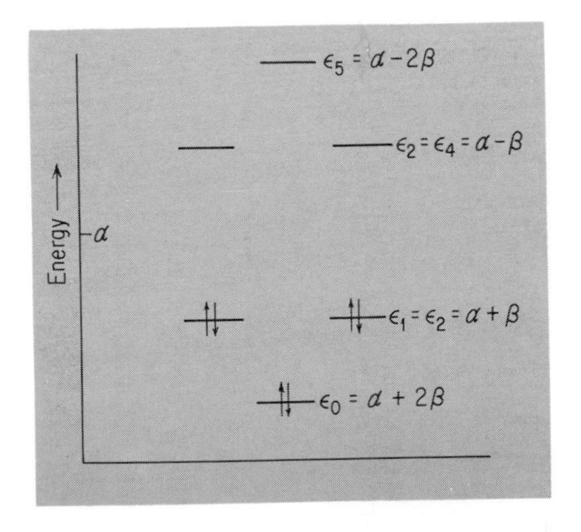

Fig. 1-4 Energy levels of the six molecular orbitals of benzene.

π electrons over the whole set of carbon atoms relative to the π electron energy for the same structure with a fixed set of double bonds. For benzene, the comparison is made between the value given by Eq. (1.6) and that for the Kekulé structure containing three isolated ethylene-like double bonds, each with E_π of $2\alpha + 2\beta$, Eq. (1.4).

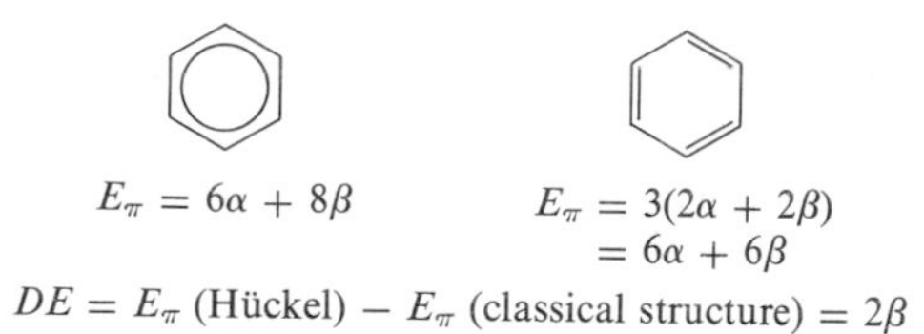

$$E_\pi = 6\alpha + 8\beta \qquad E_\pi = 3(2\alpha + 2\beta) = 6\alpha + 6\beta$$

$$DE = E_\pi\ (\text{Hückel}) - E_\pi\ (\text{classical structure}) = 2\beta$$

The estimated stabilization energy of benzene, 36.6 kcal mole^{-1} (Sec. 1.3), and the theoretical delocalization energy, 2β, may be compared to evaluate β as -18 kcal. This value is routinely used in chemical applications of the Hückel theory.

1.6 THE HÜCKEL RULE

A general result of the Hückel theory, known as the Hückel rule, predicts that monocyclic, planar molecules of sp^2 hybridized carbon atoms containing $(4n + 2)$ π electrons ($n = 0, 1, 2, \ldots$) will have aromatic character. The application of Eq. (1.5) to cyclobutadiene illustrates the rule. The four MO's of cyclobutadiene are shown in Fig. 1-5. The π electron energy E_π is $4\alpha + 4\beta$. The π electron energy for the classical structure with two ethylene double bonds is $2(2\alpha + 2\beta)$. The difference, the delocali-

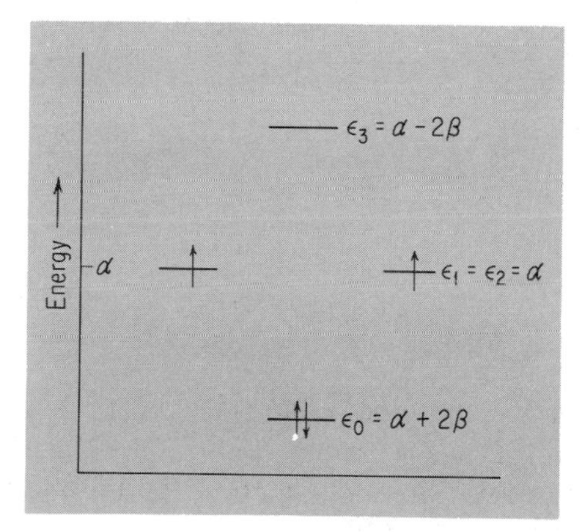

Fig. 1-5 Molecular orbital energy levels for cyclobutadiene.

zation energy, is 0. The Hückel theory predicts that cyclobutadiene should not be an aromatic compound. Use of the Hückel rule avoids this analysis. However, the more complete orbital diagram, Fig. 1-5, predicts that cyclobutadiene should have two unpaired electrons. This prediction follows from the application of Hund's rule which requires that one electron be placed in each of the equivalent orbitals, in this case ϵ_1 and ϵ_{-1}. This situation is somewhat unusual for organic molecules and many attempts have been made to test this point.

Methods for the synthesis of cyclobutadiene have been under study since 1912. This effort has not, however, led to the isolation or characterization of this substance. Some positive results were obtained in 1966 when evidence for the transient existence of cyclobutadiene as a reaction intermediate was presented. The synthetic difficulties and the apparent kinetic instability of the cyclic diene do not, of course, prove that the predictions of the Hückel rule are correct. But these results are not unexpected in view of the predictions of the Hückel theory that cyclobutadiene is a molecule with no delocalization energy and two unpaired electrons.

The next cyclic hydrocarbon, after benzene, formed from sp^2 carbon atoms is cyclooctatetraene. This substance violates the Hückel rule for aromaticity in two ways. It has eight π electrons and the molecule is not planar. The heat of combustion indicates that there is no thermodynamic stabilization energy. No ring current is detectable by nmr spectroscopy. Moreover, the compound reacts as an olefin, undergoing addition rather than substitution reactions. All these properties are in accord with the prediction of the Hückel rule.

[10]-Annulene (the term annulene is reserved for monocyclic molecules with alternating double and single bonds, the integer indicates the number of carbon atoms in the ring) was recently detected as an unstable substance in solution. This compound has 10 π electrons and, if planar, would be an aromatic compound according to the Hückel rule. However, serious steric interactions between the hydrogen atoms forced to be inside the ring are certain to deform the planar structure. The idea that the steric interactions between the inner hydrogen atoms are severe led to the prep-

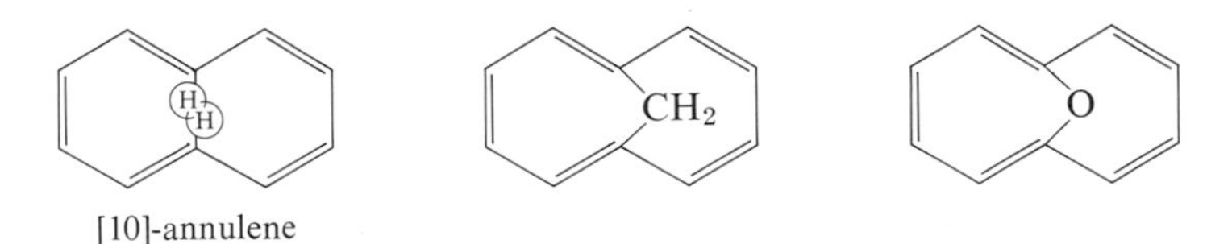

aration of model [10]-annulenes in which these hydrogen atoms are replaced by a methylene or oxygen bridge. These derivatives exhibit a ring current that is, presumably, related to the mobile π electrons of the unsaturated 10-carbon atom ring.

[14]-Annulene obeys the Hückel $(4n + 2)$ rule but is not planar.

As with [10]-annulene, the steric interactions between the hydrogens inside the ring are important. [18]-Annulene, in which the internal hydrogens are not crowded, is planar. Nuclear magnetic resonance indicates a ring current, and the heat of combustion suggests that the stabilization energy is about 100 kcal mole^{-1}.

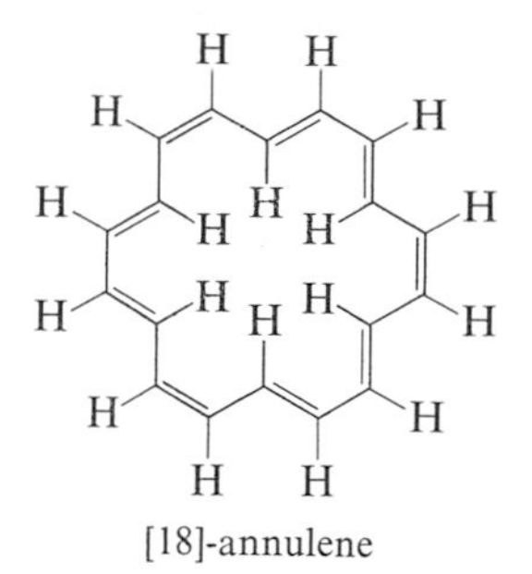

[18]-annulene

The Hückel rule also applies to carbonium ions, carbanions, and free radicals. Thus, cyclic ions or free radicals formed from sp^2 carbon atoms that have $(4n + 2)$ π electrons are predicted to have unusual thermodynamic stability. Several remarkable examples have been investigated. The cyclopropenium ion is one interesting case. The classical structure of the carbonium ion

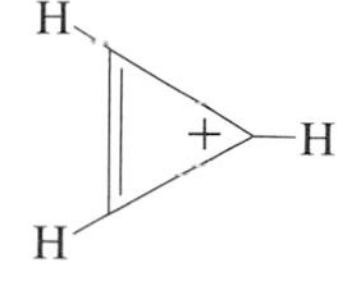

indicates that there are two π electrons in a double bond with an unoccupied p orbital at the other carbon atom. The overlap between the three equivalent p orbitals delocalizes the two π electrons over the triangular three carbon atom network to stabilize this carbonium ion.

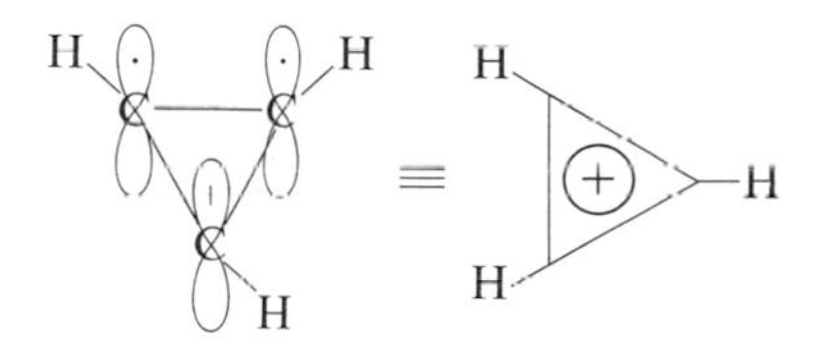

The application of Eq. (1.5) to this ion yields the MO energy levels shown in Fig. 1-6. The two π electrons occupy the first bonding MO. The π electron energy for this carbonium ion is $2\alpha + 4\beta$. E_π for the classical structure with one double bond is $2\alpha + 2\beta$. This analysis indicates a large stabilization energy, 2β, for the ion. The Hückel theory suggests that this ion and its derivatives should be unusually stable. This expectation has

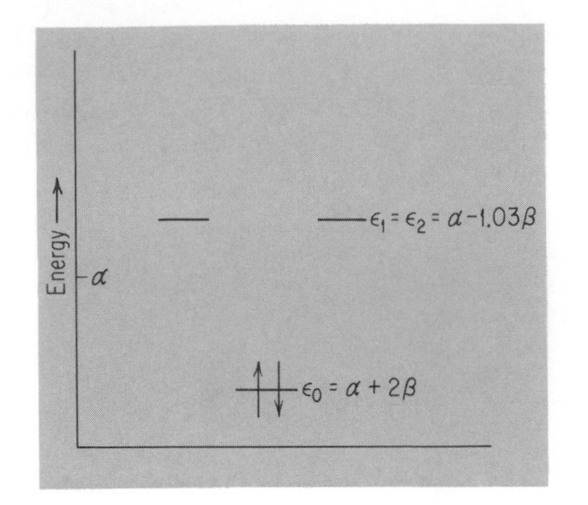

Fig. 1-6 Molecular orbital energy levels for cyclopropenium carbonium ion.

been realized experimentally. One example is tri-*n*-propylcyclopropenium perchlorate, which is an ionic compound in the solid state and which has a hydrolysis constant of about 10^{-7}.

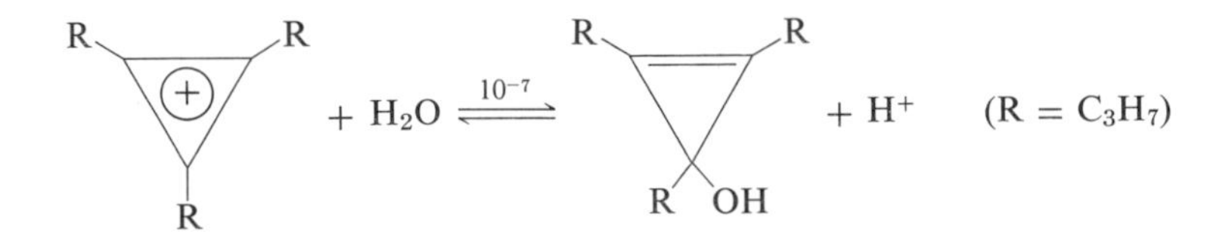

Under these conditions, *t*-butyl carbonium ion would be completely converted to *t*-butyl alcohol. This comparison illustrates the enormous importance of electron delocalization on the thermodynamic stability of carbonium ions. Other cyclic carbonium ions with $(4n + 2)$ π electrons have been examined including dipositive cyclobutadiene derivatives with two π electrons and monopositive cycloheptatriene derivatives with six π electrons. 7-Bromocycloheptatriene does not exist as a covalent compound, but rather is a saltlike material in the solid state that instantly dissociates in solution. The six π electrons are shown in the three double bonds of the classical structure of the cation called the tropylium ion

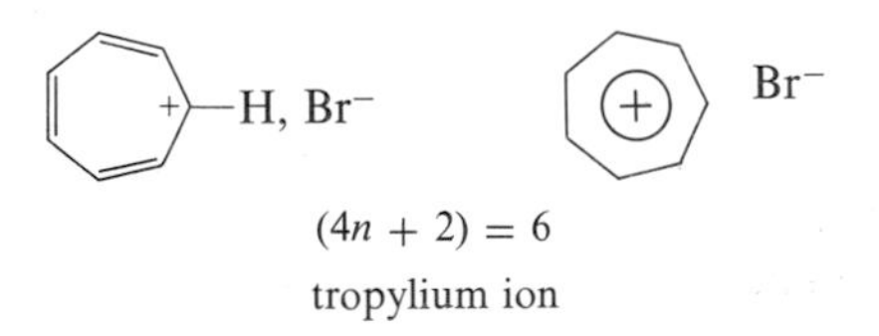

$(4n + 2) = 6$
tropylium ion

As for the cyclopropenium ion, these electrons are delocalized evenly over the entire carbon skeleton as pictured in the aromatic representation of the ion. The dipositive cyclobutadiene derivative is most remarkable. Evidence has been obtained that this material

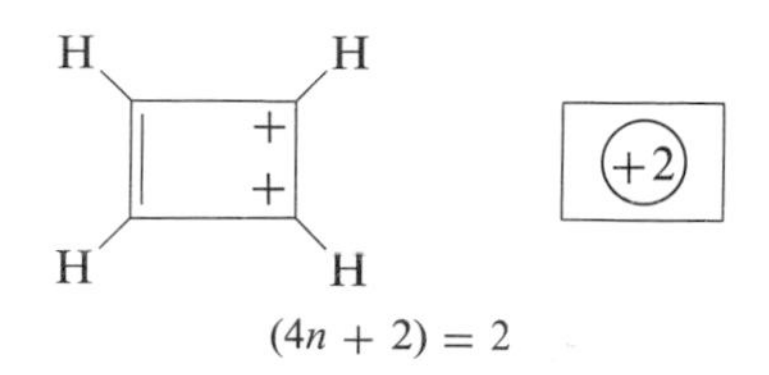

forms salts. The apparent stability of this substance is sharply contrasted by the instability of the neutral molecule, cyclobutadiene.

Carbanions with $(4n + 2)$ π electrons also exhibit unusual stability. The monoanion of cyclopentadiene has six π electrons and the dianion of cyclooctatetraene has 10 π electrons. Both of these derivatives form readily.

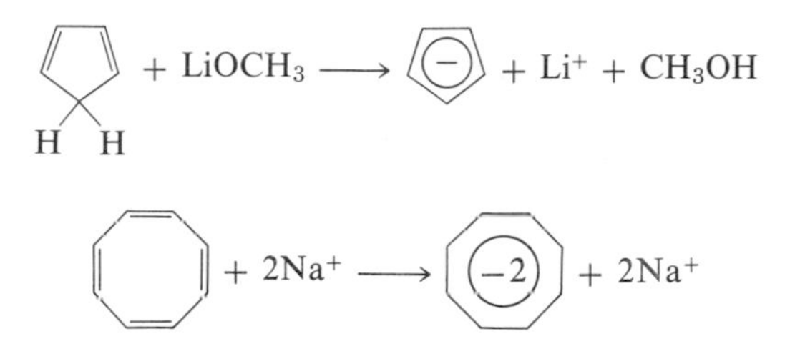

In conclusion, the Hückel rule for aromaticity has received ample confirmation in the synthesis and study of these novel carbonium ions and carbanions. Much remains to be accomplished, however, in this relatively new area of aromatic chemistry.

PROBLEMS

1.1. Draw the classical structures of the cyclic hydrocarbons of formula C_6H_6. Consider bi- and tricyclic compounds in this analysis and show that prismane alone has six equivalent hydrogen atoms.

1.2. Draw the structures of all the products obtained by the substitution of a chlorine atom for a hydrogen atom of *o*-, *m*-, and *p*-dichlorobenzene. Note that two different trichlorobenzenes may be formed from the *o*-isomer, three from the *m*-isomer, and one from the *p*-isomer. Draw the structures of the three dichloroprismanes. Show that the chlorine atoms are attached to nonbonded carbon atoms in the dichloroprismane that may yield two trichloroprismanes.

1.3. The σ bonds between carbon atoms of different hybridization differ in strength. For example, the C_{sp^2}-C_{sp^2} bond is somewhat stronger than the C_{sp^3}-C_{sp^3} bond. What effect does this fact have on the estimate of stabilization energy?

1.4. Solve Eq. (1.5) for the energy levels of the five MO's of the planar five-membered ring of sp^2 carbon atoms. Evaluate E_π and the delocalization energy for the carbonium ion, free radical, and carbanion. What unusual feature is predicted for the electron distribution in the carbonium ion? (*Answer:* E_π for carbonium ion, $4\alpha + 5.23\beta$; for free radical, $5\alpha + 5.85\beta$; for carbanion, $6\alpha + 6.47\beta$; *DE* for carbonium ion, 1.23β; for free radical, 1.85β; for carbanion, 2.47β).

1.5. Which of the following substances is expected to exhibit aromatic character on the basis of the Hückel rule?

a. [20]-Annulene

b. [20]-Annulene mononegative ion, $C_{20}H_{20}^-$

c. [20]-Annulene dinegative ion, $C_{20}H_{20}^{-2}$

d. [8]-Annulene mononegative ion, $C_8H_{20}^-$

Draw the resonance structures for this substance.

SUGGESTED READING

An excellent discussion of the structure of benzene and the structural theory is presented by G. W. Wheland, *Advanced Organic Chemistry* (3rd ed.), John Wiley & Sons, Inc., New York, 1960, Chapters 2 and 3.

An introduction to molecular orbital theory is provided by J. D. Roberts, *Molecular Orbital Calculations,* W. A. Benjamin, Inc., New York, 1962.

A more detailed discussion of the molecular orbital theory and its many applications is presented by A. Streitwieser, *Molecular Orbital Theory for Organic Chemists,* John Wiley & Sons, Inc., New York, 1961.

For a recent review of aromatic chemistry and the Hückel rule, see R. Breslow, "Aromatic Character," *Chemical and Engineering News,* **43,** 90 (June 28, 1965).

2 Electrophilic Substitution Reactions

2.1 INTRODUCTION

The most characteristic reaction of benzene is the process in which a hydrogen atom of the aromatic nucleus is replaced by a group from an electrophilic reagent. Electrophilic reagents are, as the name implies, seekers of electron density; benzene acts as the nucleophile in this reaction, providing the electron pair for the formation of the new bond between the carbon atom of the aryl ring and the electrophile. An intermediate, a benzenonium ion, forms in the course of the reaction and the hydrogen atom is subsequently removed as a proton.

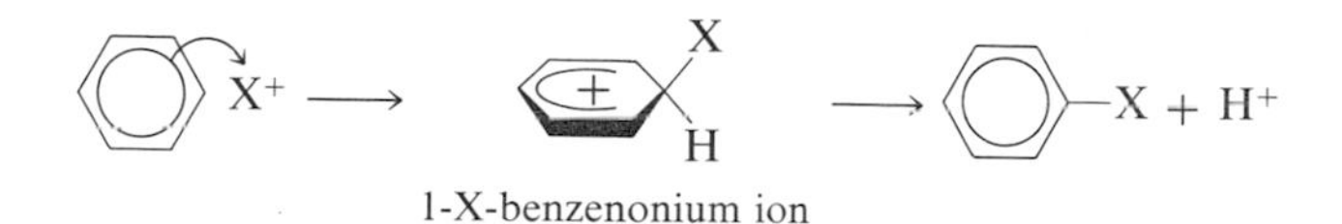

1-X-benzenonium ion

The structure of the benzenonium ion is well defined. The six carbon atoms and five of the six hydrogen atoms lie in the same plane. The sixth hydrogen atom and the X group are above and below the plane defined by the other atoms. Five of the carbon atoms of the ring are sp^2 hybridized, the sixth, the one bonded to a hydrogen atom and the X group, is sp^3 hybridized. The π electrons in this ion are delocalized and, as for benzene, no single line structure can be drawn. Resonance theory describes the ion as a set of three resonance structures with the positive charge located in the 2-, 4-, and 6-positions. Molecular orbital theory also predicts that the positive charge should be found in these three positions. Inasmuch as it will be necessary to refer to the benzenonium ion frequently in the discussion of the chemistry of benzene, the shorthand notation shown on the left will be used. It must be remembered that the charge is not distributed

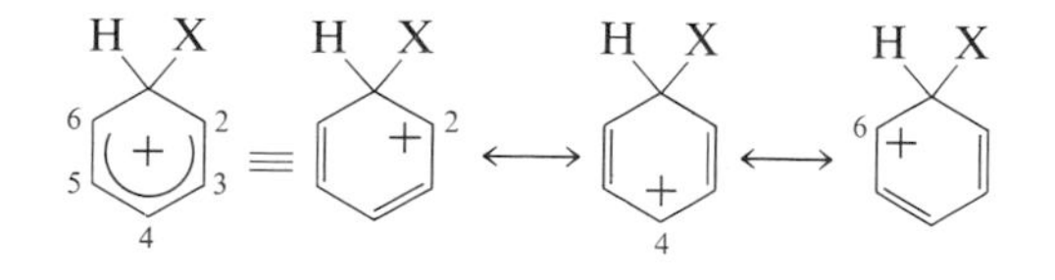

uniformly over the carbon atoms of the ring, but rather is distributed as shown in the resonance structures on the right.

The more important electrophilic substitution reactions and the evidence for their mechanisms will be discussed in this chapter.

2.2 THE MECHANISM OF THE SUBSTITUTION REACTION

Nitration is a typical electrophilic aromatic substitution reaction. The balanced equation for the reaction is

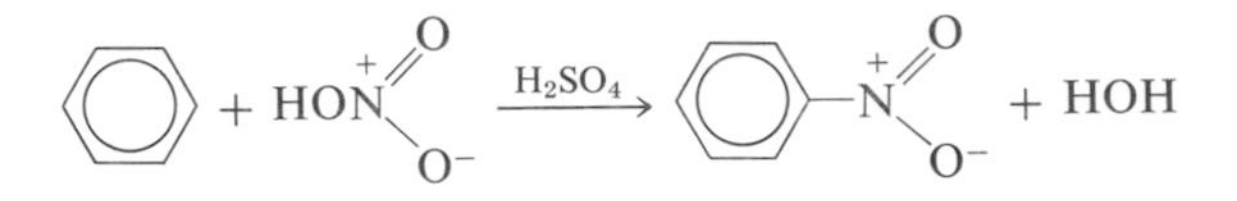

The effective reagent in nitration is actually the nitronium ion, NO_2^+, as discussed in Sec. 2.4. In this section, the mechanism of the reaction between the nitronium ion and benzene will be considered. Electrophilic reagents such as the nitronium ion are strong acids that interact with the basic π electrons of benzene. These favorable interactions are maximized by the approach of the reagent from the top (or bottom) of the plane of the benzene ring.

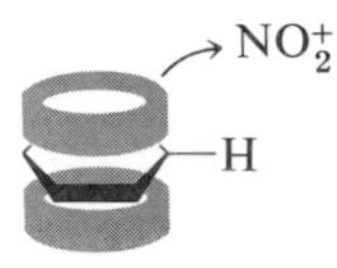

With this idea in mind, two attractive mechanisms may be formulated for the reaction. One possibility is that the substitution proceeds by a direct displacement reaction in which the carbon-nitrogen bond is formed as the carbon-hydrogen bond is broken.

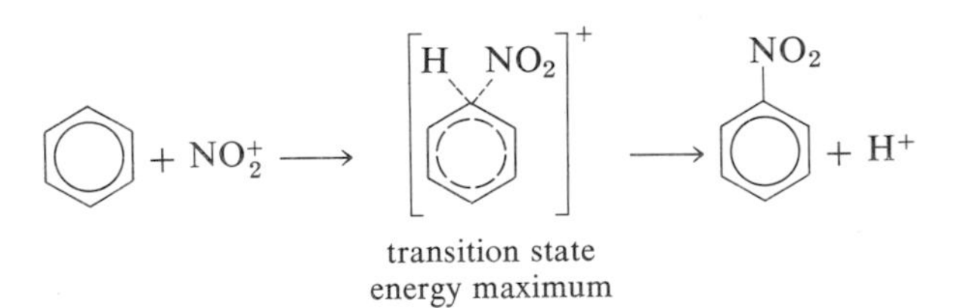

Another possible formulation is a two-step process in which an intermediate, 1-nitrobenzenonium ion, is formed in the course of the reaction.

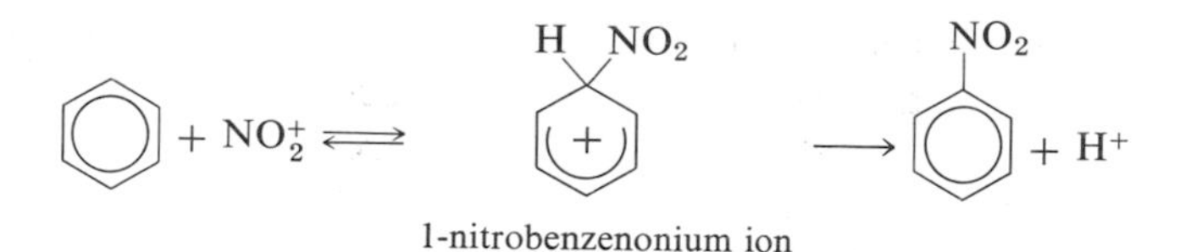

These two mechanisms differ in a subtle, but significant, way. The first formulation infers that the reaction proceeds in a continuous manner with a single energy maximum, Fig. 2-1A. The second formulation, involving the benzenonium ion as an intermediate, has two energy maxima, Fig. 2-1B. The techniques that may be used to distinguish between these possibilities are discussed by R. Stewart, in *The Investigation of Organic Reactions* (this series). Only two of the several lines of evidence indicating that the benzenonium ion is, indeed, an intermediate in the substitution reactions will be discussed here.

The comparison of the rate of nitration of benzene and benzene-d_6, C_6D_6, offers a straightforward method for the selection of the correct mechanism. Less activation energy is required for the cleavage of a carbon-hydrogen bond than for a carbon-deuterium bond. The rate difference that arises as a consequence of isotopic substitution is known as the *kinetic isotope effect.* Experimentally, reactions in which a carbon-hydrogen bond is broken in the rate-determining step proceed about 5- to 7-fold more rapidly than the corresponding reaction involving a carbon-deuterium bond. An inspection of the two energy diagrams, Fig. 2-1A and B,

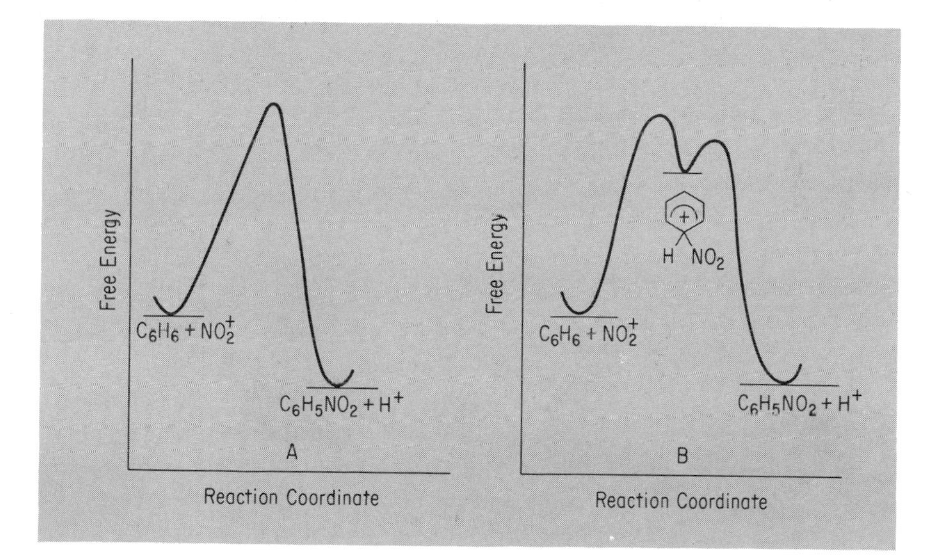

Fig. 2-1 Possible energy profiles for electrophilic substitution reactions without an intermediate (*A*) and with an intermediate (*B*).

reveals that the first mechanism requires that the carbon-hydrogen bond be partially broken at the energy maximum. Accordingly, a kinetic isotope effect should be observed for the substitution reaction if this mechanism is correct. On the other hand, no kinetic isotope effect is anticipated for the second mechanism. In that case, the carbon-hydrogen bond remains intact at the energy maximum that determines the rate of the reaction and leads to the benzenonium ion. The recognition of this difference between the two mechanisms prompted the measurement of the rate of nitration of benzene and benzene-d_6. It was found that the nitration of each proceeded at the same rate under identical conditions. The inference of this result is that the rate-determining step in nitration does not involve the cleavage of the carbon-hydrogen bond. This fact is incompatible with the one-step displacement formulation since in that picture the carbon-hydrogen bond is partially broken in the transition state. On the other hand, the result is readily accommodated by the two-step mechanism with 1-nitrobenzenonium ion formed in the slow step of the two-step process.

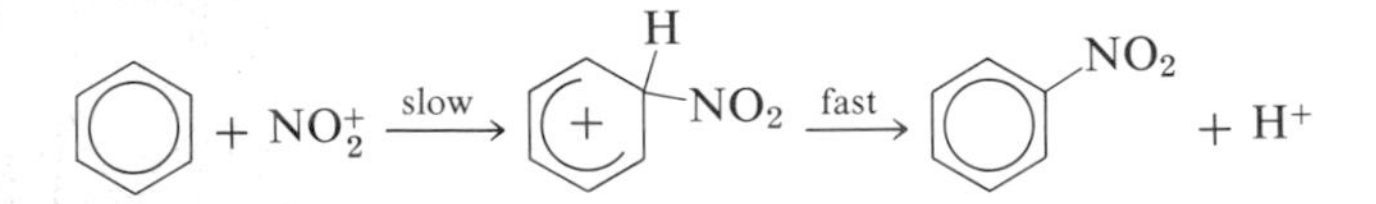

The energy profile for this reaction path is shown in Fig. 2-1B. If the energy barrier for the first step is the high point, then the subsequent reaction in which a proton is removed becomes kinetically insignificant and has no influence on the observed reaction rate. A familiar analogy is the slow climb to the highest point on a roller coaster; from that point, all subsequent lesser hills are rapidly surmounted.

Kinetic isotope effects are also absent in many other substitution reac-

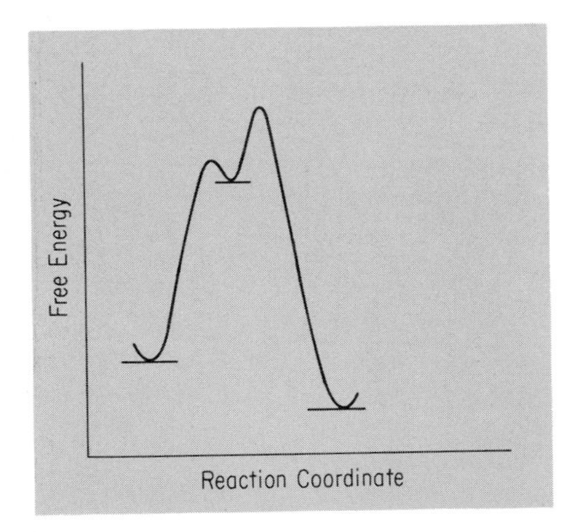

Fig. 2-2 Energy profile for an electrophilic substitution reaction in which the second step is kinetically significant.

tions, indicating the general importance of the two-step mechanism. Small kinetic isotope effects (hydrogen/deuterium = 2) are detected in a few reactions. An example is Friedel–Crafts acylation (Sec. 2.6B). Theory suggests the value for a one-step process should be larger, as noted in the previous discussion. Accordingly, these small kinetic isotope effects are also best understood in terms of the two-step mechanism, with the height of the second energy barrier somewhat greater than that for the formation of the benzenonium ion as shown in Fig. 2-2.

The classic test for the intermediacy of a substance is its detection in the reaction mixture. The application of this criterion to aromatic substitution reactions resulted in the spectroscopic identification of benzenonium ions and their isolation as salts. For example, 2,4,6-trimethylbenzenonium tetrafluoroborate is produced by the reaction of mesitylene with hydrogen fluoride in the presence of boron trifluoride.

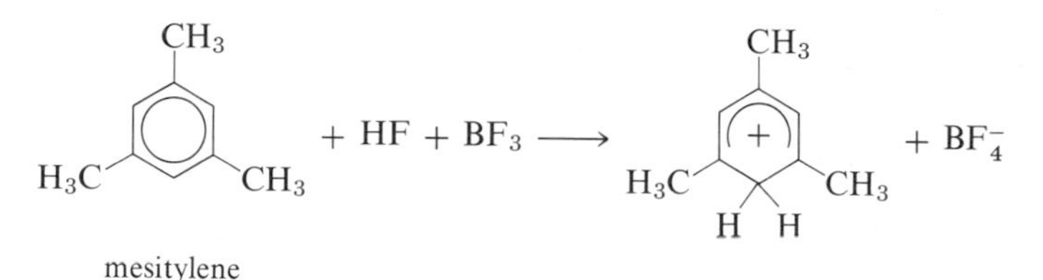

Other benzenonium ion salts with tetrachloroaluminate, $AlCl_4^-$, or hexafluoroantimonate, SbF_6^-, anions are also known. The isolation of these salts lends confidence to the idea that benzenonium ions are intermediates in the substitution reactions.

2.3 THE CHARGE-TRANSFER COMPLEX

Another chemical entity, in addition to the reagents, products, and benzenonium ions, is present in the solutions under the conditions of the substitution reaction. These additional substances are charge-transfer complexes formed by the interaction of the basic aromatic hydrocarbons with the Lewis acids in the solution. Benzene dissolved in carbon tetrachloride absorbs only ultraviolet light and the solution is colorless. Iodine dissolved in the same solvent yields a violet solution. When these solutions are mixed, the resultant homogeneous solution is brown. The color change is the consequence of the formation of a new chemical entity. Study of the properties of the solution shows that the new species consists of one molecule of benzene and one molecule of iodine, $C_6H_6 \cdot I_2$. In addition, benzene and iodine, the components of the new substance, $C_6H_6 \cdot I_2$, may be quantitatively recovered from the solution unchanged. Finally, the ability of the solution to conduct an electric current is not altered significantly. These facts indicate that the entity formed is nonionic and that the bonding between the components is very weak.

The substance formed in solution is called a *charge-transfer complex*, and it arises through the acid-base interaction between iodine and the basic π electrons of benzene. Qualitatively, the diffuse nature of the π electrons accounts for the feeble nature of the bonding. Neither covalent nor ionic bonds are formed in the conventional sense; rather, a transfer of charge from the base to the acid occurs. A useful description of the complex employs an arrow from the π electrons of benzene to the Lewis acid.

A great variety of other substances interact with benzene in this way, including hydrogen chloride, chlorine, bromine, iodine monochloride, stannic chloride, boron trifluoride, aluminum chloride, and other more unusual Lewis acids such as tetracyanoethylene, picric acid, 1,3,5-trinitrobenzene, and chloranil.

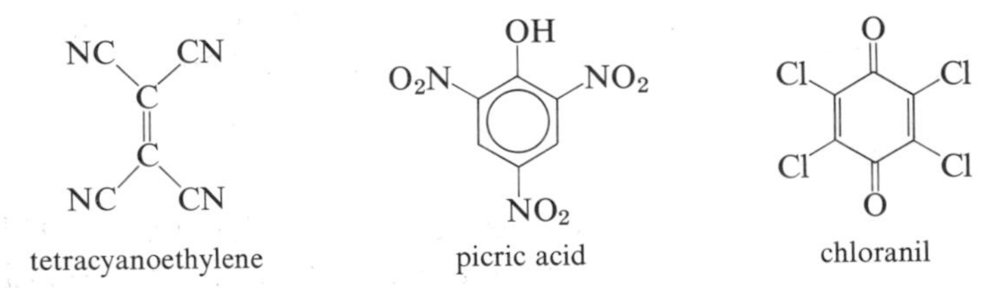

Usually the complex is not isolable, but high molecular weight adducts sometimes precipitate from solution as shown in the equation:

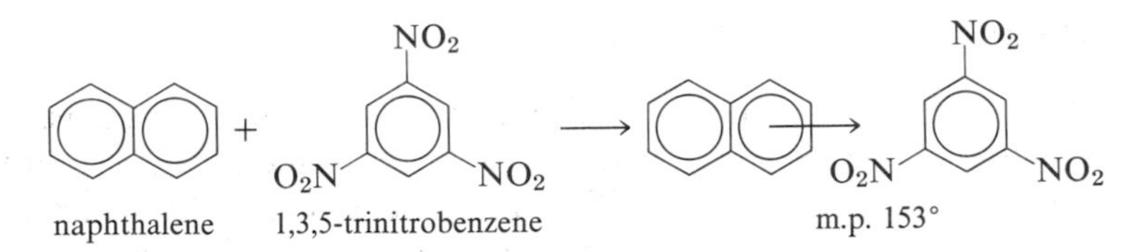

Charge-transfer complexes are present under the conditions used for aromatic substitution reactions. However, the complexes form rapidly and dissociate to their components rapidly. Because the formation and dissociation reactions are much faster than the substitution reactions, these complexes do not play a role in the determination of the rate or course of the substitution reactions. An energy diagram illustrating the complexes and an aromatic halogenation reaction is shown in Fig. 2-3.

2.4 NITRATION

Nitrobenzene is customarily prepared by the reaction of benzene with a mixture of concentrated nitric and sulfuric acids.

$$C_6H_6 + HNO_3 \xrightarrow{H_2SO_4} C_6H_5NO_2 + H_2O$$

The principal problem in the formulation of the mechanism for the individual electrophilic substitution reactions is the definition of the substance, usually a cation, that actually reacts with benzene to form the benzenonium ion. Once the character of this reagent is established, it is a relatively simple problem to invent new ways to prepare it and to exercise greater control over the reaction.

The nitration of benzene with nitric acid in the absence of sulfuric acid is very slow. A priori, several roles must be considered for the catalytic influence of sulfuric acid. The possibility that sulfuric acid drives the reaction to completion by the removal of water formed in the nitration as shown in the equation (above) is excluded because the reaction is not reversible. Another role for sulfuric acid is to convert nitric acid to a more electrophilic reagent. The generation of protonated nitric acid is an attractive idea:

$$HO{-}\overset{+}{N}(=O)O^- + H_2SO_4 \rightleftharpoons HO{-}\overset{+}{N}(=O)OH \text{ or } H_2\overset{+}{O}{-}\overset{+}{N}(=O)O^- + HSO_4^-$$

Further, the protonated acid may dissociate to produce a nitronium ion:

$$H_2\overset{+}{O}{-}\overset{+}{N}(=O)O^- \rightleftharpoons H_2O + NO_2^+$$

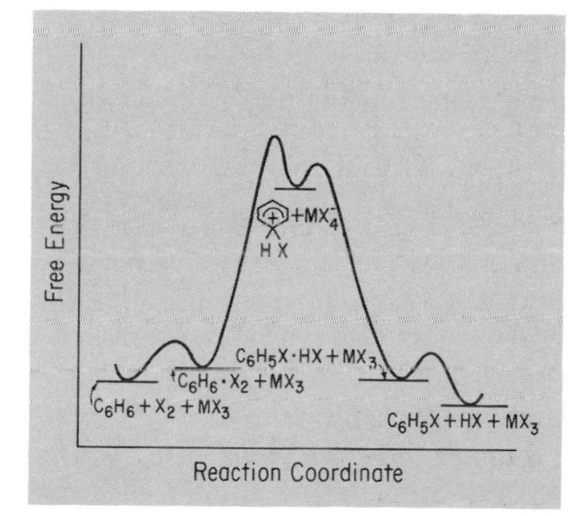

Fig. 2-3 Energy profile for the catalyzed chlorination or bromination of benzene showing charge transfer complex, $C_6H_6 \cdot X_2$, and benzenonium ion intermediates.

Evidence for the nitronium ion has been obtained by the study of the properties of solutions of nitric acid in sulfuric acid. Ions and neutral molecules in solution depress the freezing point of the solvent in direct proportion to the number of species present. For example, the addition of ethylene glycol to water depresses the freezing point of water by 1.86° per mole of added glycol. Similarly, the addition of sodium chloride to water decreases the freezing point 3.72° per mole of added salt, indicative of the dissociation of the salt to two ions. Van't Hoff suggested the *i-factor* as a measure of the number of species formed in solution per mole of the original compound. The *i*-factor for ethylene glycol in water is 1; for sodium chloride the *i*-factor is 2. A solution of nitric acid in sulfuric acid exhibits an *i*-factor of 4. Several equilibria are compatible with an *i*-factor of 4, but only one is chemically attractive:

$$HONO_2 + H_2SO_4 \rightleftharpoons H_2ONO_2^+ + HSO_4^-$$

$$H_2ONO_2^+ \rightleftharpoons H_2O + NO_2^+$$

$$H_2O + H_2SO_4 \rightleftharpoons H_3O^+ + HSO_4^-$$

Net reaction:

$$HONO_2 + 2H_2SO_4 \rightleftharpoons NO_2^+ + H_3O^+ + 2HSO_4^-$$

The formation of nitronium ion, hydronium ion, and two bisulfate anions account for the fourfold effect of nitric acid on the freezing point of sulfuric acid. Accordingly, study of solutions of nitric acid in sulfuric acid indicate that nitric acid is dissociated to the nitronium ion under the conditions of the substitution reaction. This fact lends credence to the idea that nitronium ion is the effective reagent, but it does not prove the case. The fact that the observed rate of the nitration reaction can be related to the concentration of the nitronium ion in the solution, however, provides convincing evidence that the nitronium ion is the real reagent.

The importance of the nitronium ion is supported by the fact that stable nitronium ion salts may be prepared and that these salts are powerful reagents for the nitration of aromatic compounds.

$$NO_2Cl + AgBF_4 \longrightarrow \underset{\text{nitronium tetrafluoroborate}}{NO_2^+, BF_4^-} + AgCl$$

The experimental results suggest that nitronium ion, whether preformed or generated under the conditions of the reaction, is generally the important electrophilic reagent in nitration. Other reagents, for example acetyl nitrate and dinitrogen pentoxide, are presumably precursors of the nitronium ion:

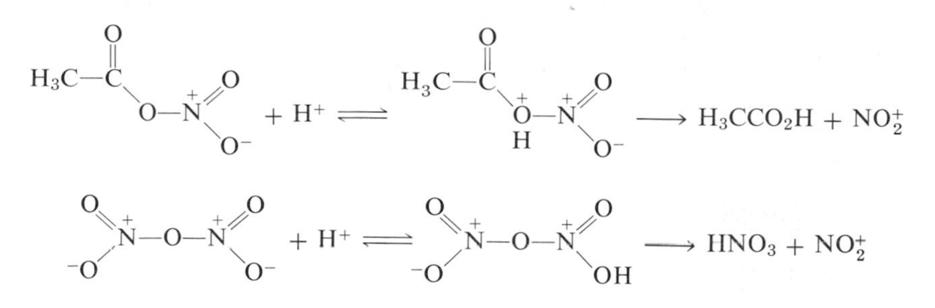

2.5 HALOGENATION

The electrophilic halogenation of benzene may be accomplished in several ways. Chlorine and bromine react with benzene in solvents that are polar or acidic.

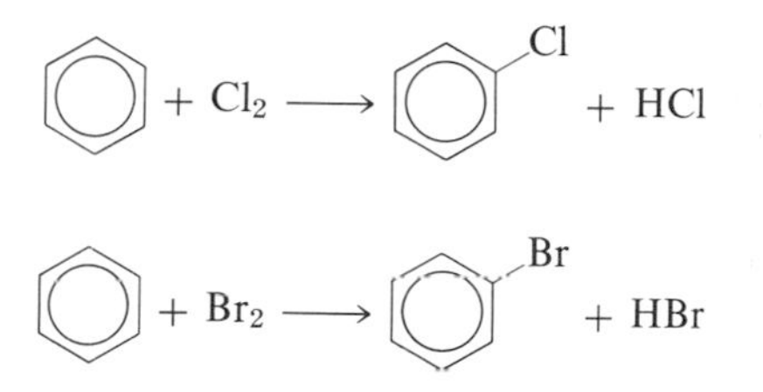

These reactions are very slow. For example, the reaction between chlorine and benzene requires several days for completion. However, Lewis acids are powerful catalysts for the halogenation reactions. The bromides or chlorides of iodine, tin(IV), iron(III), antimony(V), and aluminum catalyze the reaction when they are present in trace amounts. The catalysts commonly used are iodine (converted rapidly to iodine monochloride or iodine monobromide by the molecular halogens) or ferric and aluminum halides.

The rate law for halogenation is not always simple, but, in many instances, is

$$\frac{d[C_6H_5Cl]}{dt} = k[C_6H_6][Cl_2][E]$$

where E is the Lewis acid. The rate law reveals that one molecule each of benzene, the halogen, and the Lewis acid are involved in the reaction. This observation considerably restricts the possible mechanisms. It is also known that benzene and the halogens form charge-transfer complexes (Sec. 2.3), that the rates of chlorination and bromination of benzene and benzene-d_6 are identical (Sec. 2.2), and that the energy requirements for the formation of Cl^+ and Br^+ are prohibitive. These considerations suggest that halogenation proceeds in three steps:

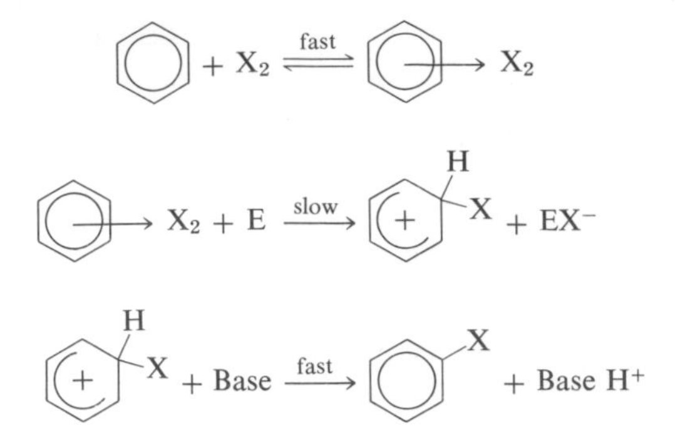

The function assigned to the electrophilic catalyst E is the removal of the halide ion as a more stable anion in the rate-determining step. The transition state leading to the benzenonium ion may be formulated as

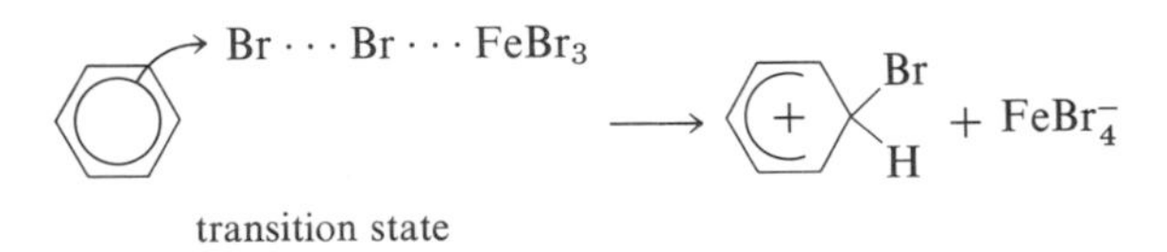

A diagram that illustrates this reaction sequence is shown in Fig. 2-3. The charge-transfer complex is a low energy intermediate that is separated from the starting state by an energy barrier that is small by comparison with the energy barrier for the formation of the benzenonium ion. In this situation, the charge-transfer complex plays no important role in the determination of the rate of the reaction.

Fluorination and iodination present some unusual problems. Fluorine reacts with benzene but the product is not fluorobenzene; rather, carbon-carbon bond rupture occurs and fragmentation products are formed. Special methods (Sec. 5.5) are used for the preparation of fluorobenzene. Iodination is very slow. However, the direct substitution of benzene may be accomplished if the reaction is carried out in the presence of an oxidizing agent. The oxidizing agent, hydrogen peroxide or more commonly nitric acid, is used to form a better electrophilic reagent, H_2OI^+.

$$2H^+ + I_2 + H_2O_2 \longrightarrow 2H_2OI^+$$

$$C_6H_6 + H_2OI^+ \longrightarrow C_6H_5I + H_3O^+$$

Many other reagents are available for aromatic halogenation. Chlorination may be accomplished by hypochlorous acid, chlorine acetate (H_3CCO_2Cl), and certain N-chloroamines (RNHCl). The analogous compounds of bromine are also effective reagents. In certain special situations these reagents offer advantages for selective halogenation reactions.

2.6 THE FRIEDEL–CRAFTS REACTION

Friedel and Crafts discovered the powerful catalytic influences of metal halides (Lewis acids) on the reaction of benzene with alkyl and acyl halides. The attention these and related reactions have received is reflected in the six large volumes of a recent survey of Friedel–Crafts chemistry (see Suggested Reading, p. 39).

2.6A Alkylation: Benzene reacts with alkyl halides and alcohols and their esters under the influence of acid catalysts.

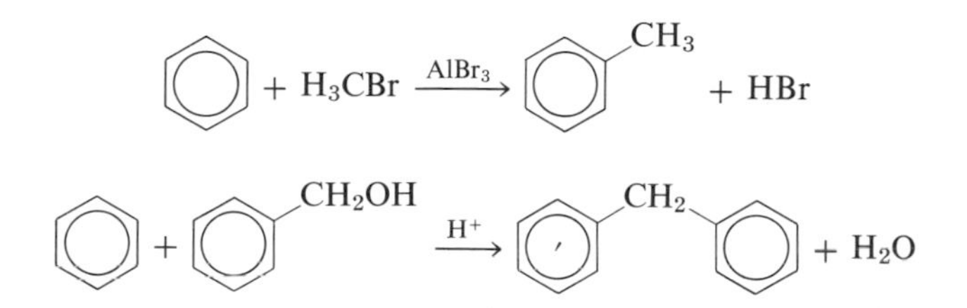

In general, reagents that may ionize to form carbonium ions alkylate benzene. Alkylations with olefins occur when a proton acid is present in addition to the Lewis acid.

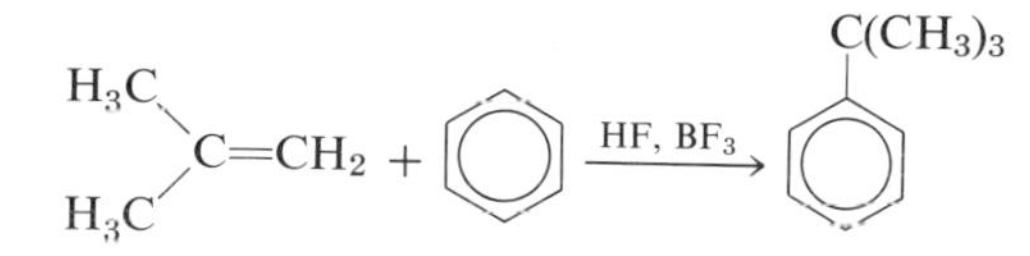

The reagents and catalysts useful for the preparation of alkylbenzenes are presented in Table 2-1.

Table 2-1
REAGENTS AND CATALYSTS IN FRIEDEL–CRAFTS ALKYLATION

Reagents	Catalysts
Alkyl halides, RCl, RBr, RI	BF_3, $SnCl_4$, $FeCl_3$, $SbCl_5$, $AlCl_3$
Aliphatic alcohols, ROH	H_2SO_4, HF, BF_3—H_2O
Olefins, $R_2C{=}CR_2$	HF—BF_3, HCl—$AlCl_3$

Side reactions limit the utility of the alkylation reaction. One important factor is that the product is more reactive than benzene. When an equal molar mixture of an alkyl halide and benzene react, the initial product, the monoalkylbenzene, substitutes further to form di- and tri-alkylated compounds.

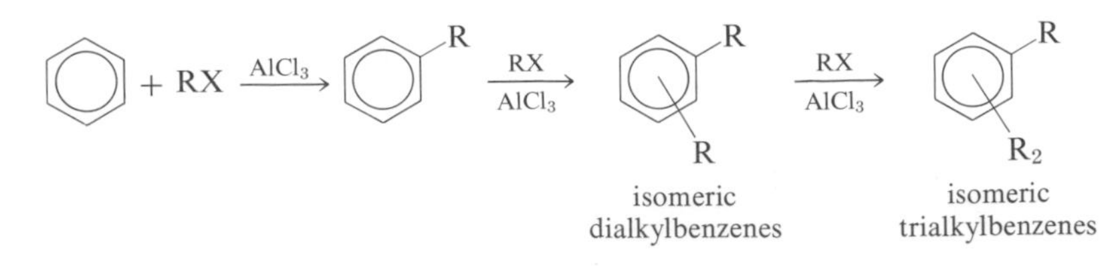

A large excess of benzene relative to the alkylating agent is necessary to reduce the formation of polysubstituted compounds. Another frequent complication in Friedel–Crafts alkylation is the isomerization of the reagents or products or both under the reaction conditions (Sec. 6.4). Methyl and ethyl halides yield methyl- and ethylbenzene, respectively. However, *n*-propyl chloride and benzene produce not only *n*-propylbenzene, but isopropylbenzene as well; isobutyl chloride yields only *t*-butylbenzene.

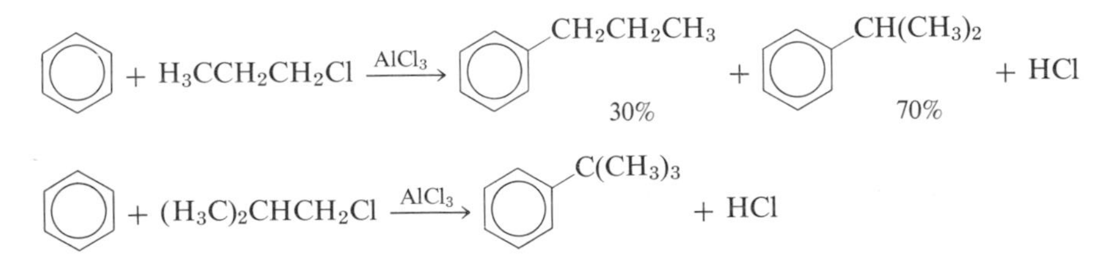

The traditional explanation for the formation of these products is shown for *n*-propyl chloride:

$$H_3CCH_2CH_2Cl + AlCl_3 \rightleftharpoons H_3CCH_2CH_2^+, AlCl_4^-$$

$$\begin{array}{ccc} H_3C\overset{H}{C}HCH_2^+ & \xrightarrow[\text{shift}]{H} & H_3C\overset{+}{C}HCH_3 \\ \downarrow C_6H_6 & & \downarrow C_6H_6 \\ H^+ + C_6H_5CH_2CH_2CH_3 & & C_6H_5CH(CH_3)_2 + H^+ \end{array}$$

This formulation suggests that *n*-propyl chloride ionizes to *n*-propyl carbonium ion, which rearranges to isopropyl carbonium ion by a hydride shift. Each ion reacts with benzene to yield the products. Quite generally isomerization occurs whenever the carbonium ion produced by isomerization is more stable than its precursor. Thus, *primary* carbonium ions are isomerized to *secondary* or *tertiary* carbonium ions and *secondary* ions are isomerized to *tertiary* carbonium ions. Alkylation products form from these rearranged ions as shown for the reaction of *n*-propyl chloride (above) and for the reaction of neopentyl chloride.

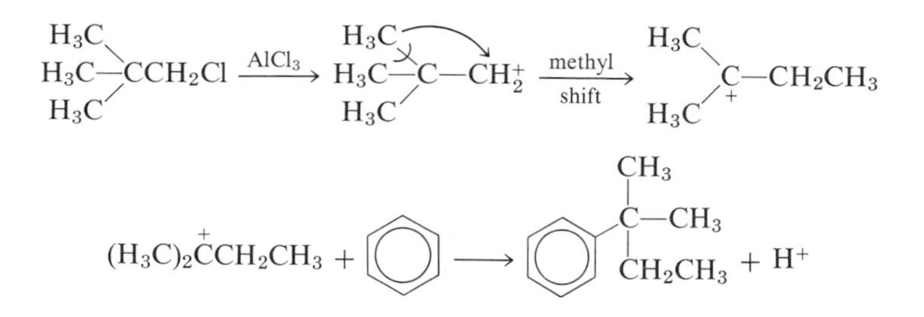

The mechanism of the Friedel–Crafts alkylation is quite accurately described as a nucleophilic substitution reaction in which benzene is the nucleophile. The alkyl halides are known to form 1 : 1 addition compounds with Lewis acids that are analogous to the charge-transfer complexes formed between benzene and these acids (Sec. 2.3).

$$H_3CCl + AlCl_3 \rightleftharpoons H_3CCl \cdot AlCl_3$$

$$H_3CCH_2Br + GaBr_3 \rightleftharpoons H_3CCH_2Br \cdot GaBr_3$$

The stable complex anion, MX_4^-, is displaced by the nucleophile, benzene, in an S_N2 reaction.

$$C_6H_6 + H_3CCl \cdot AlCl_3 \longrightarrow [C_6H_6(H)(CH_3)]^+ + AlCl_4^-$$

This mechanism is applicable for *primary* alkyl halides that are incapable of rearrangement. On the other hand, the S_N1 path predominates with *secondary* and *tertiary* alkyl halides. The 1 : 1 addition compounds of these halides readily dissociate to carbonium ions, which react with the available nucleophile, benzene.

$$(H_3C)_3CBr + BF_3 \rightleftharpoons (H_3C)_3CBr \cdot BF_3$$

$$(H_3C)_3CBr \cdot BF_3 \rightleftharpoons (H_3C)_3C^+ + BrBF_3^-$$

$$C_6H_6 + (H_3C)_3C^+ \longrightarrow [C_6H_6(H)C(CH_3)_3]^+ \longrightarrow C_6H_5C(CH_3)_3 + H^+$$

When a primary alkyl halide, such as *n*-propyl chloride, capable of rearrangement is used in a Friedel–Crafts reaction, the *n*-alkyl derivative presumably reacts via the S_N2 path while the *i*-alkyl derivative produced by a hydride shift reacts via the S_N1 path.

2.6B Acylation: Acid chlorides and acid anhydrides react with benzene in the presence of molar amounts of aluminum chloride (or other Lewis acids) to yield ketones.

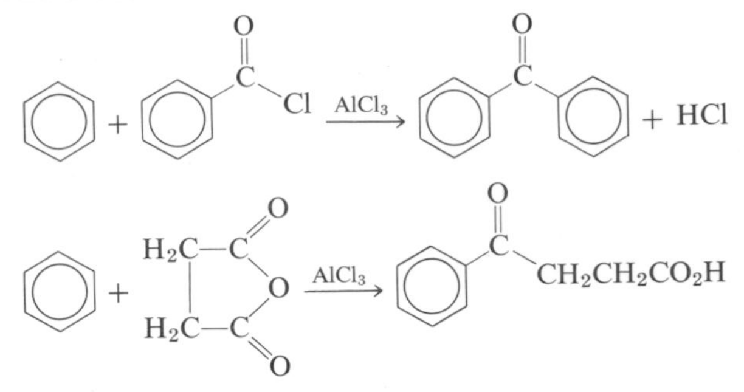

The reaction is subject to few restrictions. Rearrangements and side reactions are only rarely encountered. This Friedel–Crafts reaction often offers a convenient starting point for the synthesis of more complex molecules and is the method of choice for the preparation of phenyl ketones.

The principal features of the mechanism of acylation are established with some confidence. Acid halides are rather strong Lewis bases and form isolable 1:1 addition compounds with Lewis acids.

$$RCOCl + AlCl_3 \rightleftharpoons RCOCl \cdot AlCl_3$$

The rate law for acylation is frequently found to be

$$\frac{d[C_6H_5COR]}{dt} = k_3[C_6H_6][RCOCl][MX_3]$$

This rate law indicates that one molecule each of benzene, the acid chloride, and the Lewis acid are involved in the reaction mechanism. A related fact that assists in the definition of the course of the reaction is that when different Lewis acids are used to catalyze the reaction, the rate of product formation changes appreciably. However, the isomer distribution (see Chapter 3) does not change. For example, toluene and benzoyl chloride yield about 9% *o*-, 1% *m*-, and 90% *p*-methylbenzophenones:

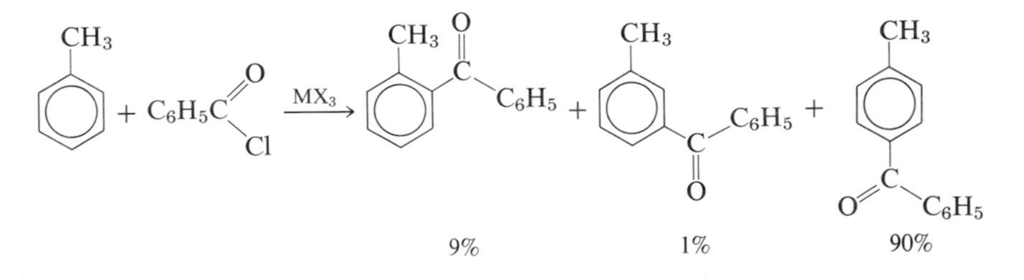

regardless of the catalyst (MX_3) used for the reaction. Further, acyl chlorides and acyl bromides yield the same set of acylated products even though the reaction rates are quite different. Such observations signal the importance of an intermediate that is common in all the reactions. The acylonium ion ($R\overset{+}{C}O$) fulfills this condition. Each acyl halide-Lewis acid addition compound may dissociate in solution:

$$C_6H_5COCl + AlCl_3 \rightleftharpoons C_6H_5COCl \cdot AlCl_3 \rightleftharpoons C_6H_5\overset{+}{C}{=}O + AlCl_4^-$$

$$C_6H_5COCl + SbCl_5 \rightleftharpoons C_6H_5COCl \cdot SbCl_5 \rightleftharpoons C_6H_5\overset{+}{C}{=}O + SbCl_6^-$$

$$C_6H_5COBr + AlBr_3 \rightleftharpoons C_6H_5COBr \cdot AlBr_3 \rightleftharpoons C_6H_5\overset{+}{C}{=}O + AlBr_4^-$$

Each acyl halide-catalyst pair yields a different anion but the same acylonium ion. This formulation accommodates the fact that the net reaction rate changes but the isomer distribution does not. The rate variations are ascribed to the differing equilibrium constants for the dissociation of the acyl halide-catalyst pair and reflect the supply of the acylonium ion available for reaction. However, the same electrophilic reagent, $C_6H_5CO^+$, is produced with each catalyst. This reagent is thus common in all the reactions and is responsible for the invariant isomer distribution.

A stoichiometric amount of the "catalyst" is needed in the acylation reaction. This requirement is the consequence of the basicity of the product ketone. The equilibrium for the reaction of a ketone with the acyl chloride-aluminum chloride addition compound is far to the right:

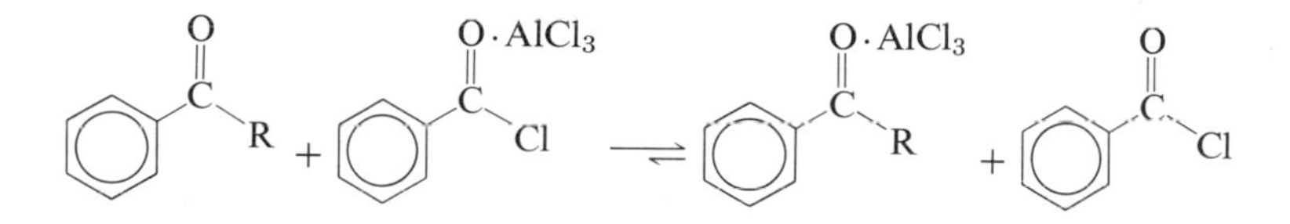

Accordingly, the catalyst is removed from the reagent and transferred to the product. A mole of the catalyst is therefore necessary for a complete reaction. The ketone-Lewis acid compound is present in the solution at the end of the reaction. Water and acid are added to hydrolyze the Lewis acid and liberate the desired ketone.

2.7 OTHER SUBSTITUTION REACTIONS

Many other electrophilic reagents substitute aromatic compounds. The mechanisms of these reactions may be formulated by analogy with the mechanisms discussed for nitration, halogenation, and the Friedel–Crafts reactions.

Benzene reacts vigorously with fuming sulfuric acid (sulfuric acid with SO_3 present).

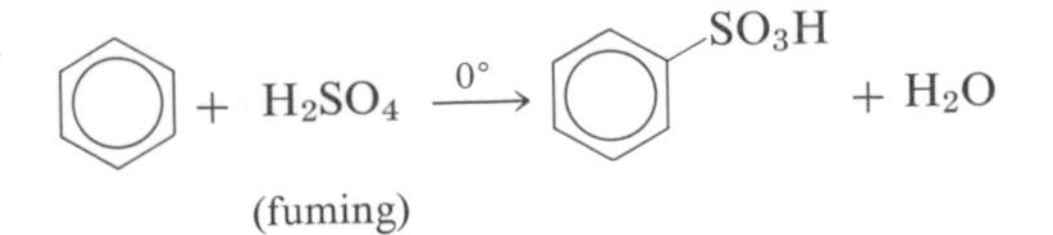

Other reagents that form carbon-sulfur bonds are chlorosulfonic acid, $ClSO_3H$; fluorosulfonic acid, FSO_3H and sulfur trioxide, SO_3. The actual electrophilic reagent in sulfonation is not established with certainty. Indeed, it would appear that several different species, SO_3 or SO_3H^+ for example, are able to effect the conversion of benzene to a benzenonium ion.

Two reactions closely related to the Friedel–Crafts syntheses are chloromethylation,

$$C_6H_6 + H_2CO + HCl \xrightarrow{ZnCl_2} C_6H_5CH_2Cl + H_2O$$

and the Gatterman–Koch aldehyde synthesis,

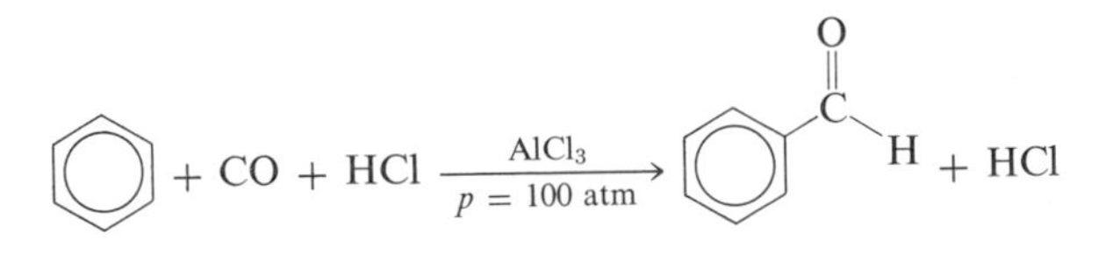

Formally, the electrophiles are produced by protonation of the carbonyl derivative under the influence of the Lewis acid.

$$2\ H_2C{=}O + 2HCl + ZnCl_2 \longrightarrow 2\ H_2\overset{+}{C}{-}OH + ZnCl_4^{-2}$$

$$:\overset{-}{C}{\equiv}\overset{+}{O}: + HCl + AlCl_3 \longrightarrow H{-}\overset{+}{C}{=}\ddot{O}: + AlCl_4^-$$

Benzenonium ions are produced when these reagents react with benzene. As in the other substitution reactions, the products are formed when a proton is removed from the benzenonium ion. Benzyl alcohol, the first product in the chloromethylation reaction, is converted to benzyl chloride under the reaction conditions.

Other less general electrophilic substitution reactions are known. These reactions are less general in the sense that the reagents are only effective for the substitution of aromatic compounds that are much more reactive than benzene. Two important processes of this class, the diazo coupling reaction and aromatic nitrosation, are examined in Sec. 5.5.

The substitution reactions that have been discussed involve the replacement of a hydrogen atom by an electrophile. Other groups may also be displaced from the aromatic nucleus in electrophilic reactions. For example, the phenyl Grignard reagent and phenyllithium react with electrophilic reagents.

$$\begin{array}{lll} C_6H_5Li & H_2O & \longrightarrow C_6H_5H \\ \text{or} & + CO_2 & \longrightarrow C_6H_5CO_2H \\ C_6H_5MgBr & H_2C{=}O & \longrightarrow C_6H_5CH_2OH \end{array}$$

The mildest kind of electrophilic reagents may be employed because the carbon-metal bond is so easily broken. Thus, hydrolysis with water is a vigorous reaction and even the polarized carbonyl group is an effective reagent.

$$\overset{\delta+}{C}{=}\overset{\delta-}{O}$$

Other organometallic groups are also substituted in preference to a hydrogen atom by electrophilic reagents.

$$C_6H_5Si(CH_3)_3 + D_3O^+ \longrightarrow C_6H_5D + DOSi(CH_3)_3 + D^+$$

$$C_6H_5HgOAc + Br_2 \longrightarrow C_6H_5Br + BrHgOAc$$

Tertiary alkyl groups are replaced at a rate that is competitive with that for the substitution of hydrogen.

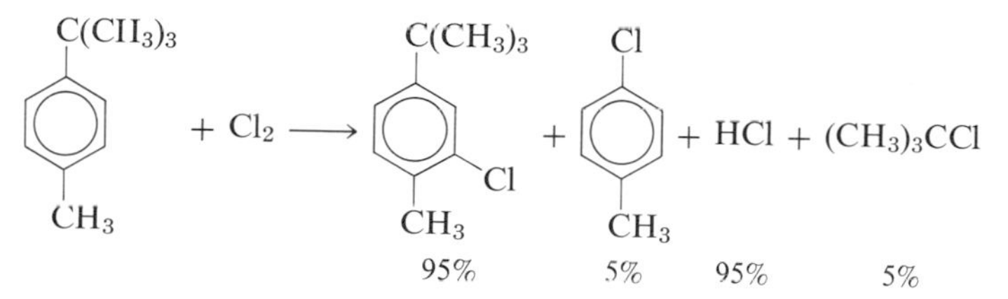

In general, groups capable of the formation of relatively stable cations may be displaced from the aromatic nucleus by less stable cations.

2.8 SUBSTITUTION AND ADDITION

Substitution products are obtained in the reactions of benzene with electrophilic reagents. These same reagents react with olefins, but addition products are obtained:

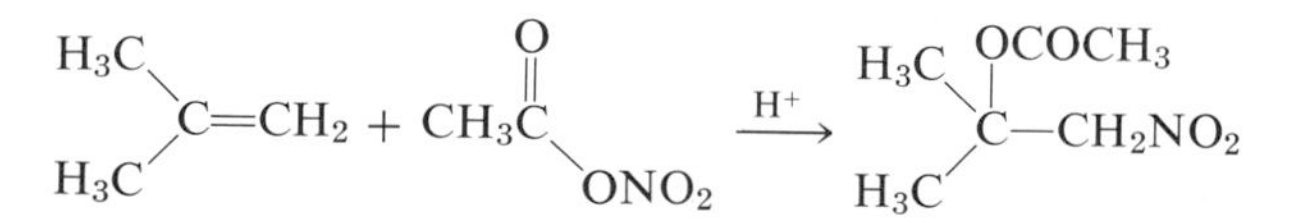

The different course taken by the reactions of olefins and of benzene with the same reagent under the same conditions is dictated by the nature of the reactions of the carbonium ion and the nucleophiles and bases present in the solution. To illustrate, the reaction of acetyl nitrate with benzene yields the intermediate benzenonium ion; while the same reaction with isobutylene leads to the aliphatic carbonium ion. Each intermediate is capable of two distinct subsequent reactions. The ions may react with acetic acid as a nucleophile to give the addition products. On the other hand, acetic acid may serve as a base to abstract a proton from the ions to yield the substitution products.

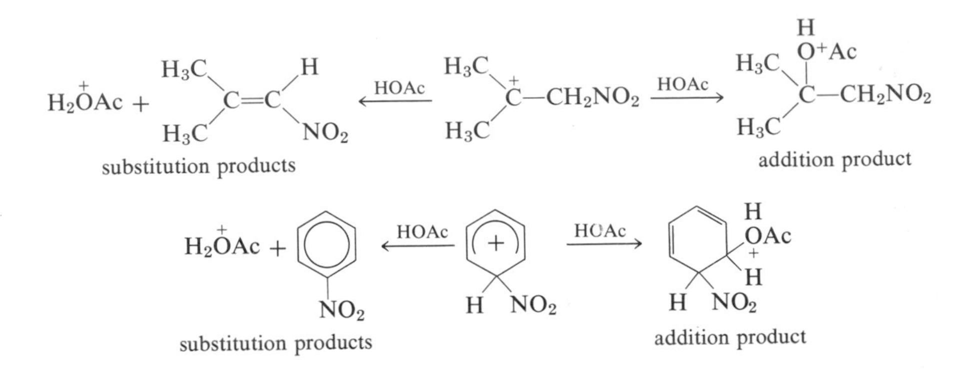

The major difference in the course of these similar reactions is dictated by the fact that the aromatic character of benzene is partially restored in the transition state that leads to the formation of the substitution product.

PROBLEMS

2.1. Draw the principal resonance structures for the three substituted benzenonium ions:

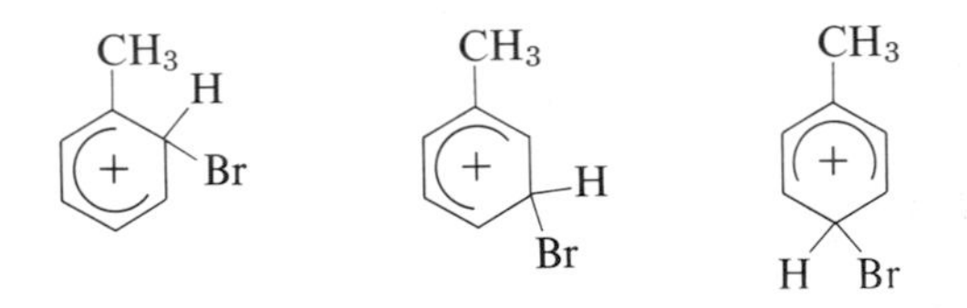

2.2. Draw the principal resonance structures for the ion formed by the introduction of the nitronium ion at the 1- and 2-positions of naphthalene.

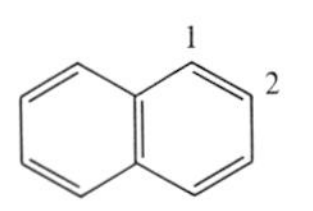

2.3. Benzene-d_6 reacts with perchloric acid to yield benzene-d_5. Draw the energy profile for this reaction.

2.4. Mercuric acetate, $Hg(OAc)_2$, reacts with benzene in acetic acid to yield phenylmercuric acetate, C_6H_5HgOAc, and acetic acid. The reaction is catalyzed by perchloric acid. The rate law for the reaction is

$$\text{rate} = \frac{d[C_6H_5HgOAc]}{dt} = k[C_6H_6][Hg(OAc)_2][HClO_4]$$

The ratio of the rate constants for the mercuration of benzene and benzene-d_6 is 2.4. Write a mechanism for this reaction that accommodates these facts and draw the free energy profile.

2.5. Suggest several reagents that may be useful for the formation of the NO^+ ion. Some examples are noted in Sec. 5.5.

2.6. Write mechanisms for the following reactions and identify the reagent that actually reacts with benzene to form the benzenonium ion.

a. $C_6H_6 + C_6H_5SO_2Cl \xrightarrow{AlCl_3} (C_6H_5)_2SO_2 + HCl$

b. $C_6H_6 + HOBr \xrightarrow{HClO_4} C_6H_5Br + H_2O$

c. $C_6H_6 + ClSO_3H \xrightarrow{H^+} C_6H_5SO_2Cl + H_2O$

d. $C_6H_6 + (CH_3)_3CCH_2OH \xrightarrow{H^+} C_6H_5C(C_2H_5)(CH_3)_2 + H_2O$

e. $C_6H_6 + CF_3CO_3H \xrightarrow{BF_3} C_6H_5OH + CF_3CO_2H$ (hypothetical)

f. $C_6H_5Li + D_2O \longrightarrow C_6H_5D + LiOD$

SUGGESTED READING

Halogenation and nitration are treated in detail by P. B. de la Mare and J. H. Ridd, *Aromatic Substitution,* Butterworth's Scientific Publications, London, 1959.

The Friedel–Crafts and related aromatic substitution reactions are discussed in the six volume treatise, *Friedel–Crafts and Related Reactions,* edited by G. A. Olah, John Wiley & Sons, New York, 1963 1964.

Recent progress in the area is discussed by E. Berliner, "Electrophilic Aromatic Substitution Reactions," *Prog. Phys. Org. Chem.*, **2,** 253 (1964).

3 Directive Effects in Electrophilic Substitution Reactions

3.1 INTRODUCTION

The nonequivalence of the hydrogen atoms of the monosubstituted benzenes was discussed in Sec. 1.2. If these hydrogen atoms were replaced with equal ease, the three disubstituted compounds would be formed in statistical amounts (2 parts *ortho,* 2 parts *meta,* 1 part *para*).

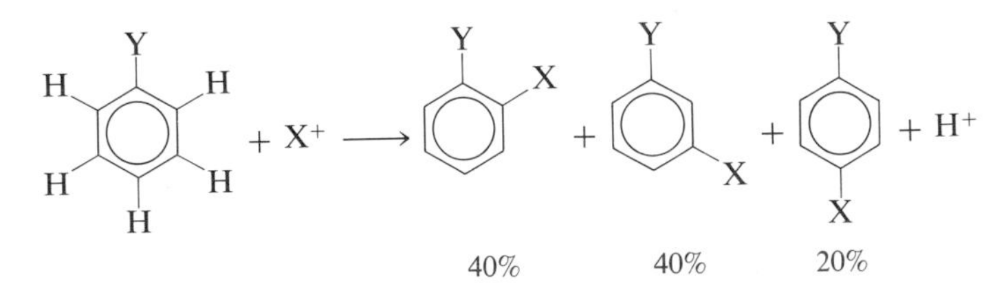

The proportion of products does not approach the statistical distribution; this is illustrated by the nitration of chlorobenzene and the chlorination of nitrobenzene.

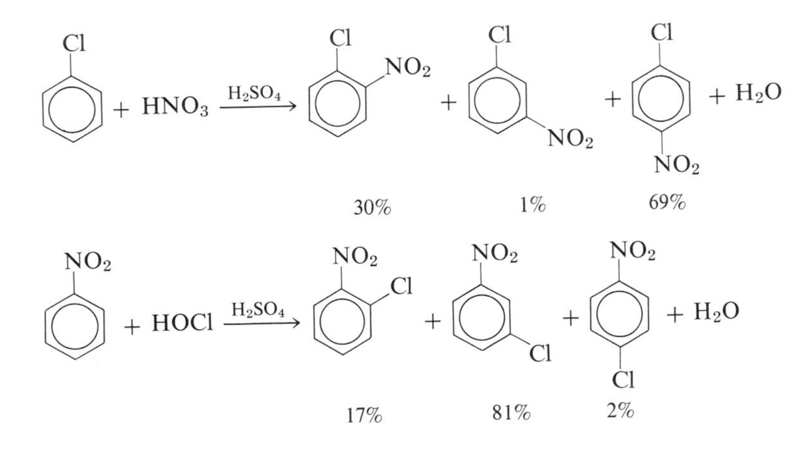

The isomer distributions and the rates of these reactions are influenced by the substituent originally present in the monosubstituted benzene. The role played by the substituent is remarkably regular and the substituent is said to exert a directive effect. A knowledge of these directive effects permits the prediction of the approximate product distribution for any electrophilic substitution reaction. These effects are the subject of this chapter.

3.2 ASSIGNMENT OF STRUCTURE

Two approaches were used for the unambiguous assignment of the structures of the isomeric di-, tri-, and polysubstituted benzenes. One, the Körner absolute isomer number method, depends on the fact that each of the three isomeric disubstituted benzenes forms a different number of trisubstituted benzenes, as shown on p. 4. In the Körner approach, the three disubstituted products of the reaction of a monosubstituted benzene are separated and then individually converted to trisubstituted benzenes. The isomeric trisubstituted products are separated and the number of different isomers obtained from each disubstituted benzene counted. To employ this method with confidence, it is essential to allow each of the three disubstituted benzenes to react and to isolate two trisubstituted benzenes from one *(ortho)*, three from another *(meta)*, and one from the third *(para)*. Unfortunately, the operation of the directive effects noted in Sec. 3.1 create serious experimental problems. Frequently, only a minor amount of one of the isomers is formed, and its separation and identification presents an insurmountable experimental difficulty.

A second approach for the proof of structure relies on the interconversion of substituent groups. If the substitution pattern is known for one of the substances, that for the second is immediately evident. Thus, the reduction of *m*-dinitrobenzene to *m*-diaminobenzene would constitute a structure proof for the dinitro compound if the structure of the diamine had been established by an independent method.

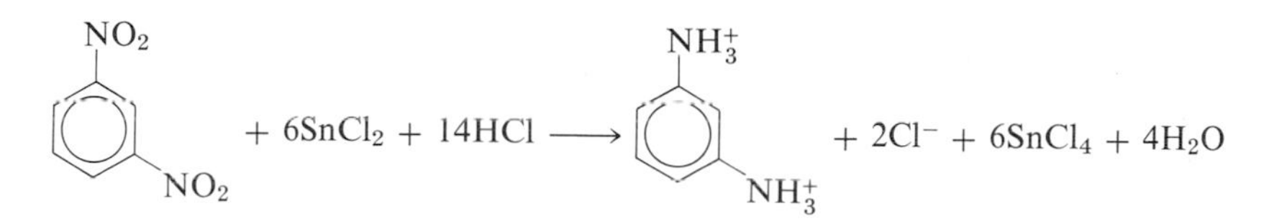

This approach was in fact used in conjunction with the Körner method to prove the structure of *m*-diaminobenzene. It was found that one diaminobenzene could be formed from three different dinitrobenzoic acids by reduction and decarboxylation. There are six possible dinitrobenzoic acids. These acids may be converted to *o*-, *m*-, or *p*-diaminobenzene as shown:

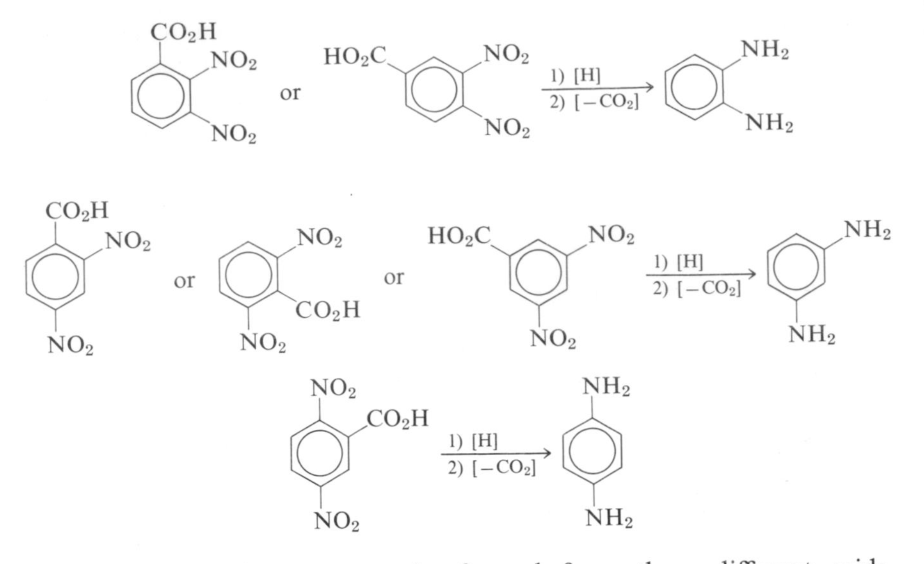

Only *m*-diaminobenzene can be formed from three different acids. Accordingly, the transformation constitutes a structure proof for this diamine. Once the structures of a few key compounds had been established by difficult methods of this kind, it became a relatively easy problem to work out the structures of others by the interconversion of substituent groups. The structures of many di- and trisubstituted benzenes were proved by these methods in the latter part of the nineteenth century.

3.3 A SURVEY OF DIRECTIVE EFFECTS

Isomer distributions for the nitration and chlorination of several typical monosubstituted benzenes are summarized in Table 3-1.

The results for nitration and chlorination indicate the general situation for the electrophilic substitution reactions of the monosubstituted benzenes. Other electrophilic substitution reactions, e.g., bromination or sulfonation, yield a similar set of isomeric disubstituted benzenes. Inspection of the results presented in Table 3-1 reveals that there is a natural division (indicated by the heavy line) in the influence of Y on the course of reaction. The substituents above the heavy line direct the entering group dominantly to the *ortho, para* positions. The substituents below the heavy line direct the reagent to the *meta* position. The substituents, therefore, are characterized as *ortho-para* directors or as *meta* directors.

Substituents also influence the rate. This directive effect is assessed by the comparison of the reaction rates of the monosubstituted compounds with the same reagent under the same conditions. For convenience, benzene is adopted as the reference compound in each substitution reaction. These data are conventionally presented as relative rates, that is,

Table 3-1

ISOMER DISTRIBUTIONS FOR NITRATION AND CHLORINATION

Benzene derivative, Y	Isomer distribution, % of each product — Nitration§ nitro-Y-benzene *o*-	*m*-	*p*-	Chlorination‡ chloro-Y-benzene *o*-	*m*-	*p*-
Anisole, $—OCH_3$	44	—†	56	21	—†	79
Acetanilide, $—NHCOCH_3$	20	—†	80	33	—†	67
Biphenyl, $—C_6H_5$	69	—†	31	53	—†	47
Toluene, $—CH_3$	59	4	37	60	—†	40
Fluorobenzene, —F	9	—†	91	11	—†	89
Chlorobenzene, —Cl	30	1	69	32	—†	68
Bromobenzene, —Br	37	1	62	39	—†	61
Benzoic acid, $—CO_2H$	22	76	2			
Nitrobenzene, $—NO_2$	6	94	—†			
Phenyltrimethyl ammonium ion, $—N(CH_3)_3^+$	—†	89	11			

† This amount is less than 1%.
‡ The reaction conditions are shown in Table 3-2.

the rate constant for a monosubstituted benzene, $k_{C_6H_5Y}$, divided by the rate constant for benzene, $k_{C_6H_6}$, for the same substitution reaction. Typical results for noncatalytic chlorination, nitration, and hypobromous acid bromination are presented in Table 3-2.

Table 3-2

RELATIVE RATES FOR TYPICAL REACTIONS OF MONOSUBSTITUTED BENZENES

Substituted benzenes Compound, Y	Relative rates* Chlorination‡ $k_{C_6H_5Y}/k_{C_6H_6}$	Nitration§ $k_{C_6H_5Y}/k_{C_6H_6}$	Bromination¶ $k_{C_6H_5Y}/k_{C_6H_6}$
Anisole, $—OCH_3$	9.7×10^6	—	—
Acetanilide, $—NHCOCH_3$	6.2×10^5	—	—
Biphenyl, $—C_6H_5$	4.2×10^2	3.5×10	1.3×10
Toluene, $—CH_3$	3.4×10^2	2.2×10	3.6×10
Benzene	1.0	1.0	1.0
Fluorobenzene, —F	7.4×10^{-1}	1.4×10^{-1}	—
Chlorobenzene, —Cl	1.0×10^{-1}	3.1×10^{-2}	—
Bromobenzene, —Br	7.2×10^{-2}	2.8×10^{-2}	—
Benzoic acid, $—CO_2H$	—	—	7.5×10^{-3}
Nitrobenzene, $—NO_2$	—	—	1.6×10^{-5}
Phenyltrimethyl-ammonium, ion, $—N(CH_3)_3^+$	—	1.5×10^{-8}	1.6×10^{-5}

* Rate for the monosubstituted benzene relative to the rate for benzene.
‡ Noncatalytic chlorination by molecular chlorine in acetic acid at 25°.
§ Nitration by nitric acid in acetic acid anhydride at 25°.
¶ Perchloric acid-catalyzed bromination by hypobromous acid in 50% dioxane-50% water at 25°.

The relative rate data, Table 3-2, allow a further characterization of the directive effects of the substituents. The substituents above the heavy line activate the aromatic ring and the substitution reactions of these monosubstituted compounds proceed more rapidly than for benzene. The substituents below the heavy line exert the opposite effect. The influence of the substituent on the rate is as regular as its influence on the isomer distribution. The substituents fall into one of three classes as presented in the survey in Fig. 3-1.

$\frac{k_{C_6H_5Y}}{k_{C_6H_6}} > 1$ *meta* products	no known groups	$\frac{k_{C_6H_5Y}}{k_{C_6H_6}} > 1$ *ortho, para* products	—OMe —NHCOCH$_3$ —C$_6$H$_5$ —CH$_3$
$\frac{k_{C_6H_5Y}}{k_{C_6H_6}} < 1$ *meta* products	—CO$_2$H —NO$_2$ —N(CH$_3$)$_3^+$	$\frac{k_{C_6H_5Y}}{k_{C_6H_6}} < 1$ *ortho, para* products	—F —Cl —Br —CH$_2$Cl

Fig. 3-1 Classification of directive effects.

An analysis of directive effects requires the comparison of the rate constants for reaction at the individual positions ($k_{o\text{-Y}}$, $k_{m\text{-Y}}$, $k_{p\text{-Y}}$) of the monosubstituted benzene relative to a single position in benzene (k_H). This comparison is necessary because each substitution product is formed through a different benzenonium ion.

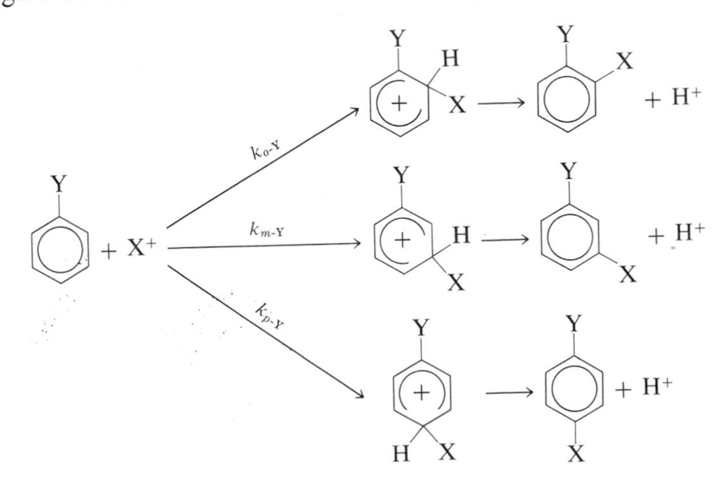

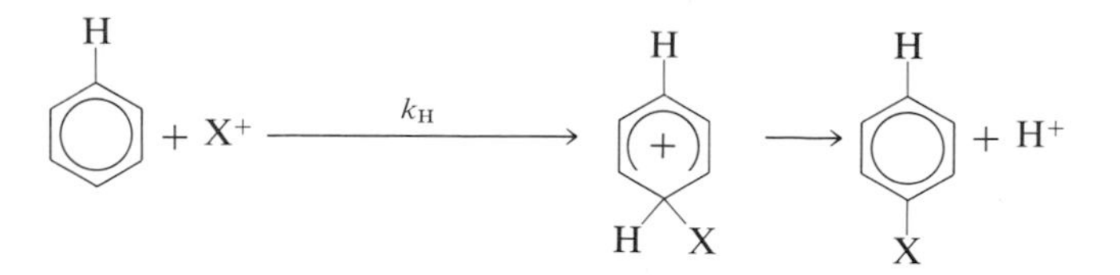

As discussed in Sec. 2.2, the rate of formation of the benzenonium ion determines the actual rate of the reaction. Thus, the rate constants for the formation of these ions determine the product distribution and the relative rates. The rate constant, $k_{C_6H_5Y}$, for the molecule C_6H_5Y is simply the sum of the rate constants for substitution at three positions:

$$k_{C_6H_5Y} = 2k_{o\text{-}Y} + 2k_{m\text{-}Y} + k_{p\text{-}Y} \tag{3.1}$$

The factor of 2 is a statistical correction for two *ortho* and two *meta* positions in the monosubstituted benzene. The isomer distribution is determined by the ratio of the statistically weighted rate constant to the total rate constant.

$$\frac{[\%\ ortho]}{100} = \frac{2k_{o\text{-}Y}}{k_{C_6H_5Y}} \tag{3.2a}$$

$$\frac{[\%\ meta]}{100} = \frac{2k_{m\text{-}Y}}{k_{C_6H_5Y}} \tag{3.2b}$$

$$\frac{[\%\ para]}{100} = \frac{k_{p\text{-}Y}}{k_{C_6H_5Y}} \tag{3.2c}$$

In the same way, the rate constant $k_{C_6H_6}$ for benzene is six times the rate constant k_H for substitution at one position:

$$k_{C_6H_6} = 6k_H \tag{3.3}$$

The relative rates for the individual positions in the monosubstituted compound relative to one position in benzene are designated as partial rate factors and symbolized:

$$o_f^Y = \frac{k_{o\text{-}Y}}{k_H} \qquad m_f^Y = \frac{k_{m\text{-}Y}}{k_H} \qquad p_f^Y = \frac{k_{p\text{-}Y}}{k_H} \tag{3.4}$$

That is, o_f^Y is the rate factor (f) for the *ortho* position (o) in the substituted benzene (C_6H_5Y). The partial rate factors are calculated from the measured relative rate, $k_{C_6H_5Y}/k_{C_6H_6}$, and the isomer distribution. The solution of Eq. (3.2a) for $k_{o\text{-}Y}$ yields

$$k_{o\text{-}Y} = \frac{k_{C_6H_5Y}}{2} \times \frac{[\%\ ortho]}{100} \tag{3.5}$$

Division of each side of Eq. (3.5) by Eq. (3.3) and rearrangement yields

$$o_f^Y = \frac{k_{o\text{-}Y}}{k_H} = \frac{3k_{C_6H_5Y}}{k_{C_6H_6}} \times \frac{[\%\ ortho]}{100} \tag{3.6}$$

Expressions for m_f^{Y} and p_f^{Y} are obtained in the same way.

$$m_f^{\mathrm{Y}} = \frac{k_{m\text{-Y}}}{k_{\mathrm{H}}} = \frac{3k_{\mathrm{C_6H_5Y}}}{k_{\mathrm{C_6H_6}}} \times \frac{[\%\ meta]}{100} \tag{3.7}$$

$$p_f^{\mathrm{Y}} = \frac{k_{p\text{-Y}}}{k_{\mathrm{H}}} = \frac{6k_{\mathrm{C_6H_5Y}}}{k_{\mathrm{C_6H_6}}} \times \frac{[\%\ para]}{100} \tag{3.8}$$

Partial rate factors calculated, in part, from the experimental results in Tables 3-1 and 3-2 are summarized in Table 3-3.

3.4 A QUALITATIVE THEORY

The qualitative interpretation of substitution effects depends on three rather fundamental ideas. These concepts are, first, the benzenonium ion is an accurate model for the transition state; second, the differences in the thermodynamic stability of these substituted benzenonium ions determine the differences in activation free energy for the reaction; and, third, the thermodynamic stabilities of the benzenonium ions depend on the polar, resonance, and steric effects of the substituent. The first suggestion is reasonable inasmuch as the benzenonium ion, formed in the rate-determining step, is a high energy intermediate that is closely related in structure and energy content to the transition state. This idea is an application of the Hammond postulate discussed by W. H. Saunders, *Ionic Aliphatic Reactions*, p. 7 (this series). The concept is illustrated in Fig. 3-2 for the *para* substitution of toluene (T) and chlorobenzene (C) by nitronium ion.

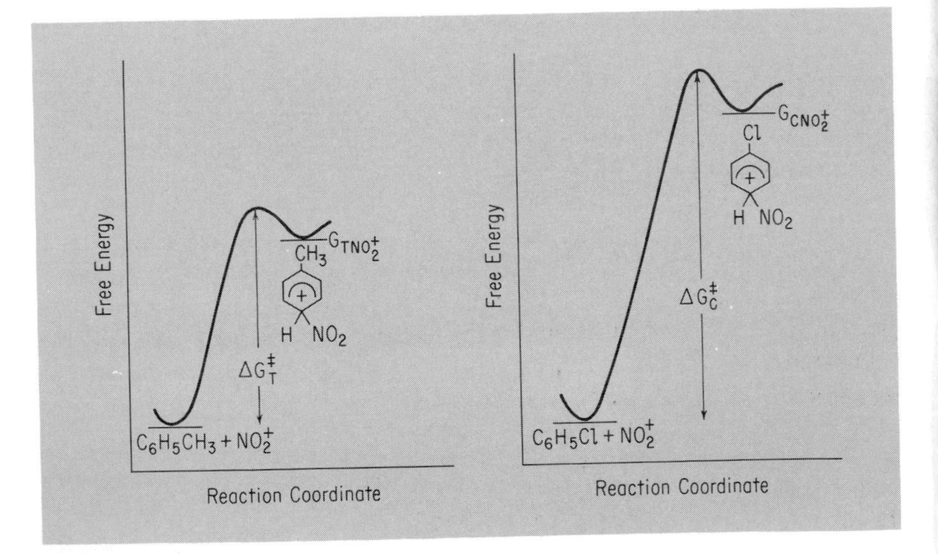

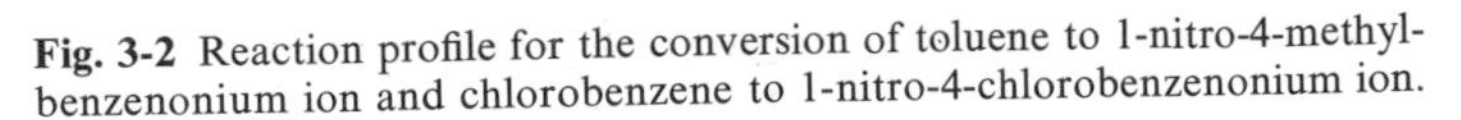
Fig. 3-2 Reaction profile for the conversion of toluene to 1-nitro-4-methylbenzenonium ion and chlorobenzene to 1-nitro-4-chlorobenzenonium ion.

Table 3-3

PARTIAL RATE FACTORS FOR TYPICAL REACTIONS OF MONOSUBSTITUTED BENZENES

Benzene derivative, Y	Partial rate factors† Chlorination			Nitration			Bromination		
	o_f^Y	m_f^Y	p_f^Y	o_f^Y	m_f^Y	p_f^Y	o_f^Y	m_f^Y	p_f^Y
Anisole, $-OCH_3$	6.1×10^6		4.6×10^7						
Acetanilide, $-NHCOCH_3$	6.1×10^5		2.5×10^6						
Biphenyl, $-C_6H_5$	310	0.7	670	36		33	11	0.3	16
Toluene, $-CH_3$	620	5	820	38	3	49	76	2.5	59
Benzene, H	1.0	1.0	1.0	1.0	1.0	1.0	1.0	1.0	1.0
Fluorobenzene, $-F$	0.2	5.6×10^{-3}	3.9	0.4		0.8			
Chlorobenzene, $-Cl$	0.01	2.3×10^{-3}	0.4	0.03	8.4×10^{-4}	0.13			
Bromobenzene, $-Br$	0.08	3.2×10^{-3}	0.3	0.03	9.8×10^{-4}	0.10			
Benzoic acid, $-CO_2H$								2.3×10^{-2}	
Nitrobenzene, $-NO_2$								4.8×10^{-5}	
Phenyltrimethyl-ammonium ion, $-N(CH_3)_3^+$					4.0×10^{-8}	1.0×10^{-8}		4.8×10^{-5}	

† The reaction conditions are shown on p. 43.

It is the premise of this theory that the free energy requirements for the nitration, $\Delta G^{\ddagger}_{T}$ and $\Delta G^{\ddagger}_{C}$, are related to the free energy content of the benzenonium ions, $G_{H_3CC_6H_5NO_2^+}$ and $G_{ClC_6H_5NO_2^+}$. The argument concludes *p*-nitrochlorobenzene is formed more slowly than *p*-nitrotoluene because the corresponding benzenonium ion, 4-$ClC_6H_5NO_2^+$, is less stable than 4-$CH_3C_6H_5NO_2^+$. The third suggestion relates the stability of the ion to the substituent's polar, resonance, and steric properties. These ideas are widely used for the qualitative discussion of rate and equilibrium problems and the well-documented results for aromatic substitution illustrate their importance and magnitude. In general, any polar or resonance contribution that reduces the positive charge density on the ring carbon atoms will stabilize the substituted benzenonium ion relative to the unsubstituted ion. Effects that increase the charge density on these carbon atoms exert the opposite influence. The steric requirements of the substituents may become important in the two ways described in Sec. 3.6C.

The analysis of directive effects on the basis of polar, resonance, and steric effects begins by an examination of the set of resonance structures that portray the benzenonium ions. The resonance structures for *meta*-Y-benzenonium ion† are

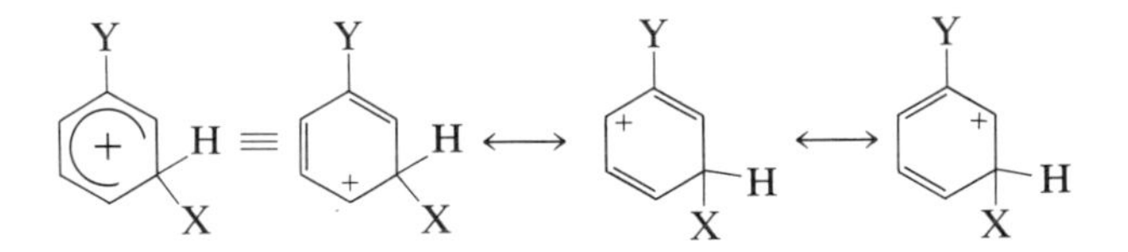

The formal positive charge, as noted in Sec. 2.1, is centered on the carbon atoms that are *ortho* and *para,* but not *meta,* to the entering group. Resonance with Y in the *meta* ion is, therefore, impossible and the magnitude of m_f^Y is determined exclusively by the polar effect of the substituent. The polar effect originates, in large part, in the dipole moment of the carbon-substituent bond.

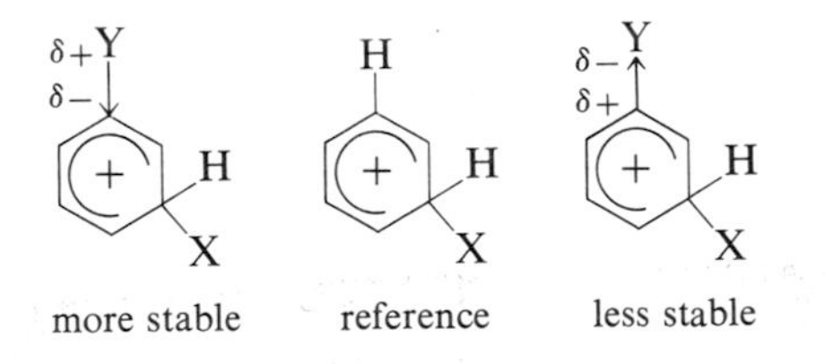

Carbon-substituent bonds that are polarized, as in the structure on the left, exert a stabilizing influence. Less activation-free energy is required

† For convenience of discussion, the 2-Y-, 3-Y-, and 4-Y-1-X-benzenonium ions will be referred to as the *ortho, meta,* and *para* ions, respectively. This designation conveys the idea that the benzenonium ion leads to the *o*-, *m*-, or *p*-disubstituted benzene.

for the incorporation of the positive charge since the negative end of the dipole decreases the charge density on the ring carbon atoms. The converse is true for the opposite orientation of the dipole (structure on the right). In this case, the positive charge density on the ring carbon atoms is greater than in the reference. Substituent effects on the acidity of acetic acid and m_f^Y values for several reactions are compared in Table 3-4. Substituent effects of this kind have been discussed by R. Stewart, *The Investigation of Organic Reactions* (this series). Polar effects determine the strength of the acetic acid derivatives; resonance is impossible since Y and the carboxyl group are insulated from one another by the saturated CH_2 unit. The ionization reaction yields a negatively charged carboxylate anion; while the substitution reaction proceeds through the positively charged benzenonium ion. The influence of Y relative to the hydrogen reference is reversed in the two reactions. Acid-weakening substituents accelerate the rate of formation of the *meta*-substituted benzenonium ion; whereas the acid-strengthening substituents decrease its rate of formation. The almost exact inversion of the substituent effects in these two reactions supports the idea that the reactivity pattern for *meta* substitution is a consequence of polar effects.

Table 3-4

COMPARISON OF POLAR EFFECTS OF GROUPS ON ACIDITY AND *meta* SUBSTITUTION

Substituent, Y	Acidity ($K_{YCH_2CO_2H}/K_{HOAc}$)	Substitution Chlorination m_f^Y	Nitration m_f^Y	Bromination m_f^Y
H_3C	0.75	5.0	3.0	2.5
H	1.0	1.0	1.0	1.0
C_6H_5	2.8	0.74	—	0.3
Cl	80	0.002	0.001	—
Br	80	0.003	0.001	—
CO_2H	85	—	—	0.02
NO_2	102	—	—	5×10^{-5}
$N(CH_3)_3^+$	850	—	4.0×10^{-8}	5×10^{-5}

The resonance structures for the *ortho* and *para* benzenonium ions

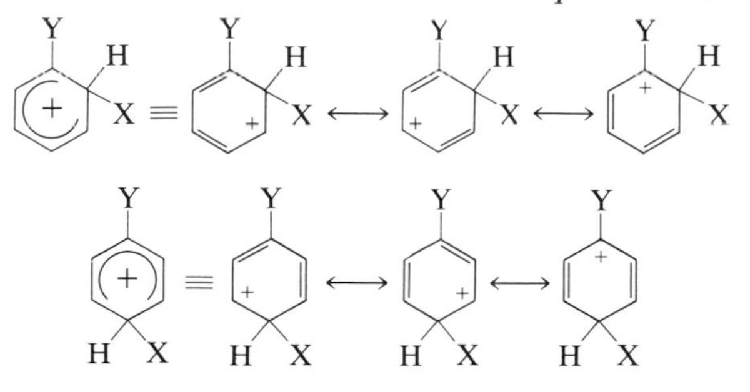

reveal that the formal positive charge is located, in part, on the carbon atom bearing the substituent (structure on the right). When the substituent possesses an unshared pair of electrons, the charge may be further delocalized through the contribution of a fourth structure,

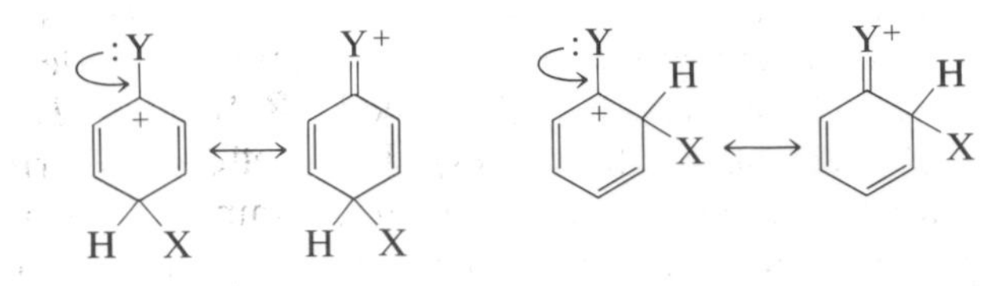

The importance of this resonance stabilization is often large, overshadowing the polar effect of the substituent. Neither polar nor resonance effects exclusively determine the stability of the *ortho* and *para* ions, and both must be considered in the interpretation of o_f^Y and p_f^Y when Y bears unshared electron pairs.

3.5 DEACTIVATING *meta* DIRECTORS

Phenyltrimethylammonium ion, nitrobenzene, benzotrifluoride, $C_6H_5CF_3$, benzotrichloride, $C_6H_5CCl_3$, benzoic acid and its derivatives, and other carbonyl compounds such as benzaldehyde, C_6H_5CHO, react much less rapidly with electrophilic reagents than does benzene to yield predominantly *meta*-disubstituted benzenes. The degree of deactivation is revealed by the small partial rate factors for acid-catalyzed hypobromous acid bromination.

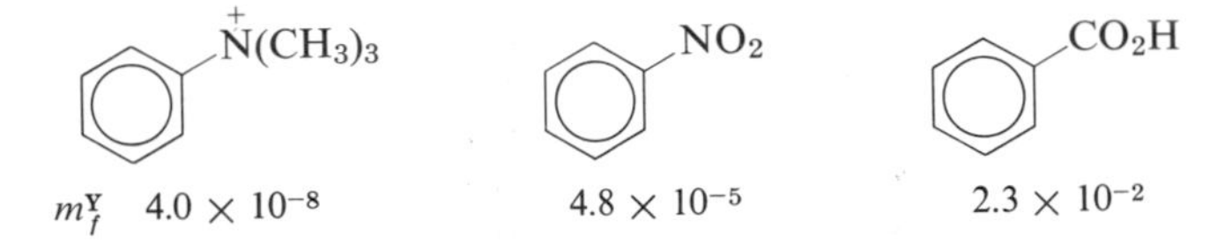

m_f^Y 4.0×10^{-8} 4.8×10^{-5} 2.3×10^{-2}

Indeed, nitrobenzene is so unreactive in electrophilic substitution reactions that it is often used as a solvent for the reactions of other aromatic compounds.

The partial rate factors, $m_f^{N(CH_3)_3^+} = 4.0 \times 10^{-8}$ and $p_f^{N(CH_3)_3^+} = 1.0 \times 10^{-8}$, for the nitration of phenyltrimethylammonium ion indicate the reactivity pattern for deactivating *meta* directors. Both partial rate factors are small, but m_f is slightly greater than p_f. The resonance structures for the two ions are shown:

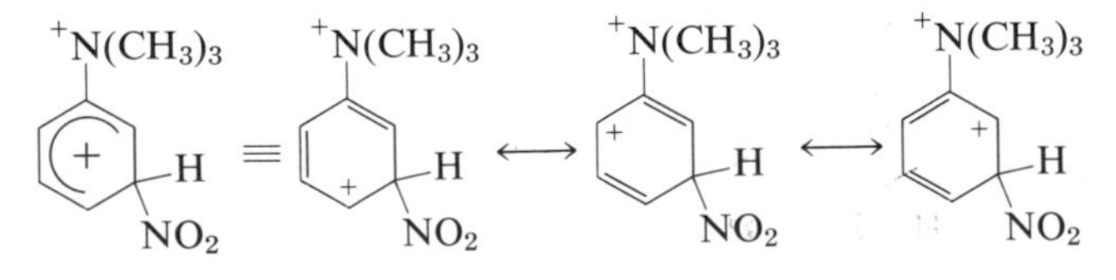

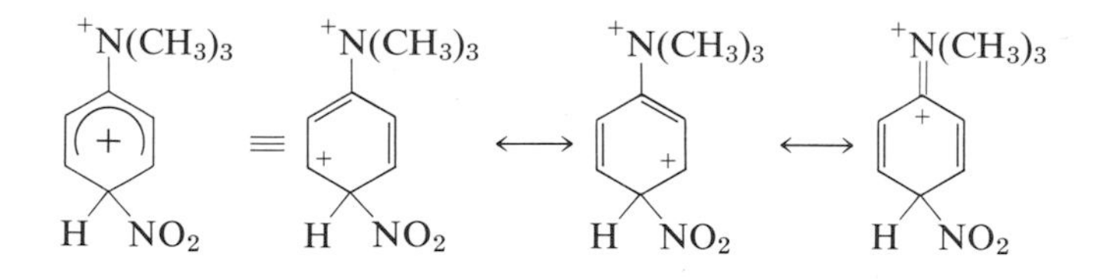

The charged trimethylamino group is incapable of resonance since the nitrogen atom is saturated. Only polar influences need be considered. Clearly, the introduction of a positive charge in the ring is unfavorable in the presence of a positive charge on the substituent. Both the *meta* and *para* ions are much less stable than the benzenonium ion. The destabilizing influence of the charged substituent is greater for the *para* ion. Inspection of the resonance structures for the *para* ion reveals that one structure has positive charges on adjacent atoms. In contrast, the charges on the nitrogen atom and carbon atoms are separated by at least two bond distances in the set of structures that describe the *meta* ion. Coulomb's law states that the energy required to locate two charges is inversely proportional to the distance between them. The proximity of the two charges in the third structure for the *para* ion increases its energy content. The net effect is that the charge in the ring is not delocalized to the same extent as in the *meta* ion. In general, the polar influences of *ortho* and *para* substituents are slightly more important, whether stabilizing or destabilizing, than *meta* substituents.

The same interpretation is applicable for the other deactivating, *meta* directors. In each case, the substituent is incapable of resonance stabilization and an unfavorably oriented dipole (rather than a full charge) increases the energy content of the *para* ion.

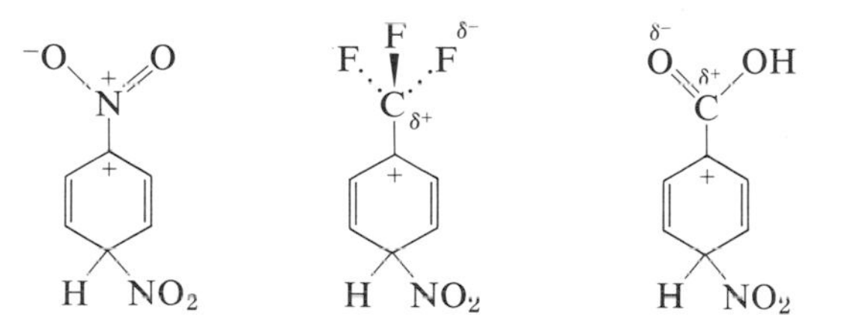

3.6 ACTIVATING *ortho-para* DIRECTORS

Familiar compounds that react more rapidly than benzene and yield *o*- and *p*-disubstituted benzenes include aniline and its derivatives, phenol and its derivatives, biphenyl, and the alkylbenzenes. The partial rate factors for noncatalytic bromination in the *para* position reveal that the substituent effect may be enormous.

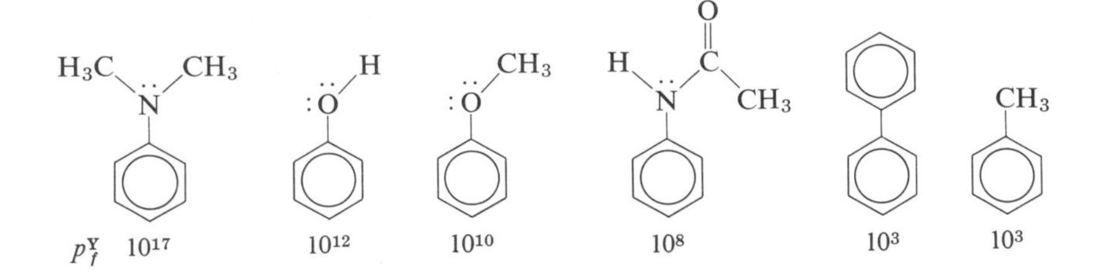

3.6A Substituents with a Destabilizing Polar Effect: Amino, hydroxy, and phenyl substituents increase the acidity of acetic acid and should exert a destabilizing polar effect on the substitution reaction. This prediction is borne out by the slow rate of substitution in the *meta* position. In sharp contrast, the p_f values for these substituents are vastly greater and illustrate the major significance of further charge delocalization on the stability of the benzenonium ion. Experience indicates that large resonance stabilization occurs for all substituents that possess unshared pairs of electrons on the atom bonded to the aromatic nucleus. Groups with trivalent nitrogen and divalent oxygen and sulfur are very effective for the delocalization of the positive charge density in *ortho* and *para* benzenonium ions. The resonance structures for the dimethylamino substituent include a fourth structure depicting the delocalization of the charge to the nitrogen atom of the substituent.

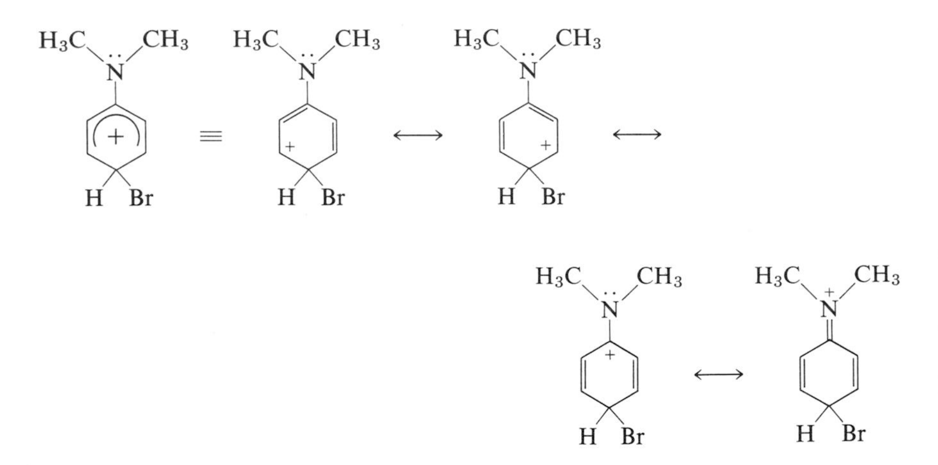

Phenylacetic acid is a somewhat stronger acid than acetic acid, Table 3-4. Accordingly, the phenyl substituent should exert a destabilizing polar effect and, as expected, $m_f^{C_6H_5}$ is less than 1.0. However, $o_f^{C_6H_5}$ and $p_f^{C_6H_5}$ are substantially greater. Resonance delocalization of the positive charge over both rings accounts for the added stability of the *ortho* and *para* ions.

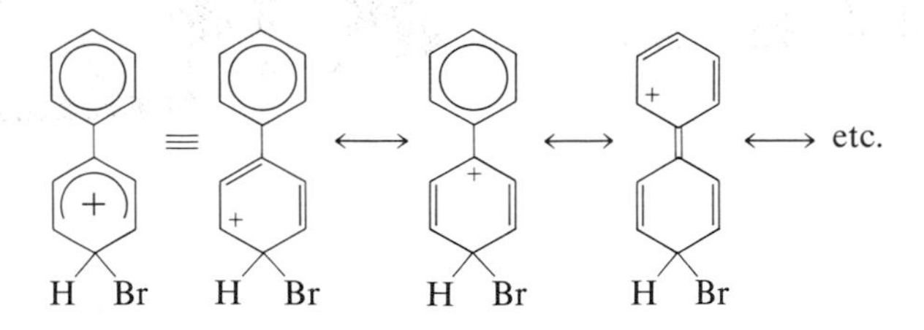

The reactivity of this compound is discussed from another viewpoint in Sec. 4.5.

3.6B The Alkyl Benzenes: The reactivities of the alkyl benzenes present a different and more difficult case. Partial rate factors for the non-catalytic bromination are summarized in Table 3-5.

Table 3-5

PARTIAL RATE FACTORS FOR THE BROMINATION OF TOLUENE AND *t*-BUTYLBENZENE

	o_f	m_f	p_f
Benzene	1.0	1.0	1.0
Toluene	800	5.5	2400
t-Butylbenzene	50	7.0	800

The three isomeric alkyl-substituted benzenonium ions form more rapidly than the benzenonium ion. Both alkyl groups exert stabilizing polar effects. However, there are some curious aspects that obviate an interpretation of these results exclusively on the basis of polar effects. The polar contribution of the *t*-butyl group is slightly greater than that of the methyl group and $m_f^{C(CH_3)_3}$ exceeds $m_f^{CH_3}$. Surprisingly, the *para* reactivities are reversed. This anomaly has been attributed to the operation of a different kind of resonance stabilization—hyperconjugation. Conventional resonance interactions are precluded since the carbon atom of the alkyl group is saturated. However, the charge at the 4-position may be delocalized by an interaction with the carbon-hydrogen and carbon-carbon bonding orbitals of the alkyl groups. This delocalization of the positive charge is known as *hyperconjugation.*

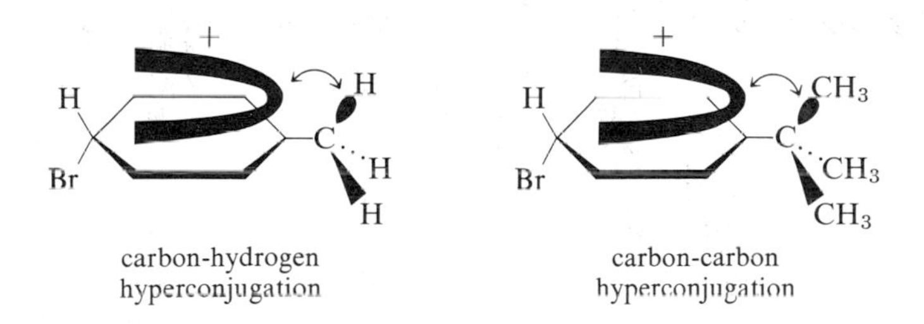

Hyperconjugation accounts for the large increase in p_f^{Alkyl} compared to m_f^{Alkyl}. The reversal in relative reactivity at the *para* position is interpreted in terms of the greater importance of carbon-hydrogen compared to carbon-carbon hyperconjugation. That is, more charge is delocalized to the carbon-hydrogen bonding orbital than to the carbon-carbon bonding orbital. The novelty of hyperconjugation has prompted considerable study. Although this concept is a convenient rationale for facts, many chemists hold the view that solvation and subtle steric effects are responsible for the reversal in reactivity between the *meta* and *para* positions.

3.6C Steric Effects: Bulk steric effects are well documented by the reactions of toluene and *t*-butylbenzene. Isomer distributions and partial rate factors for three reactions are summarized in Table 3-6.

The value of o_f^{Alkyl} is always larger for toluene than for *t*-butylbenzene and the difference is greater than that for the corresponding p_f^{Alkyl} values. The variation in o_f for these groups may be identified with the larger steric requirements of the *t*-butyl group. In the transition state for *ortho* substitution, the electrophilic reagent and the substituent are confined to a small volume element. Repulsive steric interactions between the groups may occur when either large reagents or substituents are involved. The results, Tables 3-5 and 3-6, reveal the character of the reagent is very important. In acetylation, only 1% *o*-methylacetophenone and no detectable amount of *o*-*t*-butylacetophenone are obtained. In chlorination, very different isomer distributions result in the catalytic and noncatalytic reactions.

Another more subtle steric interaction alters the influence of substituents that enhance reactivity by resonance. The effect is evident when the group capable of resonance (Y) is flanked by other substituents (R).

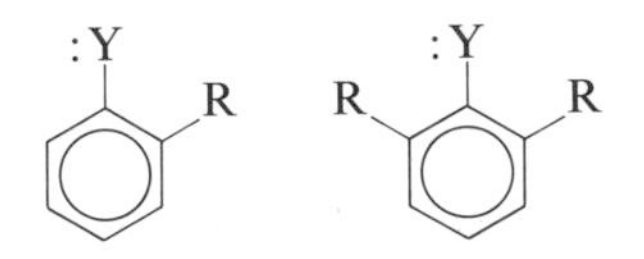

The relative rates for the *para* bromination of anisole, 2-methylanisole and 2,6-dimethylanisole illustrate this steric effect.

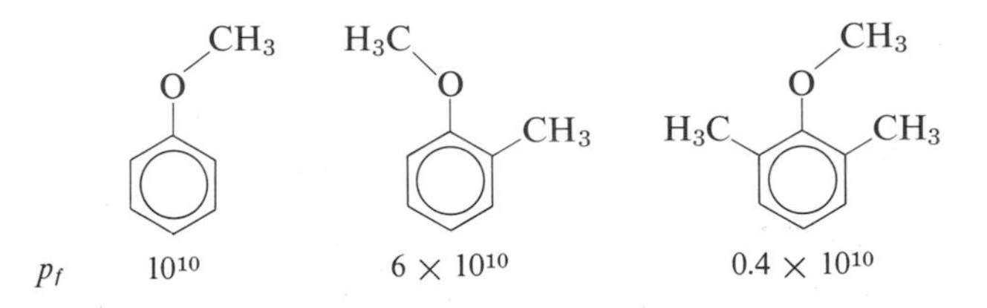

The first methyl group increases the velocity by a factor of six. The second methyl group, however, reduces the rate below that of anisole. It is a tenet of resonance theory that structures must be planar for the maximum overlap of the orbitals that effect charge delocalization. In 2-methylanisole, the ethereal methyl group may be located to the left away from the 2-methyl-substituent. In this conformation, the steric interactions between the ethereal methyl and the methyl group in the 2-position are slight. A second methyl group in the other *ortho* position, however, requires the methoxy

Table 3-6

ISOMER DISTRIBUTIONS AND PARTIAL RATE FACTORS FOR THE ACETYLATION, NONCATALYTIC AND FERRIC CHLORIDE-CATALYZED CHLORINATION OF TOLUENE AND *t*-BUTYLBENZENE†

Reaction	Toluene			*t*-Butylbenzene		
	% *o*-	% *m*-	% *p*-	% *o*-	% *m*-	% *p*-
CH_3COCl, $AlCl_3$	1	1	98	0	4	96
Cl_2, no catalyst	60	0.5	40	22	2	76
Cl_2, $FeCl_3$	68	2	30	52	6	42
	$o_f^{CH_3}$	$m_f^{CH_3}$	$p_f^{CH_3}$	$o_f^{C(CH_3)_3}$	$m_f^{C(CH_3)_3}$	$p_f^{C(CH_3)_3}$
CH_3COCl, $AlCl_3$	5	5	750	0	13	660
Cl_2, no catalyst	620	5	820	57	6	400
Cl_2, $FeCl_3$	110	4	100	47	6	75

† Results for bromination are shown in Table 3-5.

group to twist from the plane of the aromatic ring, decreasing overlap between the orbital containing the charge deficiency and the orbitals of the oxygen atom containing the nonbonding electrons.

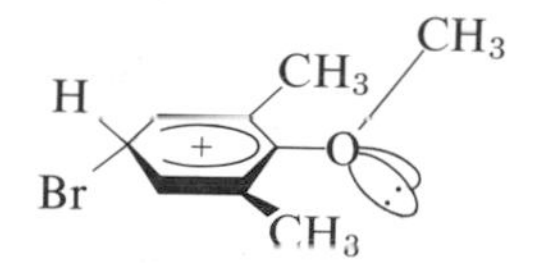

The twisting lessens the delocalization of the positive charge and resonance stabilization by the substituent is less important. Many examples of this effect, called the *steric inhibition of resonance*, are known. The rates of *para* substitution in 2,6-dimethyl-N,N-dimethylaniline and 2-*t*-butylbiphenyl are far less than in the corresponding unsubstituted compounds.

3.7 DEACTIVATING *ortho-para* DIRECTORS

The halobenzenes, certain α-substituted toluenes, and derivatives of styrene, such as cinnamic acid, react more slowly than benzene but form *o*- and *p*-disubstituted benzenes. The partial rate factors for nitration are shown:

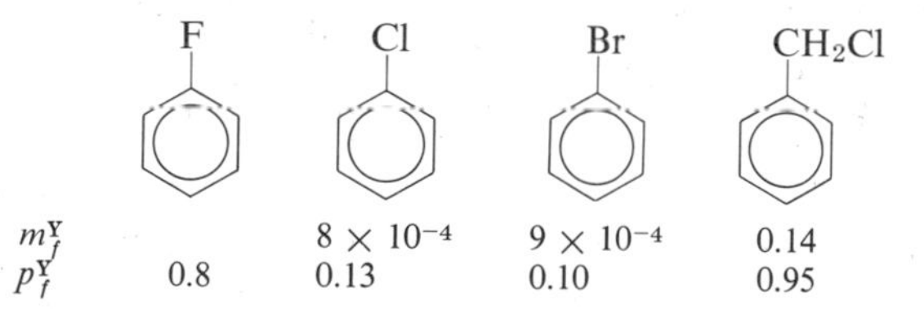

	F	Cl	Br	CH_2Cl
m_f^Y		8×10^{-4}	9×10^{-4}	0.14
p_f^Y	0.8	0.13	0.10	0.95

Halogen substituents increase the strength of acetic acid. As expected, this polar effect decreases the rate of formation of the *meta* benzenonium ions and m_f^{Halo} is very small. The values of p_f^{Halo} are, however, much larger than expected on the basis of the polar contributions of these atomic substituents. Indeed, p_f^{F} is always near unity and exceeds unity in some reactions. The results require that some effect operates to stabilize the *para* benzenonium ions and that this stabilizing influence is greatest for the fluorine atom and least for the iodine atom. The interpretation most often advanced for these data suggests that the unshared electron pairs on the halogen atom delocalize the charge by resonance as shown for the chloro substituent.

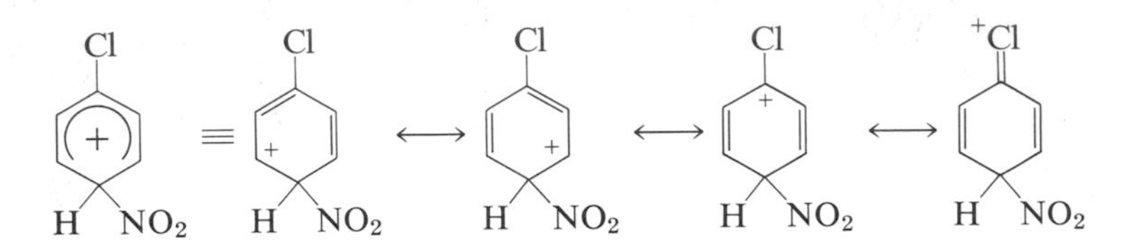

According to this suggestion, the only difference between the activating *ortho, para* directors discussed in Sec. 3.6A and the deactivating *ortho, para* directors considered here is that the resonance effect is insufficient to overcome the destabilizing polar effect. However, there are some disturbing features. Electronegativity considerations indicate that the ability of the halogens to tolerate a positive charge is in the order I > Br > Cl > F, opposite to that required for the resonance interpretation of the results for the substitution reactions. This very troublesome feature of the resonance explanation has annoyed thoughtful students for many years. Consequently, some alternative explanations have been advanced. One attractive idea is that the stabilizing component of the halogen substituent effect arises through the repulsive interaction between the p electrons of the halogen substituent and the π electrons of the aromatic nucleus. This

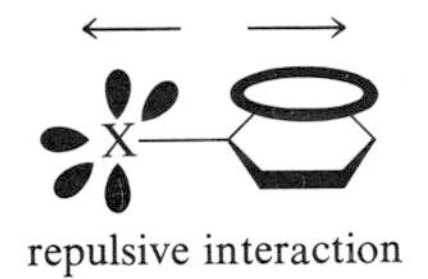

repulsive interaction

interaction would increase the electron density at the carbon atom that is *para* to the halogen atom and facilitate the formation of a bond between this carbon atom and the electrophilic reagent. The repulsive interaction is greatest for the highly electronegative fluorine atom and least for the iodine atom. Thus, this effect opposes the polar influence and would account for the observed order of reactivity of the halogens.

The observations for other deactivating *ortho, para* directors are somewhat easier to understand on the basis of conflicting polar and resonance effects. For example, the charge deficiency in the *para* benzenonium ion of cinnamic acid may be delocalized via resonance structures of a more characteristic kind:

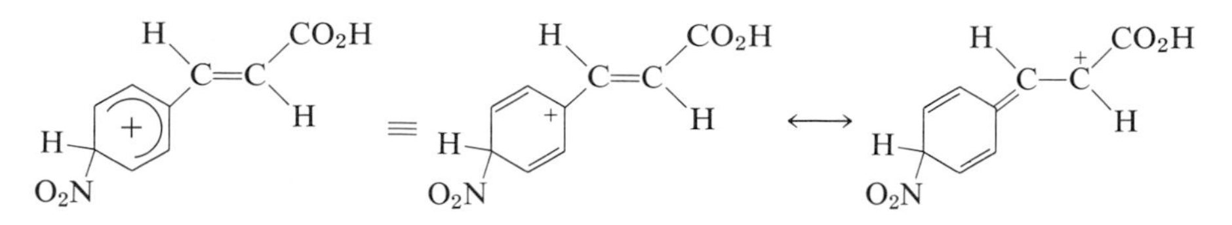

The directive effect of the chloromethyl group may also be understood in these terms, with hyperconjugative resonance with the methyl carbon-hydrogen bonds accounting for the increased stability of the *para* benzenonium ion.

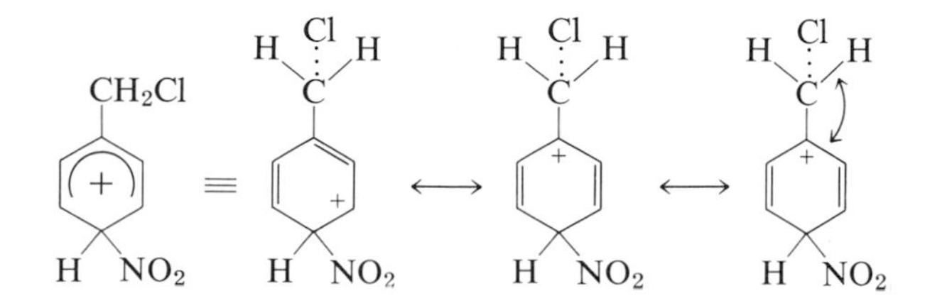

In summary, the effects of substituents on the course of the electrophilic substitution reactions are quite regular. The activation or deactivation of the aromatic nucleus and the product distributions are similar in the many different substitution reactions. The theory of directive effects based on the influences of polar, resonance, and steric effects on the stability of the intermediate benzenonium ions provides a qualitative interpretation of the results.

PROBLEMS

3.1. Friedel–Crafts ethylation (CH_3CH_2Br, $GaBr_3$) of chlorobenzene proceeds at a rate 0.21 that for the ethylation of benzene under the same conditions. The isomer distribution is 42.4% *o*- 15.9% *m*-, and 41.9% *p*-chloroethylbenzene. Calculate o_f^{Cl}, m_f^{Cl}, p_f^{Cl} for this reaction.

3.2. Account for the following results in terms of the resonance approach.

a. The value of $p_f^{OC_6H_5}$ is 1×10^8 for the bromination of diphenyl ether ($C_6H_5OC_6H_5$).

b. The value of p_f^{CN} is 3.1×10^{-6} and the value of m_f^{CN} is 8.7×10^{-7} for the bromination of benzonitrile (C_6H_5CN).

c. The nitration of benzyltrimethylammonium ion [$C_6H_5CH_2N(CH_3)_3^+$] yields 2% *o*-, 88% *m*-, and 10% *p*-$O_2NC_6H_4CH_2N(CH_3)_3^+$, and the nitration of 2-phenylethyltrimethylammonium ion ($C_6H_5CH_2CH_2N(CH_3)_3^+$) yields 13% *o*-, 17% *m*-, and 70% *p*-$O_2NC_6H_4CH_2CH_2N(CH_3)_3^+$.

d. The nitration of benzotrichloride ($C_6H_5CCl_3$) yields 6.8% *o*-, 64.5% *m*-, and 28.7% *p*-nitrobenzotrichloride, and the nitration of benzyl chloride ($C_6H_5CH_2Cl$) yields 32.0% *o*-, 15.5% *m*-, and 52.5% *p*-nitrobenzyl chloride.

3.3. The *para* partial rate factors for the nitration of biphenyl and the methylene-bridged derivative, fluorene, are

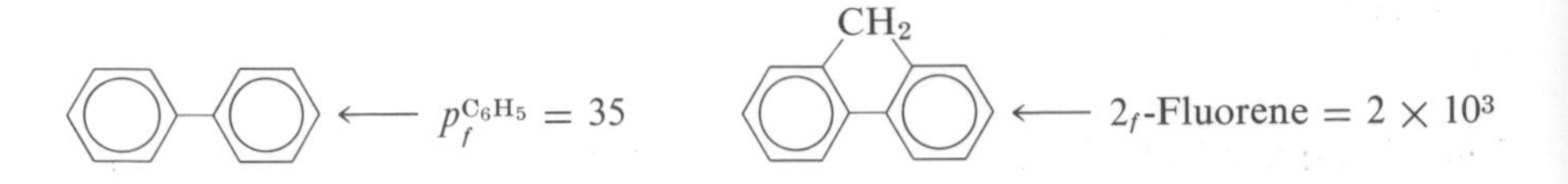

Suggest an explanation.

3.4. Account for the decreasing partial rate factors for *para* chlorination of acetanilide and the methyl derivatives shown.

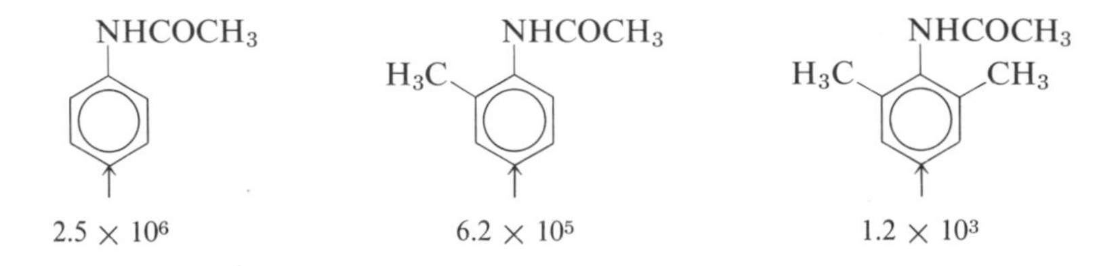

SUGGESTED READING

Relative rates, isomer distribution, and related results for many substitution reactions are summarized by L. M. Stock and H. C. Brown, *Advances in Physical Organic Chemistry*, V. Gold, editor, Academic Press, Inc., New York, 1963, Vol. 1, p. 35.

The role of substituent effects in nitration and halogenation is surveyed by P. B. D. de la Mare and J. H. Ridd, *Aromatic Substitution*, Butterworth's Scientific Publications, London 1959, Chapters 6 and 10.

Another recent discussion of substituent effects has been presented by R. O. C. Norman and R. Taylor, *Electrophilic Substitution in Benzenoid Compounds*, Elsevier Publishing Co., New York, 1965.

4 Quantitative Treatments for Benzene Derivatives and Polynuclear Hydrocarbons

4.1 INTRODUCTION

The substituent effects of *meta* and *para* groups were observed to be remarkably uniform in Chapter 3. This uniformity permits the use of an empirical quantitative relationship for the discussion of known results and for the prediction of unknown relative rates and isomer distributions. The quantitative relationship also accommodates the fact that the *para* to *meta* product ratio for the substitution of a monosubstituted benzene depends on the electrophilic properties of the reagent, in addition to the properties of the substituent. Moreover, this relationship can be extended for the prediction of the isomer distributions in disubstituted benzenes. The treatment to be presented in this chapter is empirical. A satisfactory quantitative theory for the analysis of substituent effects on the basis of first principles has not yet been developed. The problem is that the polar, resonance, and steric effects blend in a subtle way to produce the net substituent effect.

In contrast to the situation for the monosubstituted benzenes, theoretical approaches have proved quite valuable for the discussion of the electrophilic substitution reactions of polynuclear aromatic hydrocarbons. The relative reaction rates and isomer distributions for these compounds can often be treated theoretically with satisfying results.

The empirical correlation of the data for electrophilic substitution of the monosubstituted benzenes, the underlying concept of reagent selectivity, the prediction of isomer distributions for disubstituted benzenes, and the practical and theoretical chemistry of the substitution reactions of the polynuclear aromatic compounds will be discussed in this chapter.

4.2 EMPIRICAL CORRELATION OF DIRECTIVE EFFECTS

The Hammett equation is discussed by R. Stewart in *The Investigation of Organic Reactions*, p. 66, (this series). In brief review, this equation

$$\log \frac{k}{k_{\mathrm{H}}} = \rho\sigma \tag{4.1}$$

is widely used for the correlation of the rate and equilibrium constants for the side-chain reactions of benzene derivatives such as the hydrolysis of *m*- and *p*-substituted ethyl benzoates or the acid dissociation constants of *m*- and *p*-substituted phenols. The substituent constant σ measures the sum of the polar and resonance effects of the substituents; while ρ, the reaction constant, measures the susceptibility of the reaction to a change in the properties of the substituent. No attempt is made to include the results for *ortho* substituents in this correlation because the steric interactions between the *ortho* substituent and the group or atom at the adjacent reaction site are highly variable, differing in different reactions.

The Hammett substituent constants, σ values, do not correlate the partial rate factors (relative rates) for aromatic substitution reactions. The failure of these constants originates in the major difference in the charge distribution in the benzenonium ion and in the benzoate anion involved in the definition of the σ constant. The point is illustrated by a comparison of the resonance structures that describe 4-methoxy-1-X-benzenonium ion and the anion of *p*-methoxybenzoic acid.

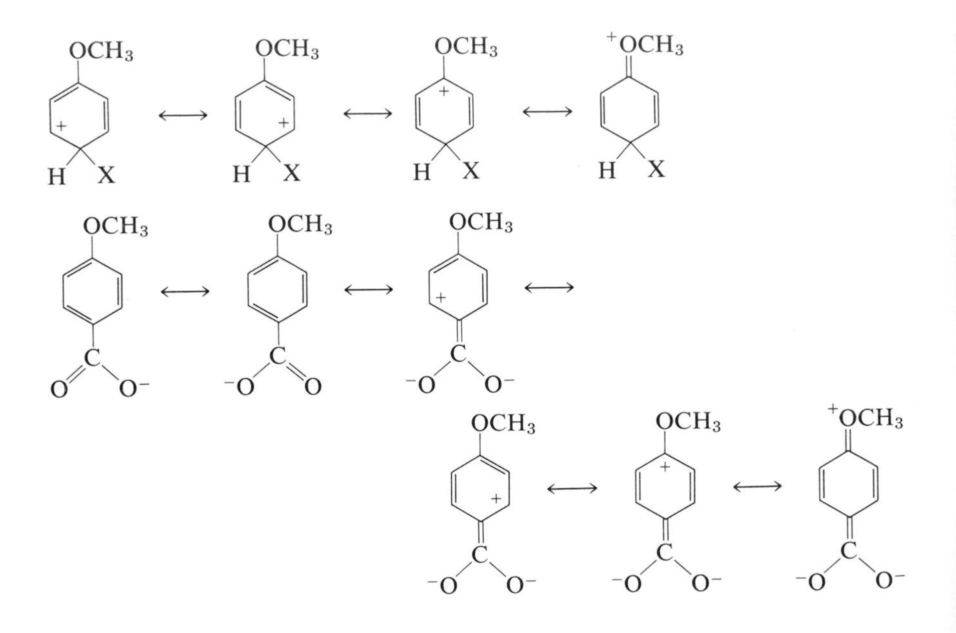

The benzenonium ion is characterized by four resonance structures. Six structures are necessary for the description of the benzoate anion. The four structures on the right are very similar to the structures for the benzenonium ion. These structures, however, require the localization of two negative charges on the oxygen atoms of the carboxylate group. Such an accumulation of charge is energetically unfavorable and these structures are much less important for the description of the charge distribution in the benzoate anion than in the benzenonium ion. The substituent constant, $\sigma_{p\text{-OMe}}$, reflects the manner in which the charge is delocalized in the anion. This constant is understandably inappropriate for the description of the influence of the *p*-methoxy group on the charge distribution in the benzenonium ion in view of the differing importance of four related resonance structures in these two cases.

The quantitative relationship for aromatic substitution simply employs another set of substituent constants to replace the inappropriate Hammett values. The substituent constants are designated σ^+ to distinguish them from the Hammett values and to indicate their intended application to reactions in which a large positive charge is introduced into the aromatic nucleus. The form of the equation is identical:

$$\log \frac{k}{k_{\text{H}}} = \rho^+\sigma^+ \tag{4.2}$$

Like the Hammett treatment for side-chain reactions, Eq. (4.2) is not used for *ortho* substituents; only the relative rates for *meta* and *para* substitution are treated.

$$\log \frac{k_{m\text{-Y}}}{k_{\text{H}}} = \log m_f^{\text{Y}} = \rho^+\sigma^+_{m\text{-Y}} \tag{4.3a}$$

$$\log \frac{k_{p\text{-Y}}}{k_{\text{H}}} = \log p_f^{\text{Y}} = \rho^+\sigma^+_{p\text{-Y}} \tag{4.3b}$$

The σ^+ constants were developed by H. C. Brown of Purdue University. Brown pointed out that there was a close relationship between the resonance structures that describe the benzenonium ion and those that describe a phenyl-substituted carbonium ion as illustrated for *p*-methoxyphenyldimethyl carbonium ion.

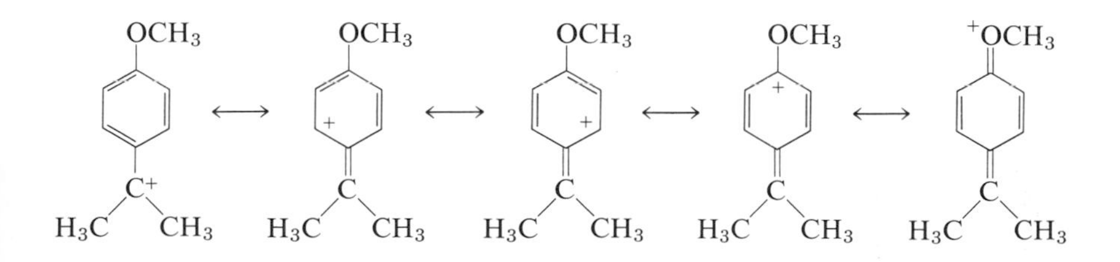

In this ion, in contrast to the benzoate anion discussed above, the delocalization of the positive charge into the aromatic nucleus does not require the creation of a new negative charge, and the four structures on the right make a major contribution to the description of the charge distribution in the carbonium ion. The σ^+ constants are based on this idea and were developed from the results of an investigation of the S_N1 reactions of *m*- and *p*-substituted phenyldimethyl carbinyl chlorides in aqueous acetone or alcohol solvents.

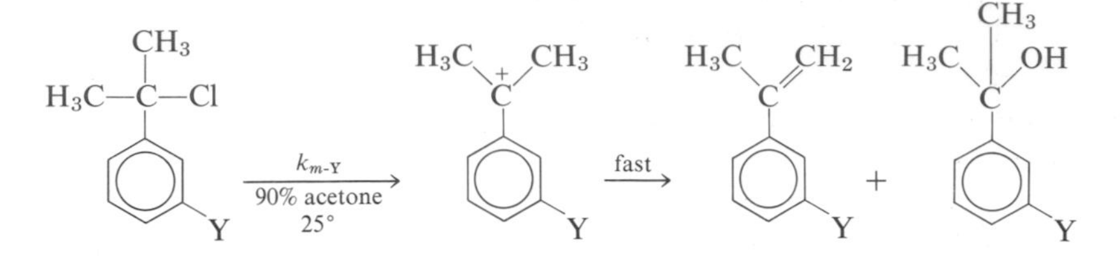

The relative rates of ionization of the *meta* derivatives, $k_{m\text{-Y}}/k_H$, are correlated with high precision by the Hammett σ_m constants, Fig. 4-1. This fact is in accord with the qualitative idea expressed in Chapter 3 that polar effects govern reactivity at the *meta* position because the charge cannot be delocalized by the substituent. On the other hand, the rates of ionization of the *p*-substituted phenyldimethyl carbinyl chlorides are not correlated satisfactorily by the Hammett constants as pictured in Fig. 4-2. The rates

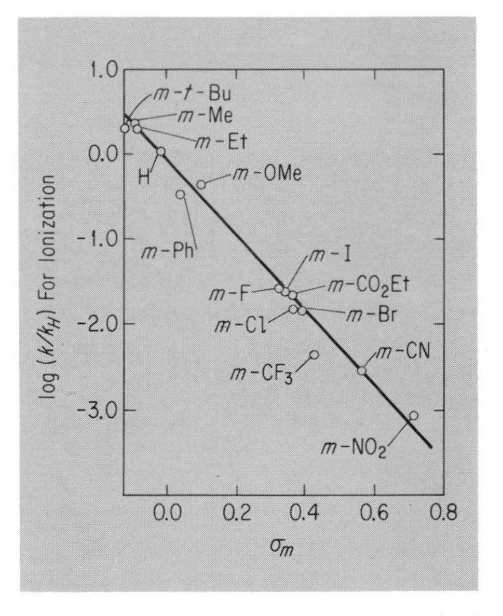

Fig. 4-1 Correlation of the relative rates of ionization of *meta*-substituted phenyldimethyl carbinyl chlorides in 90% acetone-water at 25° by Hammett σ_m constants.

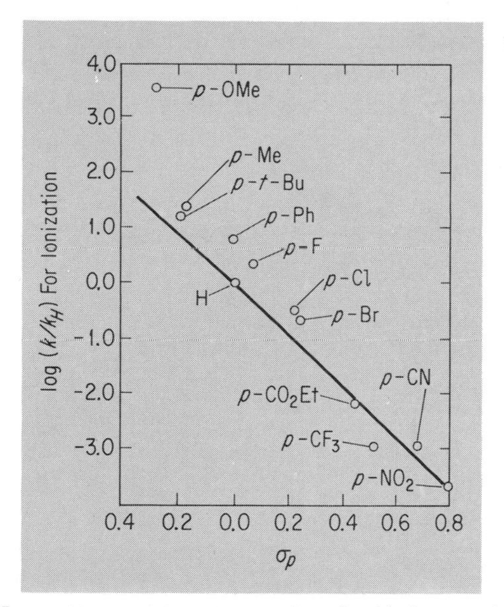

Fig. 4-2 Failure of Hammett σ_p constants to correlate the relative rate data for the ionization of *para*-substituted phenyldimethyl carbinyl chlorides.

of ionization of these *para* derivatives do, however, parallel the rates of substitution in the *para* position of the corresponding monosubstituted benzenes as shown for the mercuration (see pp. 38–39) of several compounds in Fig. 4-3.

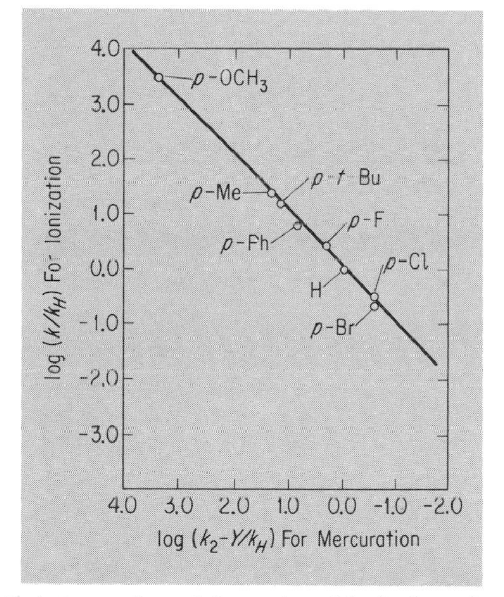

Fig. 4-3 Relationship between the relative rates of ionization of *para*-substituted phenyldimethyl carbinyl chlorides and the *para*-mercuration of the corresponding monosubstituted benzenes.

The high precision achieved in this correlation presumably reflects the fact that the substituents exert very similar influences on the distribution of charge at the energy maximum for the formation of the *tertiary* carbonium ions and the benzenonium ions. The σ^+ constants were developed from these results in the following way. The slope of the correlation line for the *meta*-substituted *tertiary* chlorides, Fig. 4-1, defines ρ for the ionization reaction. The $\sigma^+_{m\text{-Y}}$ and $\sigma^+_{p\text{-Y}}$ constants are defined by Eq. (4.4):

$$\sigma^+_{m\text{-Y}} = \frac{1}{\rho} \log \frac{k_{m\text{-Y}}}{k_{\text{H}}}$$
$$\sigma^+_{p\text{-Y}} = \frac{1}{\rho} \log \frac{k_{p\text{-Y}}}{k_{\text{H}}} \qquad (4.4)$$

where ρ (-4.54) is the reaction constant defined by the reactivity of the *meta* derivatives and the $(k_{\text{Y}}/k_{\text{H}})$ values refer to the relative rates of ionization of the *tertiary* chlorides. The constants for common substituents are presented in Table 4-1.

The σ and σ^+ constants listed in Table 4-1 illustrate the ideas used in their development and in the discussion of substituent effects in Chapter 3. Polar effects control reactivity at the *meta* position because resonance delocalization of the charge by the substituent is impossible; consequently, $\sigma_{m\text{-Y}}$ and $\sigma^+_{m\text{-Y}}$ are virtually identical. Further, $\sigma^+_{p\text{-Y}}$ and $\sigma_{p\text{-Y}}$ are also identical for substituents (nitro, cyano) incapable of resonance stabilization of the *para* benzenonium ions. In contrast, $\sigma^+_{p\text{-Y}}$ and $\sigma_{p\text{-Y}}$ are different for

Table 4-1

HAMMETT σ AND BROWN σ^+ SUBSTITUENT CONSTANTS

Substituent, Y	*meta*-Y		*para*-Y	
	σ	σ^+	σ	σ^+
Dimethylamino, $—N(CH_3)_2$			−0.83	−1.7
Amino, $—NH_2$	−0.16	−0.16	−0.66	−1.3
Hydroxy, —OH	0.12		−0.37	−0.92
Acetylamino, $—NHCOCH_3$	0.21		−0.01	−0.6
Methoxy, $—OCH_3$	0.12	0.05	−0.27	−0.78
Methyl, $—CH_3$	−0.07	−0.07	−0.17	−0.28
t-Butyl, $—C(CH_3)_3$	−0.10	−0.10	−0.20	−0.26
Phenyl, $—C_6H_5$	0.06	0.10	−0.01	−0.18
Hydrogen, H	0.00	0.00	0.00	0.00
Fluoro, F	0.34	0.35	0.06	−0.07
Chloro, Cl	0.37	0.40	0.22	0.11
Bromo, Br	0.39	0.40	0.23	0.15
Iodo, I	0.35	0.36	0.18	0.14
Carboethoxy, $—CO_2C_2H_5$	0.37	0.37	0.45	0.48
Trifluoromethyl, $—CF_3$	0.42	0.52	0.54	0.61
Cyano, —CN	0.56	0.56	0.66	0.66
Nitro, $—NO_2$	0.71	0.67	0.78	0.79

substituents (methoxy, dimethylamino) capable of resonance stabilization of the *para* ions.

The use of the constants for the correlation of the data for electrophilic substitution reactions is illustrated in Figs. 4-4 to 4-7.

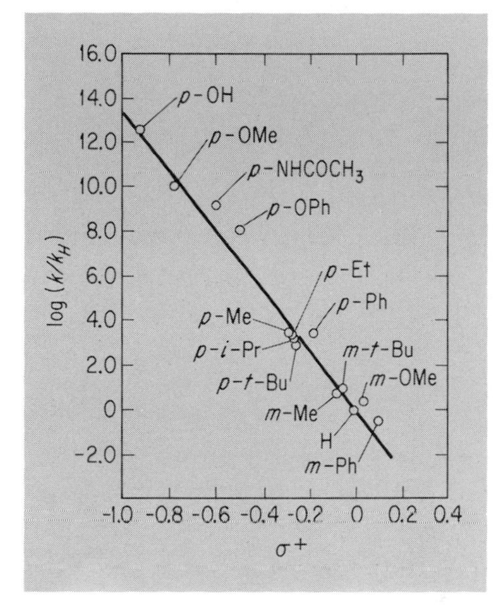

Fig. 4-4 Correlation of relative rates of non-catalytic bromination by σ^+

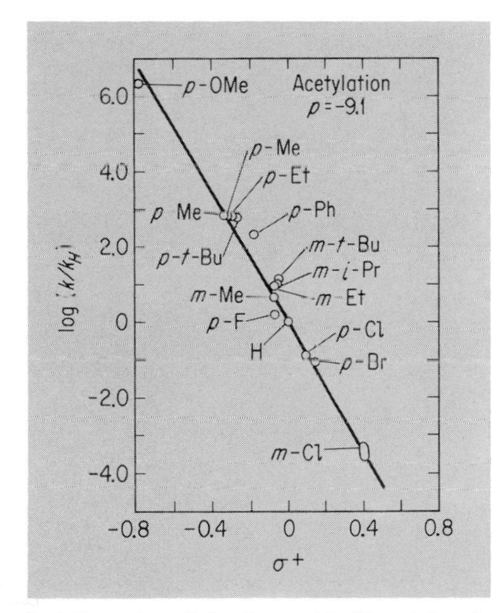

Fig. 4-5 Correlation of relative rates of aluminum chloride-catalyzed acetylation by σ^+.

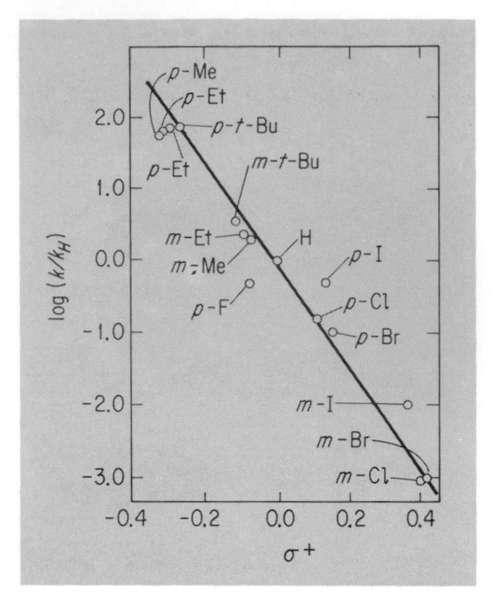

Fig. 4-6 Correlation of relative rates of nitration by σ^+.

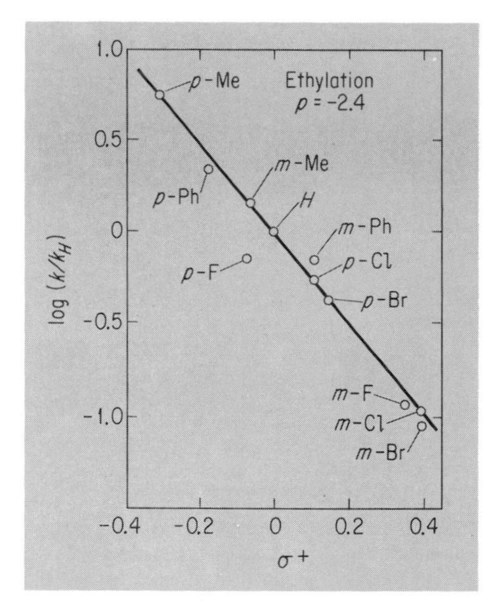

Fig. 4-7 Correlation of relative rates of gallium bromide-catalyzed ethylation by σ^+.

4.3 THE REACTION CONSTANT, SELECTIVITY

The reaction constants ρ^+ for the reactions shown in Figs. 4-4 to 4-7 are defined by the slopes ($\Delta \log (k/k_H)/\Delta\sigma^+$) of the correlation lines. The ρ^+ values for these reactions and several other typical substitution reactions are presented in Table 4-2. As noted in Sec. 4.2, the reaction constant measures the susceptibility of a reaction to a change in the nature of the substituent. The inference of this dependence of reactivity on the character of the reaction is that relative rates depend not only on the properties of the substituent but also on the properties of the electrophilic reagent. The consequences of variations in the character of the electrophilic reagent are well illustrated in the isomer distributions and relative rates for the substitution of toluene, Table 4-2.

Electrophilic reactions have negative ρ^+ values. The magnitude of ρ^+ indicates the magnitude of the substituent effects. Thus, a *p*-methyl group has a small influence on the rate ($p_f^{CH_3} = 5.0$) of the Friedel–Crafts isopropylation reaction, $\rho^+ = -2.3$, but a large influence on the rate ($p_f^{CH_3} = 2420$) of the noncatalytic bromination reaction, $\rho^+ = -12.1$. The isomer distributions, in particular the relative amounts of *meta* and *para* products, also depend on the magnitude of the reaction constant. Thus, $p_f^{CH_3}/m_f^{CH_3}$ is only 3.6 for Friedel–Crafts isopropylation with 27% *m*- and 47% *p*-isopropyltoluene produced in the reaction; but this ratio is 440 for the noncatalytic bromination reaction with only 0.3% *m*- and 67% *p*-bromotoluene produced in the reaction. These changes are quantitatively related to the magnitude of ρ^+. The *para* partial rate factor for the methyl group is determined by the product of the $\sigma^+_{p\text{-}CH_3}$ constant and ρ^+ for each reaction. Both constants are negative and $p_f^{CH_3}$ increases as ρ^+ becomes more negative. The relationship between the isomer distribution and ρ^+ is revealed by the subtraction of Eq. 4.3a from 4.3b:

$$\log p_f^{CH_3} - \log m_f^{CH_3} = \log \frac{k_{p\text{-}CH_3}}{k_{m\text{-}CH_3}} = \rho^+(\sigma^+_{p\text{-}CH_3} - \sigma^+_{m\text{-}CH_3}) \tag{4.5}$$

The difference between the σ^+ constants is -0.21. Thus, as ρ^+ becomes more negative, the logarithm of the rate ratio becomes more positive and the *para* to *meta* product ratio increases.

The variations in $p_f^{CH_3}$ and the isomer distribution depend on the selectivity of the electrophilic reagent. The concept of selectivity relates to the ability of a reagent to choose the reaction site that leads to a more stable benzenonium ion. Electrophilic reagents that have low selectivity show little inclination to discriminate between the positions that are available for reaction. The isomer distribution is more random and the partial rate factors are near unity. This case is illustrated by the Friedel–Crafts isopropylation reaction. On the other hand, weak electrophilic reagents are selective, choosing the reaction site that leads to the most

Table 4-2

REACTION CONSTANTS, ISOMER DISTRIBUTIONS, AND PARTIAL RATE FACTORS FOR THE SUBSTITUTION OF TOLUENE

Reactions, conditions†	ρ^+	Isomer distribution, %		Partial rate factors		
		meta	*para*	$m_f^{CH_3}$	$p_f^{CH_3}$	$p_f^{CH_3}/m_f^{CH_3}$
Bromination, Br_2, HOAc, 25°	−12.1	0.3	67	5.5	2420	440
Chlorination, Cl_2, HOAc, 25°	−10.0	0.5	40	5.0	820	160
Acetylation, CH_3COCl, $AlCl_3$, ethylene dichloride, 25°	−9.1	1.3	98	4.8	750	155
Chlorination, Cl_2, $FeCl_3$, CH_3NO_2, 0°	−7.1	2.1	30	3.8	100	26
Bromination, HOBr, $HClO_4$, H_2O-dioxane, 25°	−6.2	2.3	27	2.5	60	24
Nitration, $AcONO_2$, Ac_2O, 25°	−6.0	4.4	37	3.0	50	17
Ethylation, CH_3CH_2Br, $GaBr_3$, ArH, 25°	−2.4	21.0	41	1.5	6.0	4.0
Isopropylation, $(CH_3)_2CHBr$, $GaBr_3$, ArH, 25°	−2.3	26.6	47	1.4	5.0	3.6

† Reagent, catalyst when used, solvent, and temperature are listed.

stable benzenonium ion in preference to other possible sites. The isomer distributions obtained in selective reactions are far from random, heavily favoring the product that is derived from the most stable benzenonium ion. The partial rate factors for selective reagents are large for substituents that stabilize the benzenonium ion and small for reagents that destabilize the benzenonium ion. This situation is illustrated by the noncatalytic bromination reaction. As inferred in the previous paragraph, ρ^+ is a quantitative measure of selectivity.

Selectivity is determined primarily by the stability of the reagent. The unstable electrophiles do not require as much assistance from the aromatic π electrons and achieve a transition state in which the C-X$^+$ distance, r_{CX^+}, is rather large and in which only a small fractional charge is introduced into the aromatic nucleus. The more stable, more selective reagents require a much greater participation of the aromatic π electrons. The distance between Y$^+$ and the aromatic carbon atom is shorter in this transition state and a greater positive charge is introduced into the aromatic nucleus.

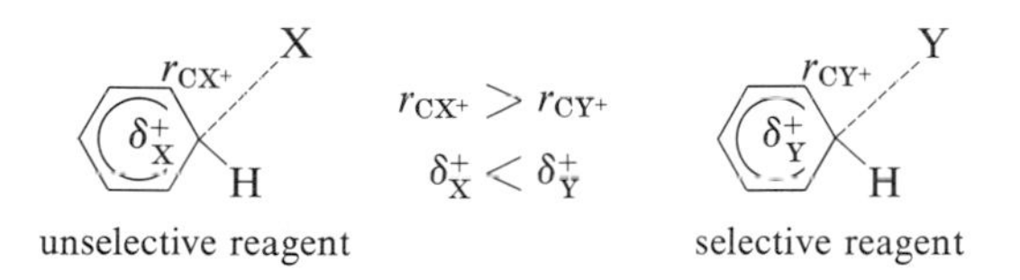

unselective reagent selective reagent

In other words, the transition state for the selective reaction more closely resembles the benzenonium ion. The idea that reagent stability is important is supported by the large difference in selectivity for Friedel–Crafts acetylation, $\rho^+ = -9.1$, and isopropylation, $\rho^+ = -2.3$. The reagents involved in these reactions are the acetylonium ion and the isopropyl carbonium ion. The resonance stabilized acylonium ion is thermodynamically

$$H_3C{-}\overset{+}{C}{=}\ddot{O}: \longleftrightarrow H_3C{-}C{\equiv}O:^+ \qquad (H_3C)_2C^+{-}H$$

more stable than the isopropyl ion. The variation in selectivity is presumably related to the difference in stability. Reaction conditions, e.g., temperature and solvent, modify selectivity but their influence is modest. Catalysts exert a more important influence because they alter the character of the electrophilic reagent. The decreased selectivity for ferric chloride-catalyzed chlorination ($\rho^+ = -7.1$) compared to the rather high selectivity for the noncatalytic reaction ($\rho^+ = -10.0$) illustrates this dependence.

4.4 THE SUBSTITUTION OF DISUBSTITUTED BENZENES

Doubts often arise when the qualitative ideas discussed in Chapter 3 are used to predict the isomer distribution for more highly substituted benzenes. To illustrate, the 2-position of *p*-chlorotoluene is substantially activated by the *o*-methyl group but substantially deactivated by the *m*-chlorine atom. On the other hand, the 3-position is slightly deactivated by the *o*-chlorine atom, but slightly activated by the *m*-methyl group. These qualitative expressions are of little value for a prediction of the isomer distribution.

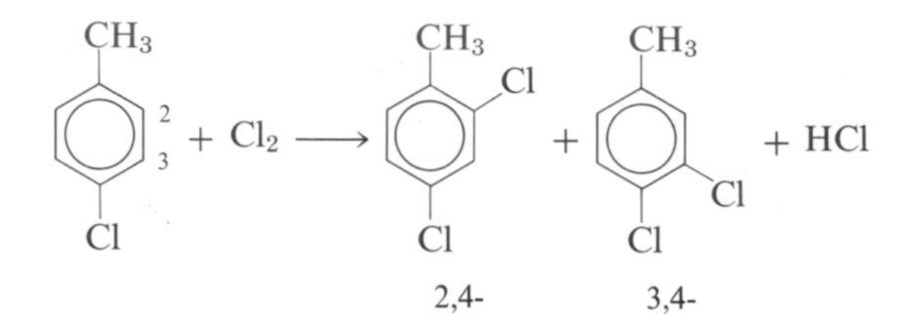

A confident estimate of the relative rate and isomer distribution for substituted benzenes can be made through an extension of the $\rho^+\sigma^+$ approach discussed in Sec. 4.2. Two assumptions are necessary in this extended treatment. First, it is presumed that the influences of the substituents remain independent in the more highly substituted compounds. That is, the influence of an *o*-, *m*-, or *p*-Y substituent on the stability of the benzenonium ion is taken to be independent of the number and kind of other groups in the molecule. Second, it is postulated that the net effect of several substituents on the stability of the benzenonium ion may be measured by the sum of their individual contributions. These assumptions are expressed formally in Eq. (4.6),

$$\log \frac{k}{k_{\mathrm{H}}} = \rho^+ \Sigma \sigma^+ \tag{4.6}$$

where k is the rate constant for substitution at one selected position of the substituted benzene, k_{H} is the rate constant for substitution at one position in benzene, ρ^+ is the reaction constant, and the individual σ^+ constants for all the substituents that influence the reactivity at the selected site for reaction are added (Σ) to assess their net effect. The use of Eq. (4.6) will be illustrated in several examples. The 2-position in *p*-chlorotoluene is *ortho* to the methyl group and *meta* to the chlorine atom; whereas the 3-position is *meta* to the methyl group and *ortho* to the chlorine atom. The net influence of the substituents is then as shown:

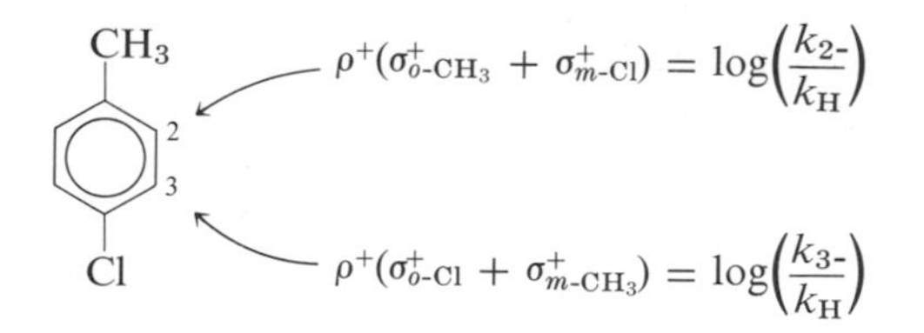

These expressions are useful, but a further simplification is possible since log (k/k_H) is equal to $\rho^+\sigma^+$. Thus,

$$\log\frac{k_{2\text{-}}}{k_H} = \rho^+(\sigma^+_{o\text{-CH}_3} + \sigma^+_{m\text{-Cl}}) = \log o_f^{\text{CH}_3} + \log m_f^{\text{Cl}}$$

$$\frac{k_{2\text{-}}}{k_H} = o_f^{\text{CH}_3} \times m_f^{\text{Cl}} \tag{4.7}$$

$$\log\frac{k_{3\text{-}}}{k_H} = \rho^+(\sigma^+_{o\text{-Cl}} + \sigma^+_{m\text{-CH}_3}) = \log o_f^{\text{Cl}} + \log m_f^{\text{CH}_3}$$

$$\frac{k_{3\text{-}}}{k_H} = o_f^{\text{Cl}} \times m_f^{\text{CH}_3}$$

These equations indicate that the relative rates for substitution in the 2- and 3-positions are given by the products of the partial rate factors for the substituents that influence the reactivity at each position. Substitution of the values for the partial rate factors for the chlorination of chlorobenzene ($o_f^{\text{Cl}} = 0.1$, $m_f^{\text{Cl}} = 0.002$, $p_f^{\text{Cl}} = 0.41$) and toluene ($o_f^{\text{CH}_3} = 620$, $m_f^{\text{CH}_3} = 5.0$, $p_f^{\text{CH}_3} = 820$) into Eq. (4.7) yields

$$\frac{k_{2\text{-}}}{k_H} = 620 \times 0.002 = 1.2$$

$$\frac{k_{3\text{-}}}{k_H} = 5 \times 0.1 = 0.5 \tag{4.8}$$

The isomer distribution is assessed from these relative rates by comparing the reactivity at each position to the sum for all the positions.

$$\%\ \text{2,4-dichlorotoluene} = \frac{(k_{2\text{-}}/k_H)}{(k_{2\text{-}}/k_H) + (k_{3\text{-}}/k_H)} \times 100 = 71\%$$

$$\%\ \text{3,4-dichlorotoluene} = \frac{(k_{3\text{-}}/k_H)}{(k_{2\text{-}}/k_H) + (k_{3\text{-}}/k_H)} \times 100 = 29\% \tag{4.9}$$

The isomer distribution obtained in the experiment is 77% 2,4- and 23% 3,4-dichlorotoluene.

This extension of the $\rho^+\sigma^+$ method involves the use of o_f. It was noted in Sec. 4.2 that the empirical method was not applicable for the correlation of the data for *ortho* substitution because of the large variations in steric requirements. In this extension of the method, the steric requirements do remain constant. Thus, the steric interaction between the methyl group and the reagent is sensibly the same for substitution in the *o*-position of toluene and in the 2-position of *p*-chlorotoluene. This equivalence of steric effects is necessary for a successful prediction (see Prob. 4.3c).

The chlorination of *m*-xylene provides another illustration. This hydrocarbon has three different reaction sites. The substituent effects are shown in the illustration and the sum for all the positions is given by Eq. (4.10).

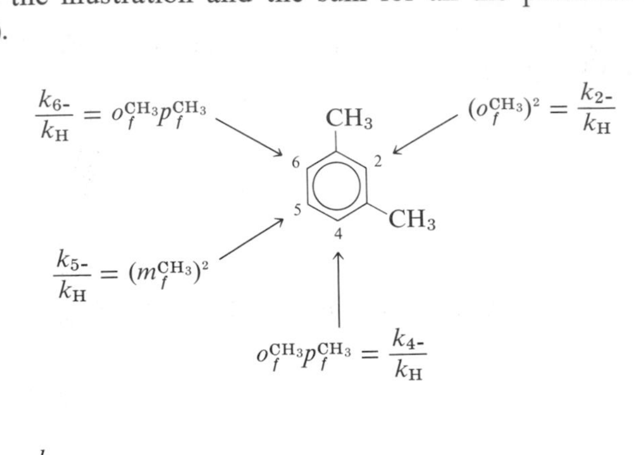

$$\frac{k_{m\text{-xylene}}}{k_H} = (o_f^{CH_3})^2 + 2o_f^{CH_3} p_f^{CH_3} + (m_f^{CH_3})^2 = 142 \times 10^4 \qquad (4.10)$$

The isomer distribution is given by the ratio of the reactivity at the individual positions divided by the sum for all the positions.

$$\%\ 4\text{-} = \frac{2o_f^{CH_3} p_f^{CH_3} \times 100}{\text{sum of all positions}} = \frac{103 \times 10^6}{142 \times 10^4} = 73\%$$

$$\%\ 2\text{-} = \frac{(o_f^{CH_3})^2 \times 100}{\text{sum of all positions}} = \frac{38.5 \times 10^6}{142 \times 10^4} = 27\%$$

$$\%\ 5\text{-} = \frac{(m_f^{CH_3})^2 \times 100}{\text{sum of all positions}} = \frac{25 \times 10^2}{142 \times 10^4} = 0.002\%$$

The experimental result for chlorination is 77% 4-chloro- and 23% 2-chloro-*m*-xylene. Additional examples are presented in Prob. 4.3.

4.5 POLYNUCLEAR AROMATIC HYDROCARBONS

The conjugated, unsaturated hydrocarbons with fused six-membered rings are aromatic compounds (Sec. 1.4). Kekulé structures for three important compounds of this kind are shown. Several lines of evidence indi-

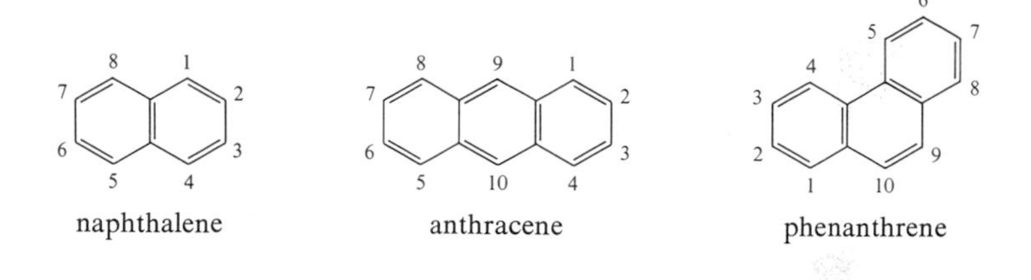

cate that these compounds are aromatic substances. The nmr signals for the ring protons occur at low field, as do those of benzene (Sec. 1.4), and the heats of combustion reveal a large stabilization energy (Sec. 1.3): 61 kcal mole^{-1} for napthalene, 84 kcal mole^{-1} for anthracene, and 91 kcal mole^{-1} for phenanthrene. These facts indicate that π electrons in these compounds are delocalized. Their aromatic character is portrayed by the placement of a circle in each ring. It is pertinent to note that the circle is not to be identified with any specific number of π electrons but that it only indicates their delocalization. The two circles in naphthalene represent 10 π electrons; whereas the three circles in anthracene and phenanthrene represent 14 π electrons. The symmetry properties of naphthalene are such that the 1-, 4-, 5-, and 8-positions are identical, as are the 2-, 3-, 6-, and

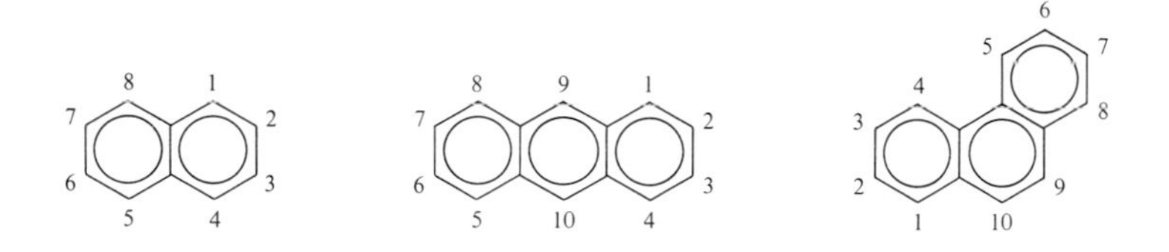

7-positions. There are three different kinds of hydrogen atoms in anthracene: the four in the 1-, 4-, 5-, and 8-positions differ from the set in the 2-, 3-, 6-, and 7-positions and from the pair in the 9-, and 10-positions. There are five different kinds of hydrogen atoms in phenanthrene: 1 and 8, 2 and 7, 3 and 6, 4 and 5, and 9 and 10.

The polynuclear hydrocarbons undergo both electrophilic substitution and electrophilic addition reactions. A semiquantitative theory based on molecular orbital theory is quite successful for the prediction of the relative rates and isomer distribution for these reactions. It is presumed in this theory that the rate differences are related to the change in the energy of the π electrons in the conversion of the hydrocarbon to the benzenonium ion-like intermediates that are involved in the rate-determining step of the reaction, as illustrated for the two nonequivalent positions of naphthalene.

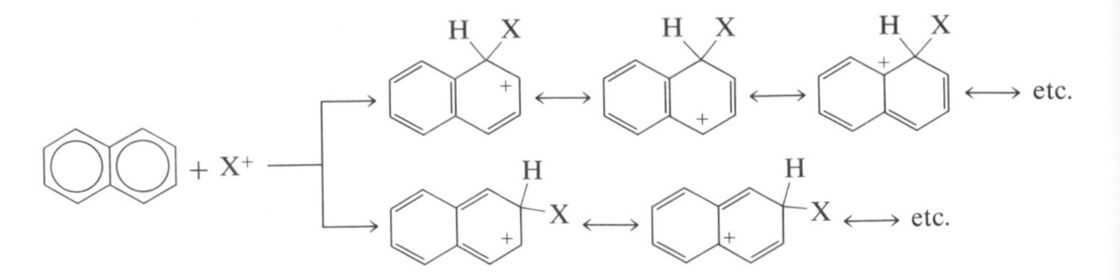

The approach used for the calculation of the change in π electron energy will be examined for the protonation of benzene.

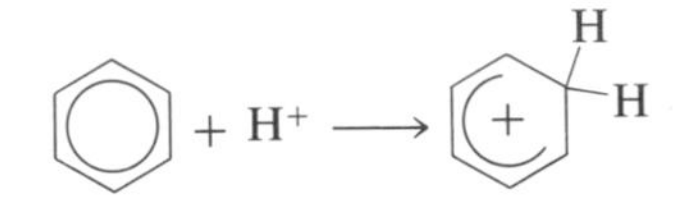

In this reaction two π electrons are removed from the molecular orbitals of benzene to form a new localized carbon-hydrogen σ bond. The energy of the π electrons of benzene is $6\alpha + 8\beta$ (Eq. 1.6). Five sp^2 hybridized carbon atoms remain in a chain in the benzenonium ion. The application of Eq. (1.1) to a five carbon atom chain yields the MO energy levels shown in Fig. 4-8. There are four π electrons in the benzenonium ion. The energy of these four electrons, $E_\pi^{C_6H_7^+}$, is $4\alpha + 5.46\beta$. The change in π electron energy for the reaction is given by the difference.

$$E_\pi^{C_6H_6} - E_\pi^{C_6H_7^+} = (6\alpha + 8\beta) - (4\alpha + 5.46\beta) = 2\alpha + 2.54\beta \qquad (4.11)$$

This calculation treats only the π electrons; the energy change associated with the formation of a new carbon-hydrogen σ bond is not considered. The term 2α, Eq. (4.11), arises because two π electrons are removed from

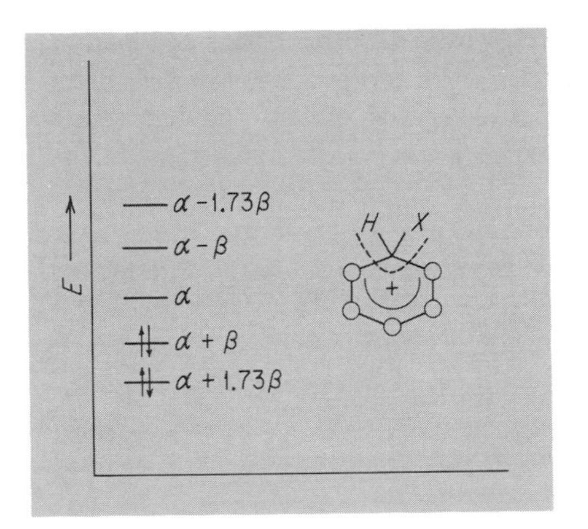

Fig. 4-8 Molecular orbital energy level diagram for the five carbon atom chain occupied by four electrons as in the benzenonium ion.

the π system of benzene in the formation of this bond. These electrons, which were delocalized in benzene, become localized in the ion. The term 2α occurs in the calculated π electron energy change for the electrophilic reactions of all polynuclear hydrocarbons. In view of this fact, it is convenient to define L^+, the cation (electrophilic) localization energy, as

$$L^+ = \text{change in } \pi \text{ electron energy} - 2\alpha \qquad (4.12)$$

and to discuss the reactivity of the hydrocarbons on the basis of L^+. For benzene, L^+ is 2.54β.

The change in π electron energy and L^+ may be calculated for the conversion of a polynuclear hydrocarbon to any specific benzenonium-like ion, for example, for the conversion of naphthalene to the two possible ions,

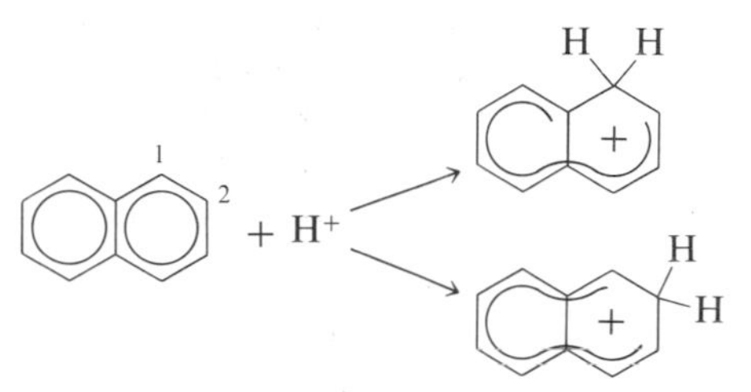

The procedure is the same as illustrated for benzene. However, the calculation is somewhat more difficult and will not be presented here. These calculations specifically consider the large delocalization energies of the hydrocarbons. In each case the calculated values of L^+ reflect the difference in the delocalization energy of the π electrons in the starting hydrocarbon and product ion. Values of L^+ for reaction at each position of biphenyl, naphthalene, anthracene, and phenanthrene are summarized in Table 4-3.

The smaller L^+ values indicate less energy is required for the reaction. Since L^+ is given in units of β, a small change in L^+ represents a large change in the energy required for reaction. The localization energies do not measure the activation-free energy change for the achievement of the transition state for each reaction. The method does not consider the energy quantities associated with the formation of a new σ bond. Moreover, the actual change in π electron energy for the achievement of the transition state is proportional, but not equal, to L^+ because the transition state is of somewhat greater energy content than the intermediate benzenonium ion on which the calculations are based. These simplifications restrict the use of the theory to the prediction of the relative reactivity of the hydrocarbons with a common reagent and to the prediction of isomer distributions.

The localization approach predicts that biphenyl should substitute in the *ortho, para* positions and at a rate greater than that of benzene [L^+ for

Table 4-3
CATION LOCALIZATION ENERGIES

Compound	Position	L^+
Benzene	1	2.54β
Biphenyl	2	2.40β
	3	2.54β
	4	2.45β
Naphthalene	1	2.30β
	2	2.48β
Anthracene	1	2.25β
	2	2.40β
	9	2.01β
Phenanthrene	1	2.32β
	2	2.50β
	3	2.45β
	4	2.36β
	9	2.30β

the *ortho* (2) and *para* (4) positions of biphenyl is smaller than L^+ for benzene]. As already discussed in Sec. 3.6A, the electrophilic substitution of biphenyl occurs virtually completely in the *ortho* and *para* positions and $o_f^{C_6H_5}$ and $p_f^{C_6H_5}$ are far greater than unity. The localization approach suggests the reactivity of the *meta* (3) position is identical to that of one position in benzene. Values for $m_f^{C_6H_5}$ are actually slightly smaller than unity. This small discrepancy results from the fact that the localization approximation neglects the destabilizing polar influence of the phenyl substituent on the *meta*-substituted benzenonium ion.

Naphthalene, according to the L^+ values, should substitute predominantly in the 1-position. Both the 1- and 2-positions are predicted to be much more reactive than a single position in benzene. These predictions are correct. The reaction of naphthalene with chlorine, bromine, or nitronium ion yields mostly the 1-isomer.

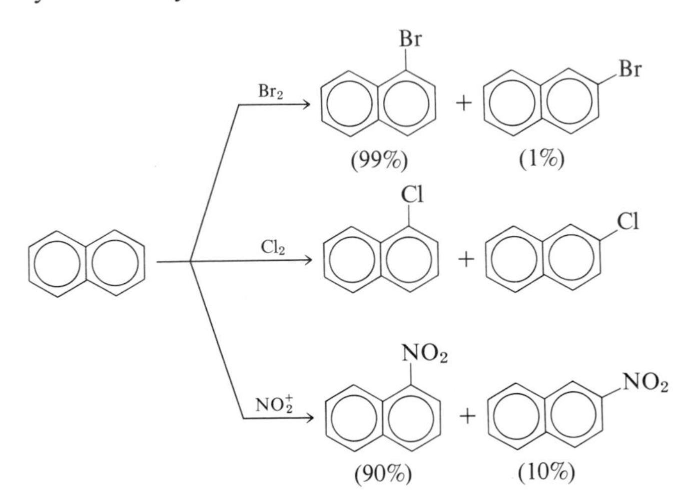

These reactions are far more rapid than the substitution of benzene; the partial rate factors for bromination are $1_f^N = k_{1\text{-Naphthalene}}/k_H = 2 \times 10^5$ and $2_f^N = k_{2\text{-Naphthalene}}/k_H = 2 \times 10^3$.

The reactions of anthracene and phenanthrene with electrophilic reagents often follow a distinctly different path than the reactions of benzene, biphenyl, and naphthalene. Addition rather than substitution products are usually obtained. For example, anthracene adds chlorine to give 9,10-dichloro-9,10-dihydroanthracene.

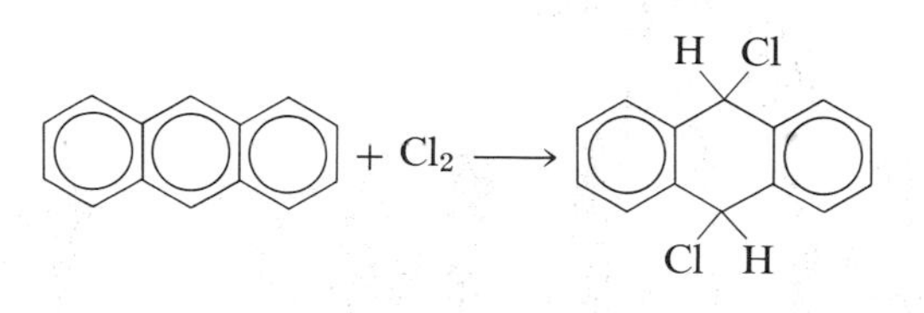

Electrophilic substitution and electrophilic addition reactions both proceed by the rate-determining formation of the anthracenonium ion. As discussed in Sec. 2.8, the energy relationships for the subsequent fast reactions of the ion determine the nature of the product.

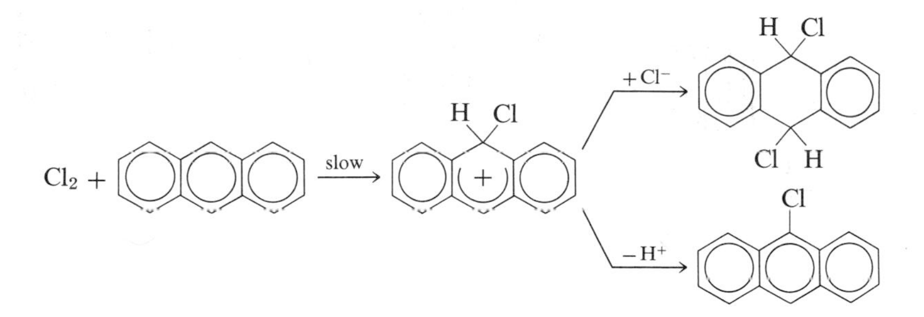

The L^+ values, Table 4-3, predict that the 9-substituted ion should form far more rapidly than the 1- or 2-substituted anthracenonium ion and vastly more rapidly than the benzenonium ion. This expectation is borne out by the fact that anthracene reacts extremely rapidly with chlorine and that only the 9,10-addition product is obtained in isolable amounts. The importance of the aromatic stabilization energy in the determination of the course of electrophilic reactions of benzene was noted in Sec. 2.8. Substitution products are obtained with benzene because these products enable the restoration of the aromaticity with 36 kcal mole^{-1} stabilization energy. The stabilization energy of anthracene is 84 kcal mole^{-1}.

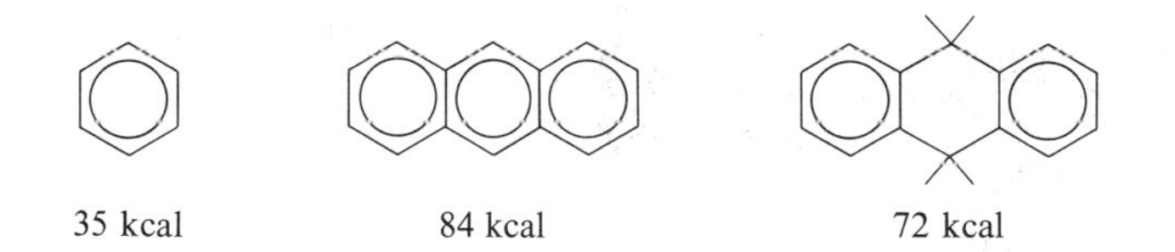

Dihydroanthracene has two isolated benzene rings and the stabilization energy is twice the stabilization energy of benzene, 72 kcal mole^{-1}. The difference between the stabilization energy of anthracene and 9,10-dihydroanthracene is only 12 kcal mole^{-1}. The formation of a second σ bond to yield the addition product then becomes the favored path for reaction.

9-Substituted anthracenes are prepared by an addition followed by an elimination reaction. 9-Chloroanthracene, for example, is obtained by the thermal elimination of hydrogen chloride from 9,10-dichloro-9,10-dihydroanthracene. Other derivatives are synthesized by similar procedures: 9-nitroanthracene is prepared by the nitration of anthracene in the presence of hydrogen chloride. The dihydro compound precipitates; subsequent treatment with base yields 9-nitroanthracene.

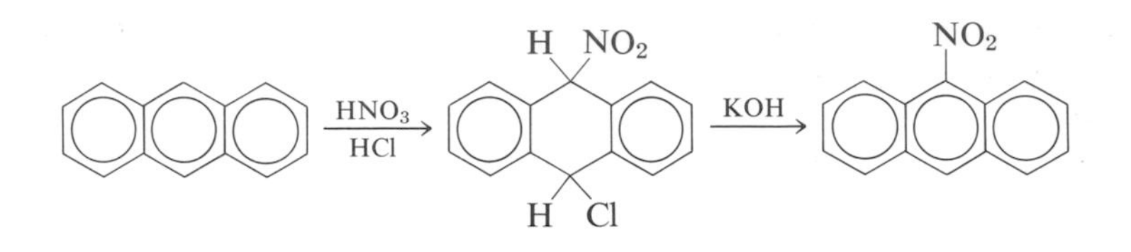

Phenanthrene, as anthracene, yields addition products with many electrophilic reagents. Bromine and chlorine, for example, add to the 9, 10-positions.

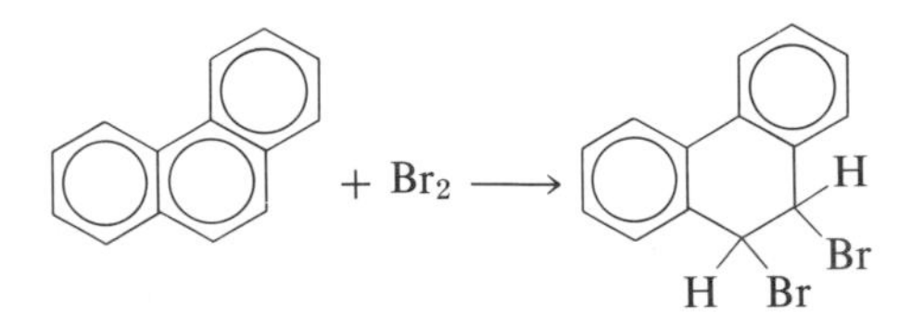

Nitration, in contrast to chlorination, yields the substitution products shown. This substitution pattern is compatible with the prediction of the L^+ treatment ($9 > 1 > 4 > 3 > 2$) except that too little of 4-nitrophenanthrene is formed. This is not surprising because the hydrogen atom at the 5-position sterically interferes with reaction in the 4-position.

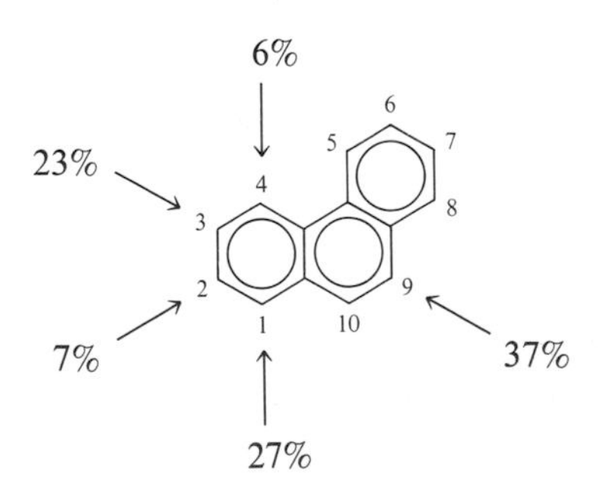

PROBLEMS

4.1. Assess ρ^+ for the mercuration reaction (see Prob. 2.4) from the experimental results: $p_f^{OCH_3} = 2.3 \times 10^3$; $p_f^{NHCOCH_3} = 2.8 \times 10^2$; $p_f^{CH_3} = 23$; $m_f^{CH_3} = 2.23$; $p_f^F = 2.98$; $m_f^F = 0.04$; $p_f^{Cl} = 0.36$; $m_f^{Cl} = 0.06$. (*Answer:* $\rho^+ = -4.0$.)

4.2. Suggest an order for ρ^+ for the Friedel–Crafts reactions of the following ions:

a. $(C_6H_5)_3C^+$, $(CH_3)_3C^+$, $(CH_3)_2CH^+$, CH_3^+

b. CF_3CO^+ and CH_3CO^+

4.3. a. The partial rate factors for noncatalytic chlorination are $o_f^{CH_3} = 620$, $m_f^{CH_3} = 5.0$, $o_f^F = 0.22$, $m_f^F = 0.0056$. Estimate the isomer distribution for the chlorination of *p*-fluorotoluene. (*Answer:* 76% 2-chloro-, 24% 3-chloro-4-fluorotoluene. For comparison, the experimental results are 64% 2-chloro- and 36% 3-chloro-4-fluorotoluene).

b. The partial rate factors for nitration are $o_f^{CH_3} = 38$, $m_f^{CH_3} = 3.0$, $p_f^{CH_3} = 47$, $o_f^{Cl} = 0.03$, $m_f^{Cl} = 0.009$, $p_f^{Cl} = 0.14$. Estimate the isomer distribution for the nitration of *m*-chlorotoluene. (*Answer:* 14% 2-nitro-, 18% 4-nitro-, 0.4% 5-nitro-, and 67% 6-nitro-3-chlorotoluene. For comparison, the experimental results are 9% 2-, 32% 4-, and 59% 6-nitro-3-chlorotoluene with none of the 5-isomer detected).

c. The partial rate factors for noncatalytic chlorination are $m_f^{NHCOCH_3} = 0.5$, $p_f^{NHCOCH_3} = 25.2 \times 10^5$, $o_f^{CH_3} = 620$, $m_f^{CH_3} = 5.0$, $p_f^{CH_3} = 820$. Calculate the isomer distribution for the chlorination of 2, 6-dimethylacetanilide. The experimental result is 98% 3-chloro-2, 6-dimethylacetanilide and 2% 4-chloro-2,6-dimethylacetanilide. Suggest an explanation for the failure of the approach in this case.

d. The partial rate factors for the Friedel–Crafts acetylation of toluene are $o_f^{CH_3} = 5.0$, $m_f^{CH_3} = 5.0$, and $p_f^{CH_3} = 750$. Calculate the rate of acetylation of isodurene (1,2,3,5-tetramethylbenzene) relative to benzene (*Answer:* 3.1×10^4). Compare this result with the experimental result 7.4×10^3.

4.4. Indicate the products of the following reactions.

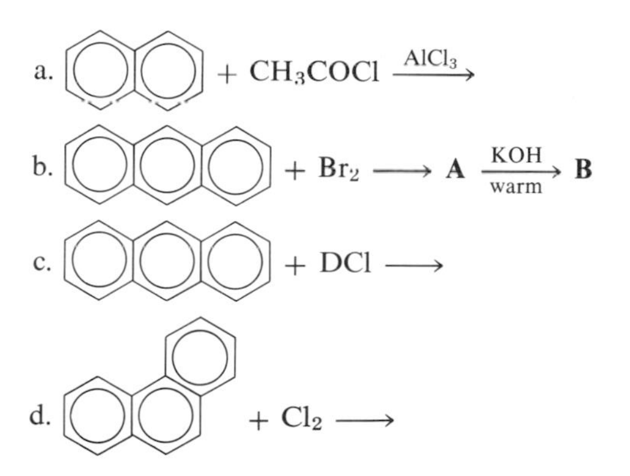

SUGGESTED READING

The chemistry of the polynuclear aromatic hydrocarbons is discussed by L. F. Fieser and M. Fieser in Chapter 27, "Naphthalene", of their book, *Advanced Organic Chemistry,* Reinhold Publishing Corp., New York, 1961 and in Chapter 1, "Polynuclear Hydrocarbons" of their book *Topics in Organic Chemistry,* Reinhold Publishing Corp., New York, 1963.

The results for many substitution reactions and the use of $\rho^+\sigma^+$ correlations are examined by L. M. Stock and H. C. Brown, *Advances in Physical Organic Chemistry,* V. Gold, editor, Academic Press, New York, 1963, Vol. I.

The extension of the $\rho^+\sigma^+$ treatment to more highly polysubstituted compounds is discussed by P. B. D. de La Mare and J. H. Ridd, *Aromatic Substitution, Butterworth's Scientific Publications,* London, 1959, and by Stock and Brown in the previous reference.

The localization approximation is discussed by A. Streitwieser, *Molecular Orbital Theory for Organic Chemists,* John Wiley & Sons, Inc., New York, 1961, Chapter XI.

5 Nucleophilic Substitution and Elimination Reactions

5.1 INTRODUCTION

Benzene derivatives react with nucleophiles and with bases in reactions that are formally similar to the nucleophilic substitution and elimination reactions that are so important in aliphatic chemistry. These aliphatic S_N1, S_N2, and $E2$ processes are examined in detail by W. H. Saunders, in *Ionic Aliphatic Reactions* (this series). The related reactions of aromatic compounds will be discussed in this chapter. These reactions are particularly important in the chemistry of benzene derivatives because they often provide convenient methods for the interchange of substituent groups and for the synthesis of important compounds.

5.2 AROMATIC S_N1 REACTIONS

Many *tertiary* alkyl halides undergo first-order nucleophilic substitution reactions. This well-characterized process proceeds by the heterolytic cleavage of the carbon-halogen bond to yield a carbonium ion in the rate-determining step of the reaction. The carbonium ion reacts with the nucleophiles present in solution to yield the substitution products in a subsequent fast reaction.

$$(H_3C)_3CCl \rightleftharpoons (H_3C)_3C^+ + Cl^-$$

$$(H_3C)_3C^+ + H_2O \longrightarrow (H_3C)_3COH + H^+$$

The halobenzenes do not react in this manner even under the most forcing conditions.

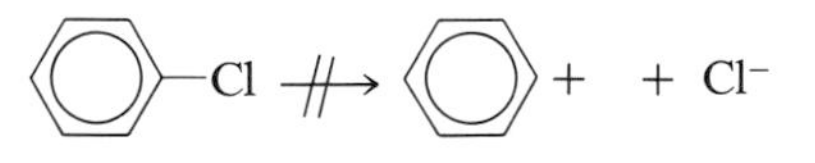

Two factors contribute to the prohibitively great activation free energy for the aromatic S_N1 reaction of the aryl halides. First, the carbon-chlorine bond is much stronger in the aryl halides as revealed by the shorter carbon-chlorine bond distance of 1.70 Å in chlorobenzene compared to 1.78 Å in *t*-butyl chloride. A second factor that increases the activation energy for the ionization reaction is the instability of the phenyl carbonium ion. This instability may be related to the greater electronegativity of the *sp*-like carbon atom that bears the charge in the phenyl cation compared to the sp^2 hybridized carbon atom of the aliphatic carbonium ion. Moreover, there is no opportunity for delocalization of the positive charge in the phenyl cation since the vacant orbital does not overlap with the aromatic π electron orbital.

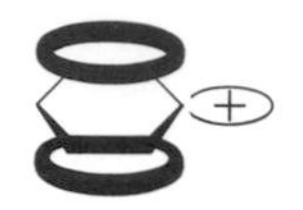

The only known practical method for the formation of the phenyl cation is through the thermal decomposition of the benzenediazonium ion (the methods of preparation of these ions are discussed in Sec. 5.5).

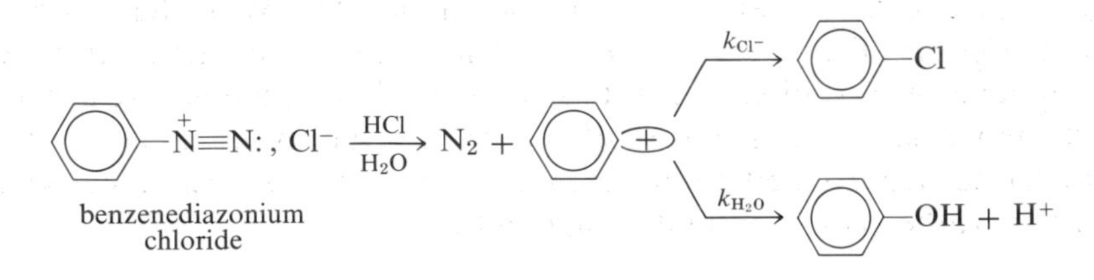

These decomposition reactions exhibit the same kinetic characteristics as the S_N1 reactions of aliphatic halides. Thus, the rate of disappearance of the benzenediazonium ion depends on the concentration of the ion but not on the concentration of the nucleophiles in solution. The success of this method for the generation of the phenyl cation is related to the fact that the decomposition reaction produces the very unstable cation and the very stable diatomic nitrogen molecule simultaneously. The energy required for the formation of the cation is counterbalanced by the energy gained in the formation of nitrogen. The decomposition is carried out in acid solution (see Sec. 5.5). The subsequent reactions of the phenyl cation are rapid and unselective as expected for a highly energetic reagent (Sec. 4.3). The low selectivity is illustrated by the fact that the ratio of the rate constants for the reaction with chloride ion and with water ($k_{Cl^-} : k_{H_2O}$) is 3 for the phenyl cation compared to 180 for *t*-butyl carbonium ion. The lack of selectivity is further shown by the fact that a recombination reaction occurs. The reactive phenyl cation actually recaptures the feebly nucleophilic nitrogen molecule, as shown by the partial scrambling of the label in the benzenediazonium ion.

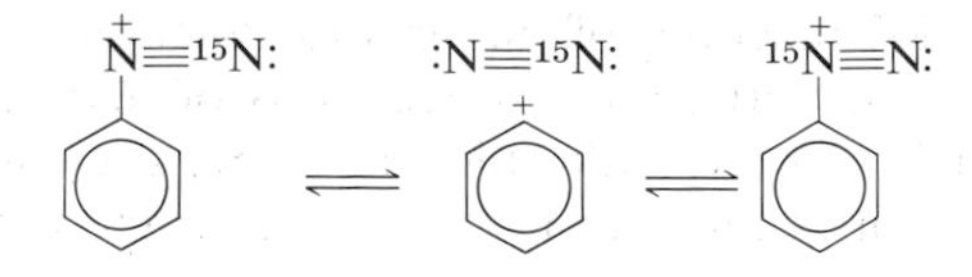

5.3 AROMATIC S_N2 REACTIONS

Many *primary* and *secondary* alkyl halides undergo second-order nucleophilic substitution reactions. This reaction proceeds via a displacement mechanism in which the nucleophile and the alkyl halide form a transition state with a penta-coordinate carbon atom.

$$Y^- + CH_3CH_2X \longrightarrow \left[\begin{array}{c} H \quad H \\ Y\text{---}C\text{---}X \\ | \\ CH_3 \end{array}\right]^- \longrightarrow CH_3CH_2Y + X^-$$

energy maximum
transition state

The corresponding reaction also occurs in the aromatic series. There is, however, an important difference in the mechanism of these reactions. In the aromatic series an intermediate, a benzenanion, forms in the course of the reaction, Fig. 5-1. No simple line structure can be written for the benzenanion. The anion is described by a set of resonance structures similar to those used for the description of the benzenonium ion.

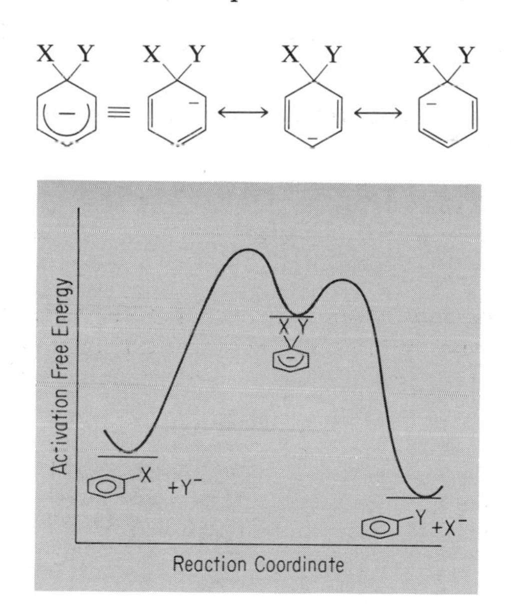

Fig. 5-1 Reaction profile for the aromatic S_N2 reaction.

The aromatic S_N2 reactions of the unsubstituted aryl halides are very much slower than the corresponding reactions of alkyl halides. The reaction of sodium hydroxide with chlorobenzene, a commercial method for the preparation of phenol, requires elevated temperature.

$$C_6H_5{-}Cl + NaOH \xrightarrow[350^\circ]{H_2O} [C_6H_5(Cl)(OH)]^- \longrightarrow C_6H_5{-}OH + Cl^- + Na^+$$

The reduced reaction velocity is associated with the energy necessary to disrupt the aromatic character of the substrate and with the repulsive interactions between the six π electrons of the benzenanion. These factors are, of course, unimportant in the aliphatic substitution reactions. The high energy requirements not withstanding, nucleophilic substitution reactions often offer convenient routes for the replacement of one substituent by another one. The alkaline cleavage of sodium benzenesulfonate is an example of a general method for the synthesis of phenols.

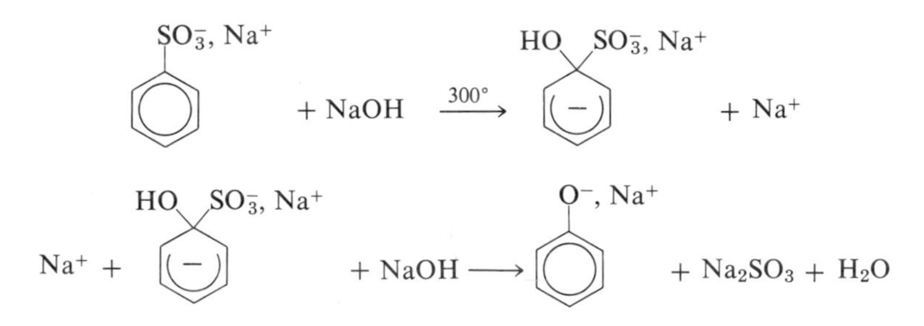

Aniline is prepared from chlorobenzene on a commercial scale by an aromatic S_N2 reaction.

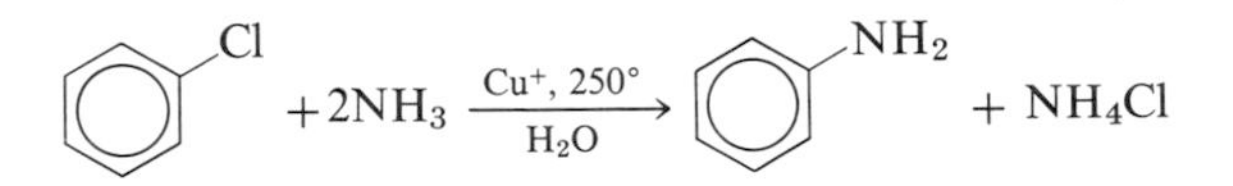

These nucleophilic substitution reactions proceed very slowly in protic solvents such as water or alcohol, and elevated temperatures are required for a practical reaction rate. However, *tertiary* amide solvents greatly in-

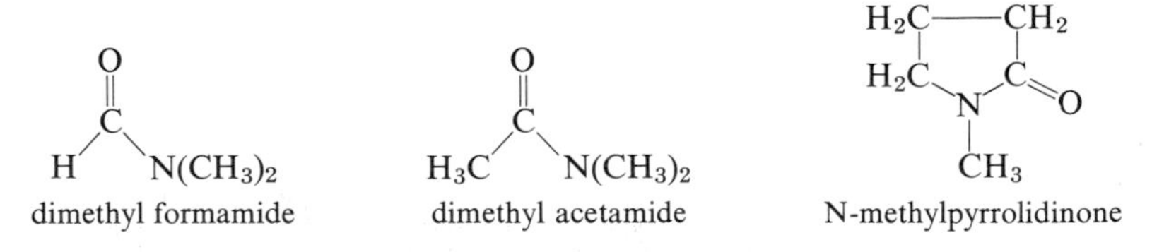

crease the reaction rate. The amides are poor solvents for anions and "activate" the nucleophilic reagent by not solvating it. Direct substitution reactions of simple unsubstituted aryl bromides may be accomplished quite readily in these solvents. Aromatic amines, cyanides, thioethers, and other compounds are readily prepared in this way:

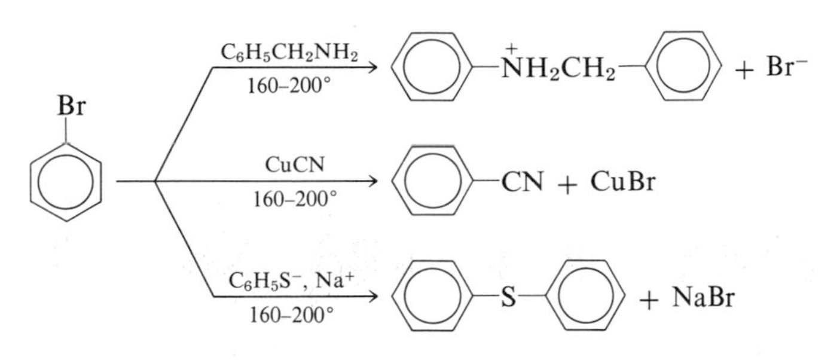

The mechanism of the aromatic S_N2 reaction has been established with some confidence. These reactions are second-order processes as implied by the S_N2 designation:

$$\frac{d[\text{product}]}{dt} = k_2^{\text{ArX}}[\text{ArX}][\text{nucleophile}]$$

Several lines of evidence indicate that the benzenanion is an intermediate. One convincing observation is the isolation of many stable salts containing the benzenanion. For example, the potassium salt of 1-methoxy-1-ethoxy-2,4,6-trinitrobenzenanion is formed in the two ways shown in the following equation:

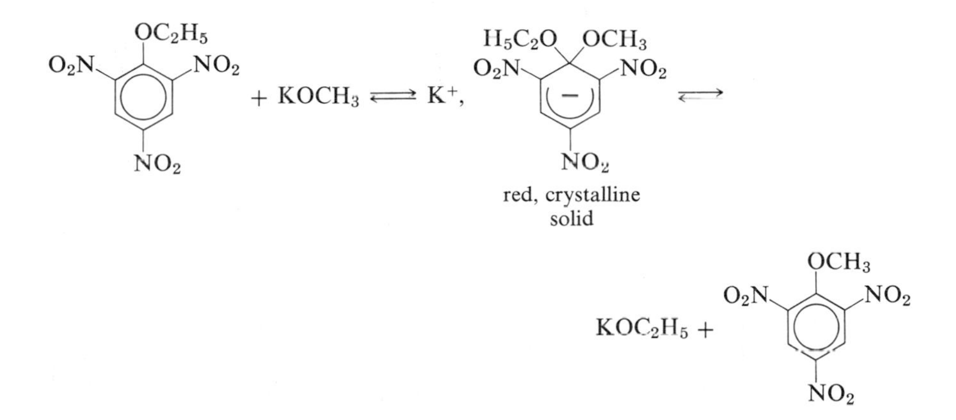

Other stable salts with aromatic anions have been isolated in similar experiments. The anion of this potassium salt is stabilized by the delocalization of the negative charge by the nitro substituents (see the subsequent discussion of substituent effects).

Certain kinetic facts also indicate that an intermediate is involved in these reactions. Under equivalent conditions, the aryl fluorides react far more rapidly than the corresponding aryl chlorides or bromides; that is,

$k_2^{\mathrm{ArF}} > k_2^{\mathrm{ArCl}} > k_2^{\mathrm{ArBr}}$. In contrast, the S_N2 reactivities of the alkyl fluorides, chlorides, and bromides are in the opposite order: $k_2^{\mathrm{RBr}} > k_2^{\mathrm{RCl}} > k_2^{\mathrm{RF}}$. The rate sequence for the alkyl halides is related to the nature of the leaving group and bromide ion is regarded to be a better leaving group than fluoride ion. The reversal of reactivity for the aryl halides is easily understood in terms of a two-step mechanism,

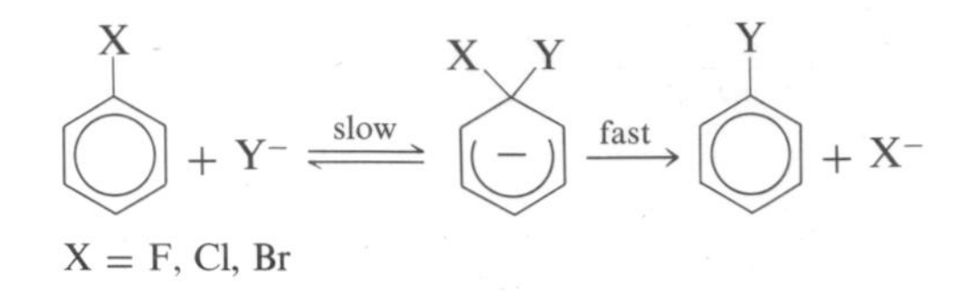

with the first step slow and rate determining as shown in the energy profile, Fig. 5-1. The rate of formation of the 1-fluorobenzenanion may be larger than that of the other 1-halobenzenanions because the fluorine atom exerts a larger stabilizing polar effect. That the fluoride anion is a poor leaving group, as shown by the results for the aliphatic halides, is not critical in the aromatic S_N2 reactions since the departure of the halide anion occurs in the second, fast step of the sequence.

Substituents exert an important influence on the rate of the aromatic S_N2 reactions. Indeed, prior to the discovery of the enhanced reaction velocities in *tertiary* amide solvents, it was thought that activating *o*- or *p*-nitro groups were essential for a practical reaction rate. The origin and magnitude of substituent effects are well illustrated by the results for the reaction of piperidine with 4-Y- and 5-Y-2-nitrochlorobenzene.

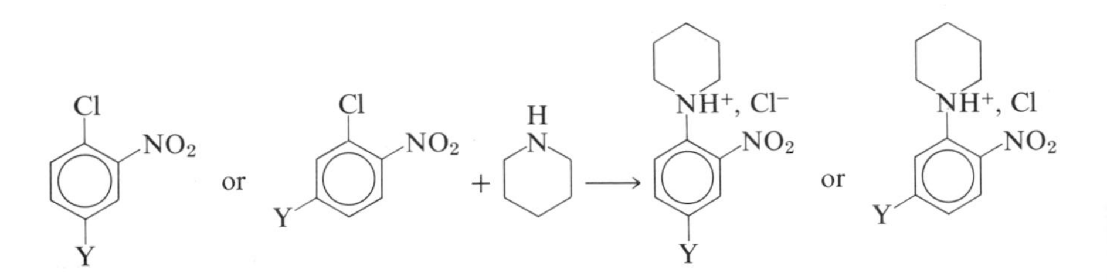

The 2-nitro derivative of chlorobenzene was employed to permit a comparison of all the Y groups under similar conditions. The influence of *para* and *meta* substituents are reflected in the rate data for the 4- and 5-derivatives, respectively, in Table 5-1.

These substituent effects may be discussed on the basis of the same three postulates that were used for the interpretation of substituent effects in electrophilic aromatic substitution reactions in Chapter 3. Thus, it is postulated that the benzenanion is a good model for the transition state, that the thermodynamic stability of the benzenanion determines the re-

Table 5-1

RELATIVE RATES FOR THE S_N2 REACTION OF 4-Y- AND 5-Y-SUBSTITUTED 2-NITROCHLOROBENZENES WITH PIPERIDINE AT 45° IN BENZENE

meta Series		*para* Series	
5-Y	k/k_H	4-Y	k/k_H
NO_2	—	NO_2	41,000
CN	60	CN	6,000
$CO_2C_2H_5$	5	$CO_2C_2H_5$	920
Br	35	Br	10
Cl	32	Cl	6
OCH_3	4	OCH_3	0.025
H	1.00	H	1.00
CH_3	0.9	CH_3	0.2

action rate, and that polar and resonance effects dictate the thermodynamic stability of the substituted benzenanions.

Inspection of the resonance structures for the *meta*-substituted benzenanions reveals that resonance interactions with the substituent are impossible.

Accordingly, polar effects dictate the relative thermodynamic stability of these ions. Inasmuch as the benzenanion is negatively charged, substituent effects in the aromatic nucleophilic substitution reactions are the reverse of the substituent effects in the aromatic electrophilic substitution reactions. As noted in Sec. 3.4, polar influences are determined by the magnitude and direction of the dipole moment of the aryl carbon-substituent bond.

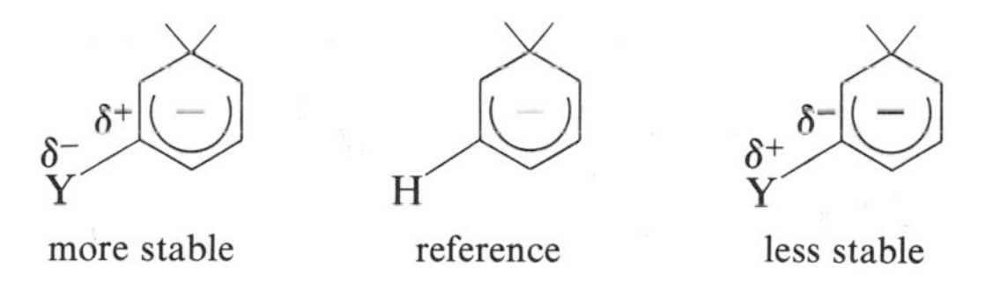

Groups that are polarized, as in the structure on the left, stabilize the ion relative to the unsubstituted derivatives; whereas the opposite polarization causes the ion to be less stable than the reference ion. Thus, *m*-halogen substituents stabilize the benzenanion and accelerate the reaction, while the *m*-methyl group decreases the stability of the anion and slows the reaction velocity. The results shown in Table 5-1 for the other *meta* substituents may be interpreted on the same basis.

The observations for the *para* substituents, Table 5-1, are conveniently discussed on the basis of the same polar, resonance, and *p* electron-π electron repulsion effects that were used in the interpretation of substituent effects in the electrophilic reactions discussed in Chapter 3. The resonance structures that describe the *para* benzenanion include a structure with the negative charge on the carbon atom that bears the substituent.

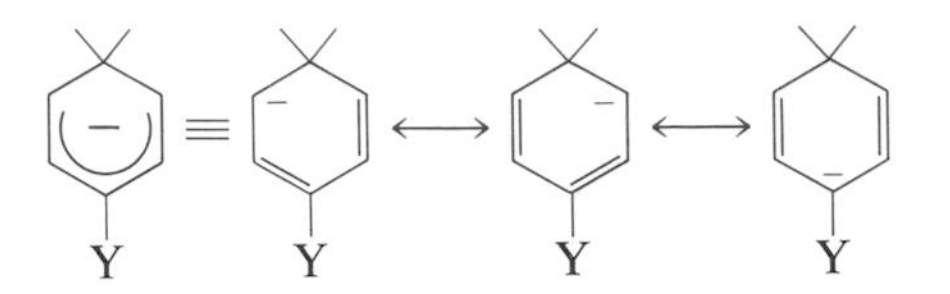

The substituent groups in which the atom bonded to the aromatic ring is saturated, for example, alkyl groups, or in which the atom bonded to the ring has all its orbitals occupied by *p* electrons, for example the halogen atoms and the methoxy group, are incapable of resonance interactions. It was pointed out in Sec. 3.5 that the polar effects of *para* substituents are usually somewhat more important than the polar effects of *meta* groups. The influence of the methyl group on the reaction rate is usually interpreted on the basis of this idea; that is, the destabilizing polar effect of this group is modestly more important in the *para* position than in the *meta* position. This viewpoint predicts that the *p*-halogen and *p*-methoxy substituents should be more stabilizing than the corresponding *meta* groups. The results, Table 5-1, indicate that this expectation is not realized; the reaction rates of the *p*-halogen- and *p*-methoxy-substituted compounds are actually slower than the rates of the *meta* derivatives. An attractive explanation for this result focuses on the potential importance of repulsive electrostatic interactions between the *p* electrons of the substituent and the π electrons of the aromatic system. These destabilizing interactions are illustrated for the halogen and methoxy groups. This repulsive effect may

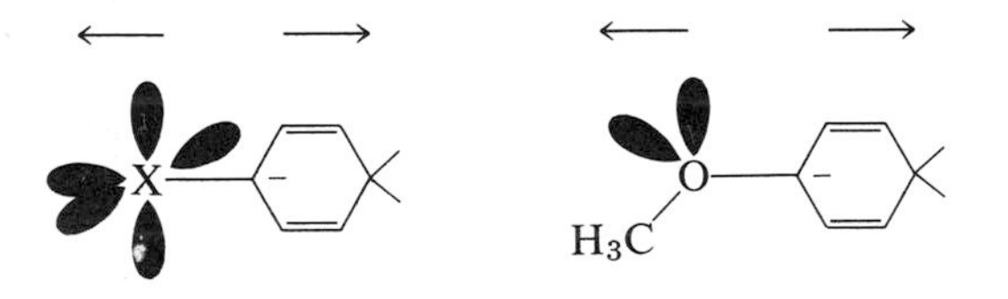

offset the polar influence of the substituent, accounting for the unexpected pattern of reactivity. The rate effects of these substituents are, however, minor in comparison with the resonance effects discussed in the next paragraph.

para-Nitro, cyano, acetyl, and carboethoxy groups have an enormous accelerating influence on the reaction rate. Resonance delocalization of the negative charge by these substituents is important. This delocalization of the negative charge is illustrated for 4-nitrobenzenanion.

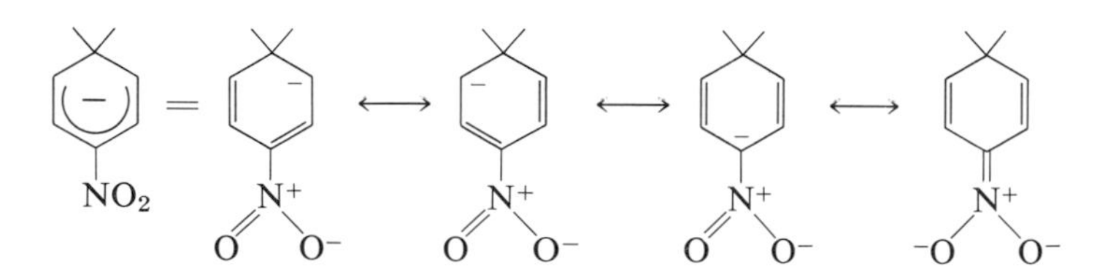

A fourth resonance structure is also necessary for the description of the delocalization of the charge in the *p*-cyano, acetyl, and carboethoxy groups:

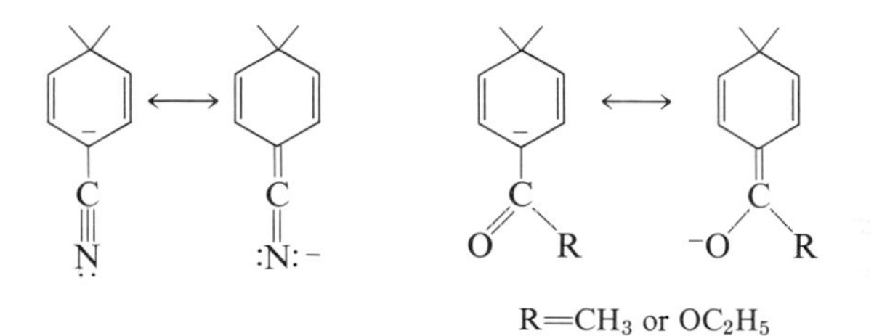

Benzene derivatives bearing these substituents are substituted readily and these reactions do not require the use of amide solvents or elevated temperatures as in the case for the unsubstituted halobenzenes. Hydrazine, for example, reacts with 2,4-dinitrochlorobenzene to yield 2,4-dinitrophenylhydrazine, the well-known reagent for the preparation of derivatives of aldehydes and ketones.

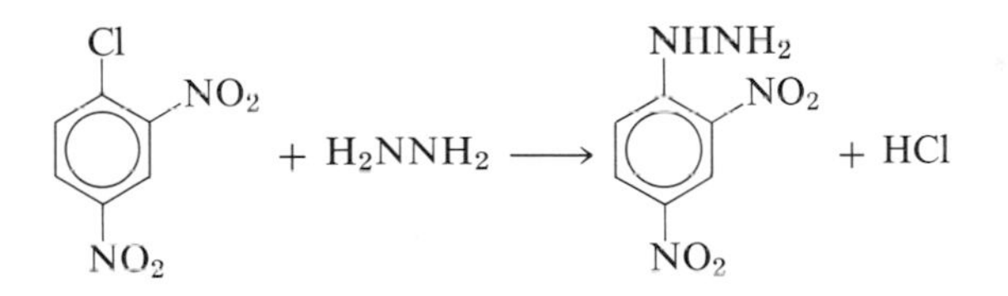

Dinitrobenzenes are also used for end group analysis in the elucidation of amino acid sequences in peptides and proteins. The nucleophilic amino group of the terminal acid (the amide nitrogen atoms are not sufficiently nucleophilic to react) displaces fluoride ion from the dinitrobenzene. Hydrolysis of the product yields the individual amino acids with the terminal amino acid tagged with a 2,4-dinitrophenyl group. This product is easily separated from the amino acids and identified.

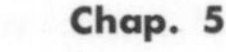

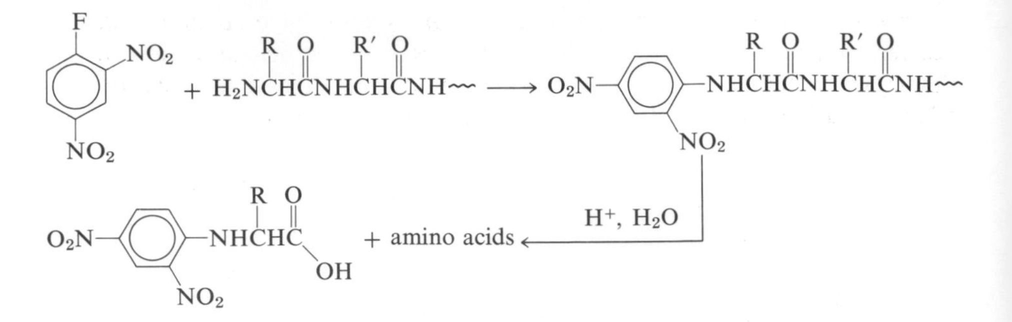

5.4 ELIMINATION REACTIONS

A remarkable reaction occurs when aryl halides that are not activated for nucleophilic substitution are treated with very strong bases. The unusual character of the process is illustrated by the reaction of 2-bromo-6-methylanisole with sodium amide in liquid ammonia.

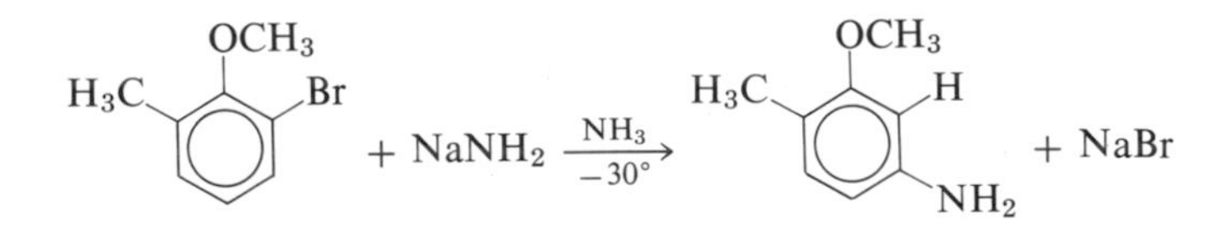

The amino group that is introduced in this reaction occupies the 3-position rather than the 2-position. This and other similar reactions proceed via an elimination-addition sequence. In the first step, the strong base removes a proton from the halobenzene.

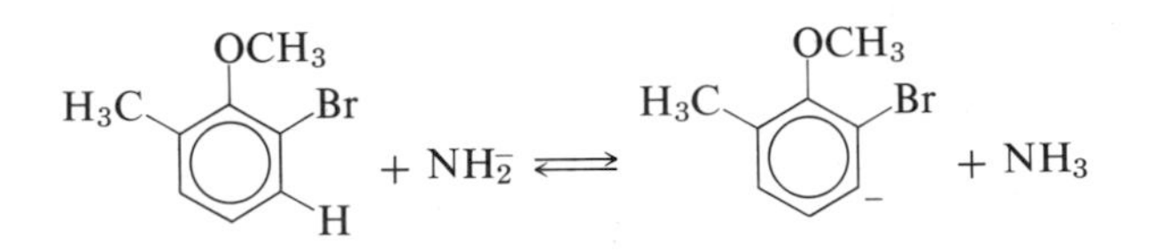

Bromide ion is lost in the second step of the elimination reaction to provide an acetylenic substance called a benzyne.

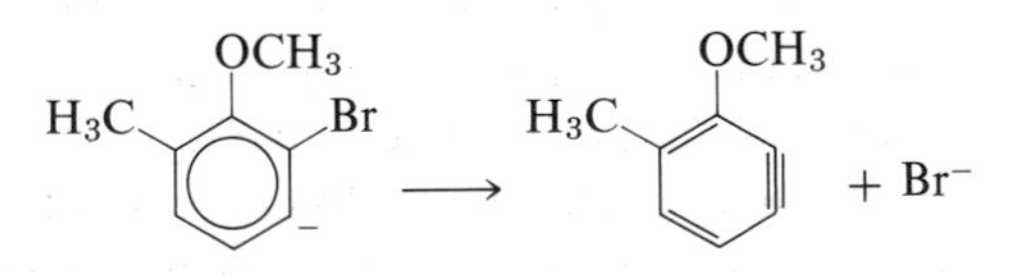

The substituted benzyne then adds ammonia to form the product.

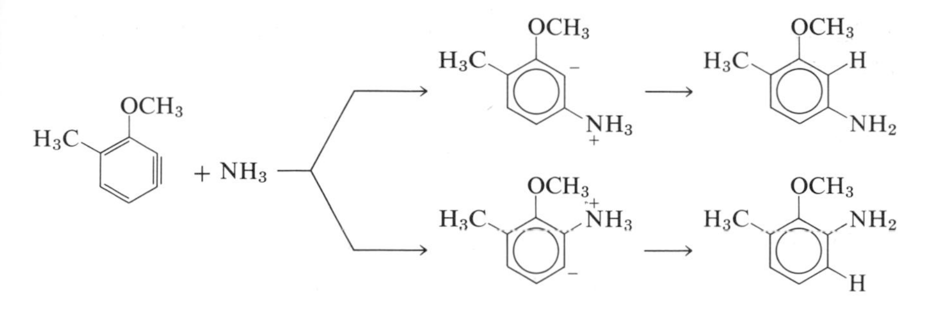

In principle, both 2-amino- and 3-amino-6-methylanisole should form; in fact, only the 3-amino derivative is obtained in this particular reaction.

The evidence for the intermediacy of benzynes in reactions of this kind is quite secure. First, it is well established that aryl hydrogen atoms are removed by strong bases such as sodium amide in liquid ammonia.

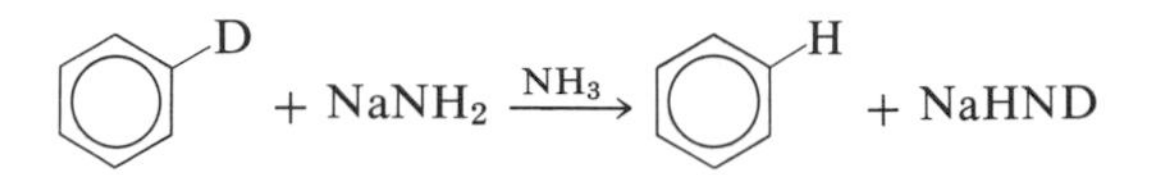

Second, a symmetrical intermediate is involved in the amination reactions of aryl halides. When chlorobenzene labeled with ^{14}C at the 1-position reacts with potassium amide, the label is distributed equally between the 1- and 2-positions in the product.

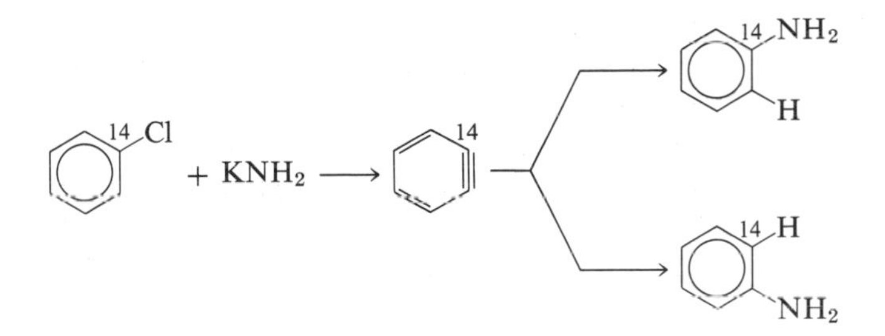

Third, the involvement of the *ortho* hydrogen atom is revealed by the failure of the reaction with 2,6-disubstituted bromobenzenes such as 2-methoxy-6-methylbromobenzene. These facts are best explained by the

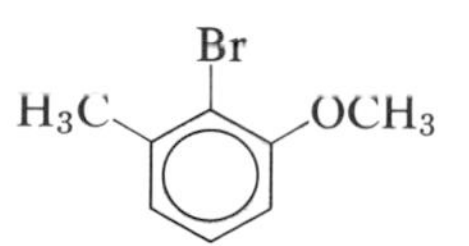

acetylenic intermediate. Benzyne has not been isolated as a pure compound; however, it has been trapped by reaction with dienes. The Diels–

Alder reaction proceeds rapidly with acetylene derivatives and the dienophilic benzyne reacts readily with dienes.

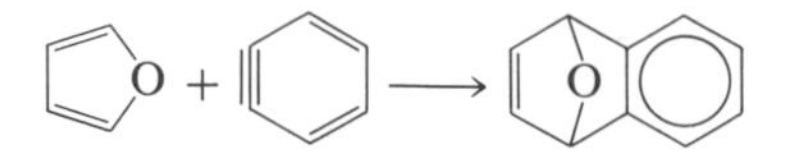

The synthetic potential of benzyne has led to the development of several techniques for its generation.

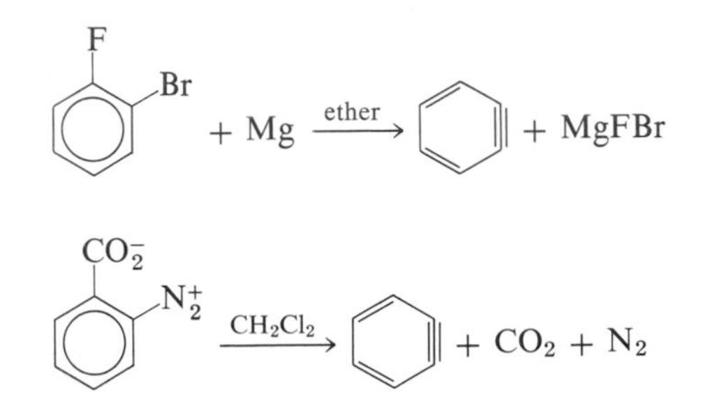

5.5 NITROSATION AND THE ARYL DIAZONIUM SALTS

The diazonium ions from which the aryl carbonium ion may be produced (Sec. 5.2) are prepared from *primary* aromatic amines by nitrosation. These diazonium ions also react with many nucleophilic reagents to provide a variety of substituted aromatic compounds. Thus, nitrosation and the chemistry of the diazonium ions constitute a vast area of particular synthetic interest. Nitrosation is the nitrous acid counterpart of nitration by nitric acid. In nitrosation, the NO^+ group is introduced and a proton expelled. The electrophilic reagent actually involved depends on the acidity of the solution and the anions present in the medium. The equilibria

$$HONO + H^+ \rightleftharpoons H_2\overset{+}{O}NO$$

$$H_2\overset{+}{O}NO + X^- \rightleftharpoons H_2O + XNO$$

$$H_2\overset{+}{O}NO + NO_2^- \rightleftharpoons H_2O + \underset{(N_2O_3)}{O_2NNO}$$

are rapidly established and each of the reagents, $H_2\overset{+}{O}NO$, XNO, and N_2O_3 is known to nitrosate. For brevity, the reagent is designated as $H_2\overset{+}{O}NO$ in the subsequent equations. Nitrosation occurs with highly activated aromatic compounds and with molecules possessing centers of high electron density, for example, the free electron pair on nitrogen atoms. Three different products result from the treatment of *primary*, *secondary*, and *tertiary* aromatic amines with sodium nitrite in acid solution, the usual method for nitrosation.

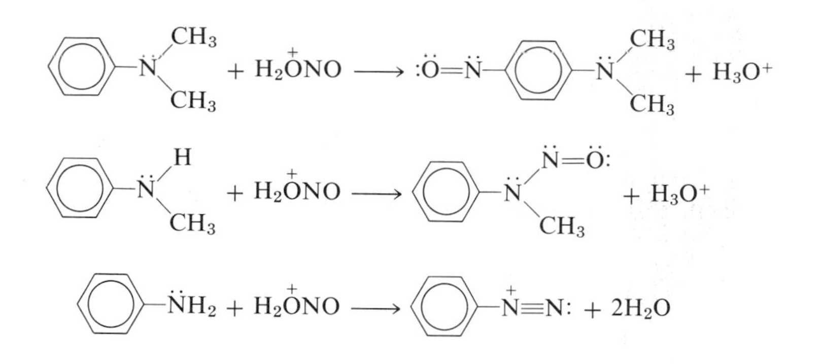

With *tertiary* aromatic amines, nitrosation occurs in the *para* position. Similar electrophilic aromatic nitrosation also occurs with phenol and its derivatives.

$$C_6H_5\text{—}OH + H_2\overset{+}{O}NO \longrightarrow ON\text{—}C_6H_4\text{—}OH + H_3O^+$$

Secondary amines yield N-nitroso derivatives. With *primary* amines, diazonium compounds are formed. The reaction proceeds by the nitrosation of the amino nitrogen atom, followed by the tautomeric shift of two protons and the subsequent elimination of water.

$$C_6H_5NH_2 + H_2O\overset{+}{N}O \longrightarrow C_6H_5\underset{\displaystyle H}{\overset{\displaystyle :N{=}\ddot{O}:}{N^+}}\text{—}H + H_2O$$

$$C_6H_5\underset{\displaystyle H}{\overset{\displaystyle :N{=}\ddot{O}:}{N^+}}\text{—}H \rightleftharpoons C_6H_5\underset{\displaystyle H}{\ddot{N}}\text{—}\ddot{N}{=}\overset{+}{\ddot{O}}H \rightleftharpoons C_6H_5\ddot{N}{=}\ddot{N}\text{—}\overset{+}{\ddot{O}}H_2 \rightleftharpoons C_6H_5N_2^+ + H_2O$$

Diazonium ions are most conveniently prepared by treatment of the amine, dissolved in a cold, aqueous, acidic solution, with sodium nitrite.

$$C_6H_5\text{—}NH_2 + 2H^+, X^- + Na^+, NO_2^- \xrightarrow[5^\circ]{H_2O} C_6H_5\text{—}N_2^+ + X^- + 2H_2O + Na^+, X^-$$

The solution is chilled to avoid the decomposition of the diazonium salt. Crystalline diazonium salts are rarely isolated because they often decompose explosively. Certain sulfate and tetrafluoroborate salts are, however, sufficiently stable to permit safe handling. More routinely, the salts are prepared in solution and maintained at low temperature; the subsequent reactions are carried out by the addition of other reagents and by warming the solution, if necessary, to decompose the diazonium compound.

Application in Synthesis: The diazonium ions react in several different ways. These positive ions are electrophilic reagents and substitute reactive aromatic compounds. The benzenediazonium ions may be decomposed in basic solution to produce phenyl free radicals. In addition, the diazonium ions react with many nucleophilic reagents to provide aromatic compounds that are not easily prepared by electrophilic or nucleophilic substitution reactions. The diazo group may be replaced by hydrogen, fluorine, chlorine, bromine, iodine, nitro, hydroxide, or cyano groups. The techniques useful for the introduction of the desired substituents have some very special features and the mechanisms of these reactions are not established with full confidence. However, the important feature of this method is that the nucleophilic group enters the molecule at the position formerly occupied by the diazo group. This route avoids many of the practical difficulties that are encountered in the direct electrophilic substitution reactions. For example, the bromination of *o*-xylene yields 20% 3-bromo- and 80% 4-bromo-1,2-dimethylbenzene.

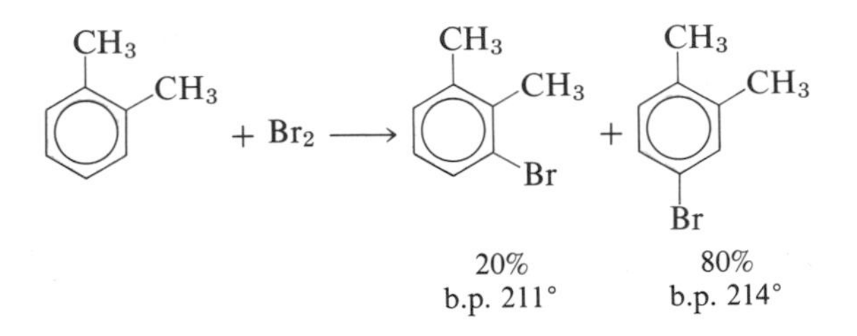

These bromo compounds have very similar physical properties and the separation of the two compounds by fractional distillation is extremely difficult. On the other hand, the nitration reaction yields 55% 3-nitro- and 45% 4-nitro-1,2-dimethylbenzene. The nitro compounds may be separated and purified by crystallization. The separated isomers may be reduced by a variety of techniques, for example iron and hydrochloric acid, to the pure amines. Diazotization followed by the introduction of the bromine atom yields pure samples of each of the isomeric bromides.

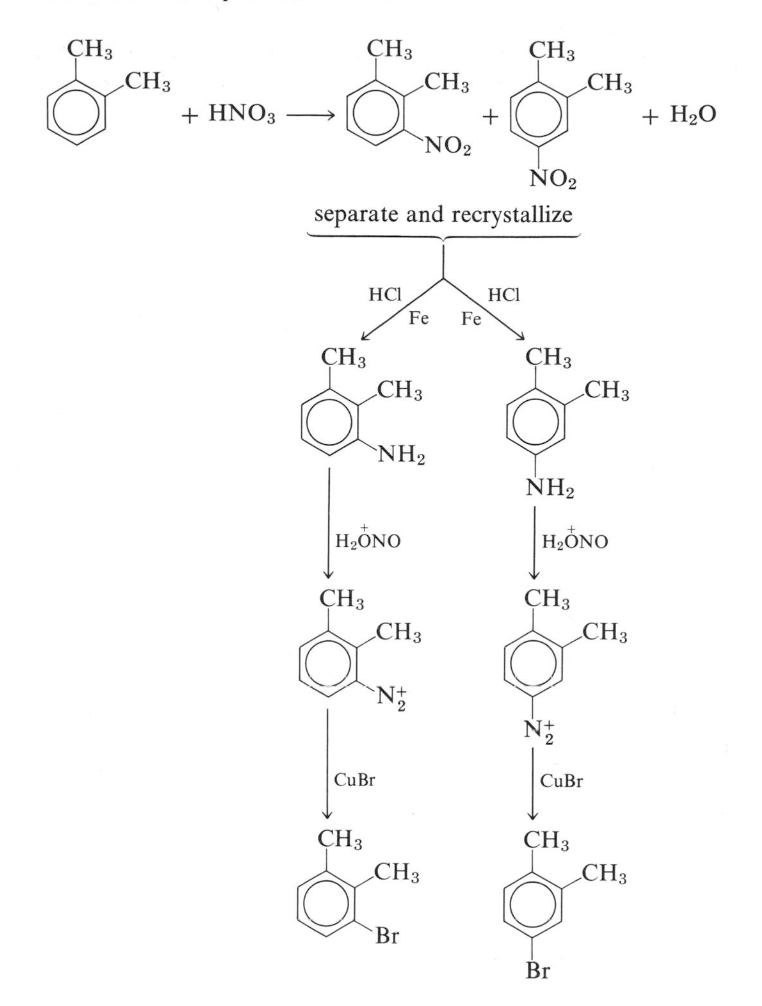

Phenol Formation: Diazonium salts are decomposed in 40–50% sulfuric acid to form the corresponding phenol. It is necessary to carry out the reaction in the absence of other nucleophiles to avoid the formation of other aromatic derivatives. This method is an alternative to the nucleophilic substitution of the aryl sulfonic acid discussed in Sec. 5.3.

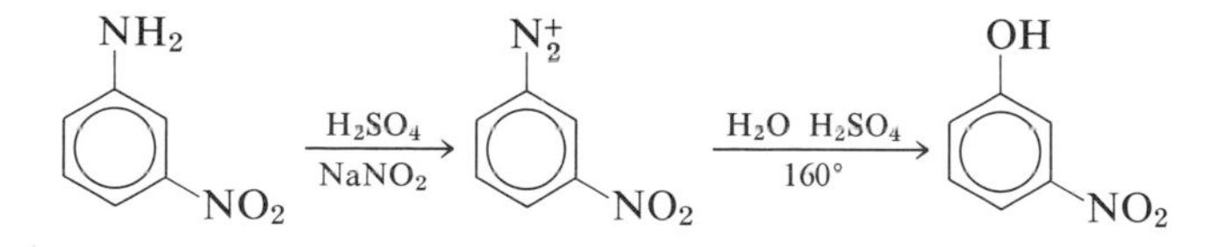

Aryl Halide Synthesis: The decomposition of aryl diazonium chlorides or bromides in aqueous hydrochloric or hydrobromic acid yields both phenol and the aryl halide. These replacement reactions can be readily accomplished when cuprous chloride or bromide (Sandmeyer reaction) or copper powder (Gatterman reaction) is added to the solution.

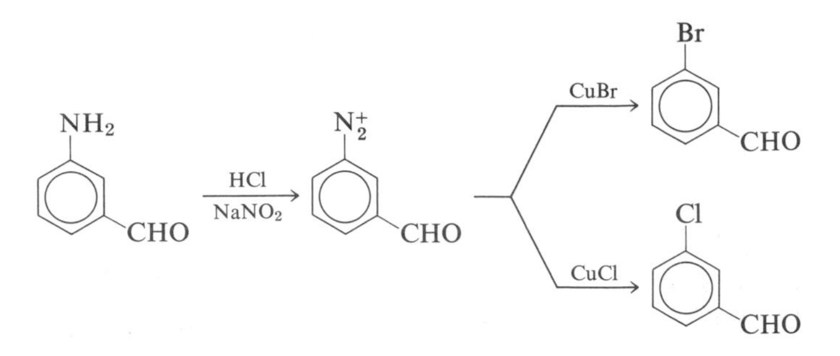

The aryl iodides are easily formed by reaction with potassium iodide.

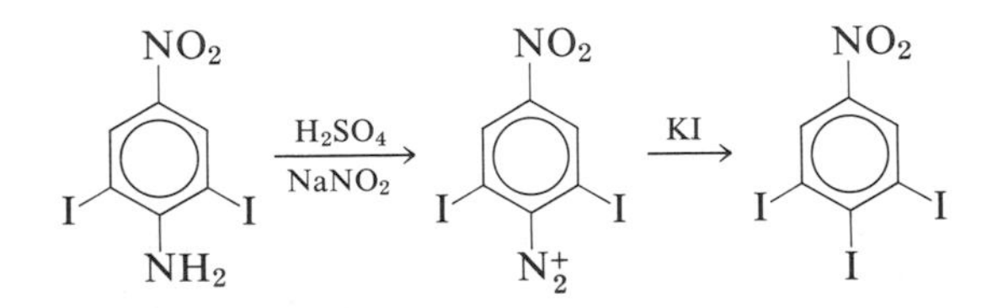

Aryl fluorides are prepared by the thermal decomposition of aryl diazonium tetrafluoroborates (Schiemann reaction). These salts do not decompose explosively. When they are gently warmed, nitrogen and boron trifluoride are evolved and the aryl fluoride is produced.

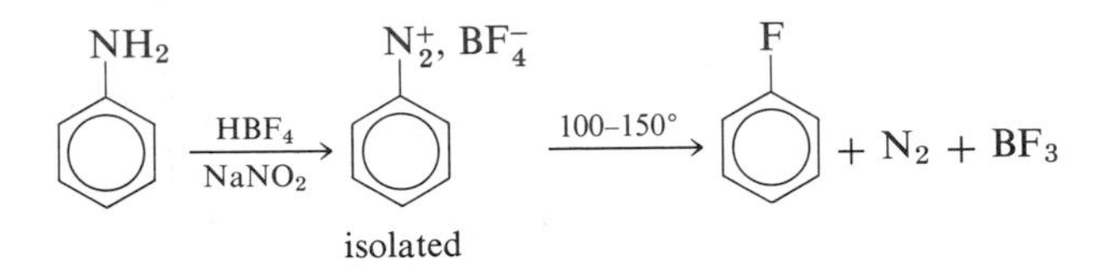

Aryl Cyanide Formation: The cyano group is introduced via the reaction of the diazonium compound with cuprous cyanide (Sandmeyer reaction) in solution.

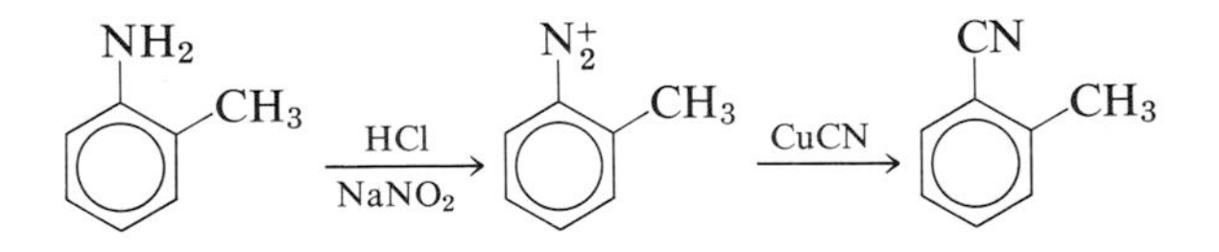

Nitro Compounds: The nitro group may also be introduced via the diazonium route. This method is particularly useful for the synthesis of compounds where the entering nitro group is *ortho* or *para* to another deactivating substituent, for example, in the synthesis of *p*-dinitrobenzene.

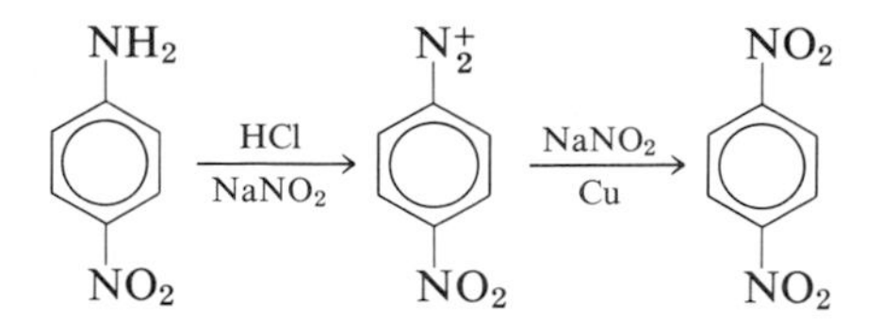

Reduction: The diazo group may be replaced by hydrogen. The most general procedure uses hypophosphorous acid (H_3PO_2) as the hydrogen source.

H_2N–(biphenyl)–NH_2 (with H_3CO, OCH_3) ⟶ (N_2^+, OCH_3)$_2$ $\xrightarrow{H_3PO_2}$ H–(biphenyl)–H (with H_3CO, OCH_3)

Synthetic Methods: The techniques adopted for the preparation of substituted benzenes often take advantage of the best features of both the direct substitution reaction and the diazonium replacement reactions. An example is the preparation of *o*-chloro-*t*-butylbenzene. The reaction of *t*-butylbenzene with chlorine yields a complex mixture of *o*-, *m*-, and *p*-chloro-*t*-butylbenzenes. Although these isomers may be separated and purified by vapor phase chromatography, the method is tedious and unsuitable for the purification of large amounts of material. The following scheme avoids this purification problem. The direct nitration of *t*-butylbenzene yields *p*-nitro-*t*-butylbenzene, which may be purified by fractional vacuum distillation. Chlorination of this nitro compound produces 2-chloro-4-nitro-*t*-butylbenzene. The directive effects of the *t*-butyl and nitro groups both favor reaction in the 2-position. Reduction and deamination with hypophosphorous acid yield the desired product.

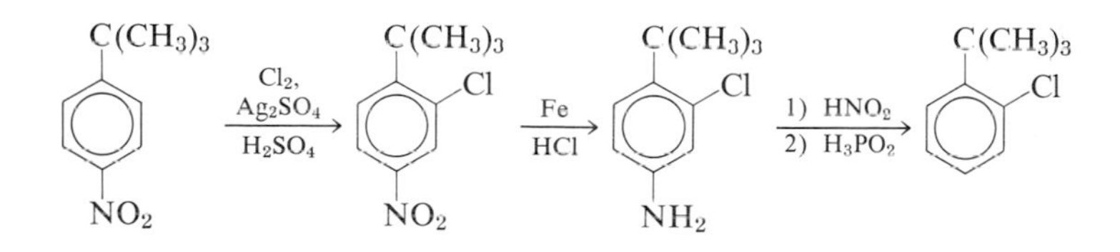

Another example is the synthesis of 2-chloro-6-iodo-1,3,5-tribromobenzene. The chlorination of nitrobenzene yields *m*-chloronitrobenzene, which is reduced to *m*-chloroaniline. The amino group greatly activates the ring and tribromination is rapid. The product is then treated with nitrous acid and the iodo substituent introduced. In this example the nitro group is used to direct the chlorination reaction and the amino group is used to direct the bromination reaction.

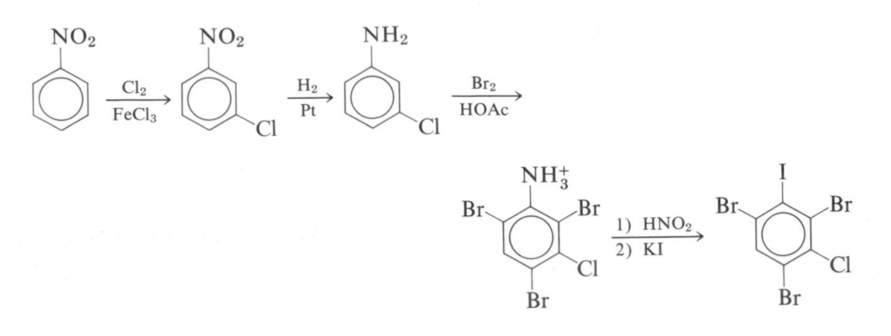

Free Radical Phenylation: When benzenediazonium salts are decomposed in basic solution in the presence of benzene or other aromatic compounds, a free radical phenylation reaction occurs to yield biphenyls.

$$C_6H_5N_2^+ + C_6H_6 + NaOH \longrightarrow C_6H_5{-}C_6H_5 + N_2 + H_2O + Na^+$$

This reaction, known as the Gomberg–Bachmann reaction, is a method for the synthesis of biaryls. An aqueous acidic solution of the diazonium salt is treated with sodium hydroxide to yield the treacherously unstable benzene diazohydroxide.

$$C_6H_5{-}N_2^+, Cl^- \xrightarrow{NaOH} C_6H_5{-}N{=}N{-}OH + NaCl$$

The diazohydroxide decomposes to liberate the phenyl radical, nitrogen and hydroxy radical.

$$C_6H_5{-}N{=}N{-}OH \longrightarrow C_6H_5\cdot + N_2 + \cdot OH$$

The phenyl radical produced in the decomposition reaction attacks the aromatic substrate forming a radical intermediate that corresponds to the benzenonium ion or benzenanion.

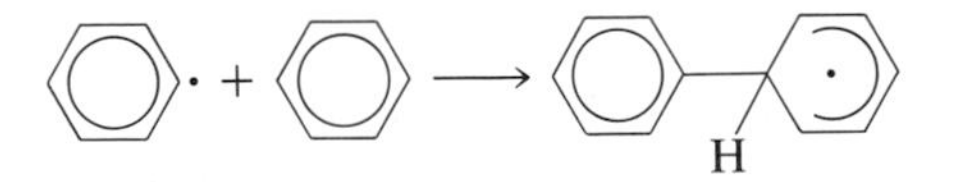

This intermediate exhibits a more diverse chemistry than the charged ions. It undergoes dimerization and disproportionation in addition to the hydrogen atom abstraction reaction that leads to biphenyl.

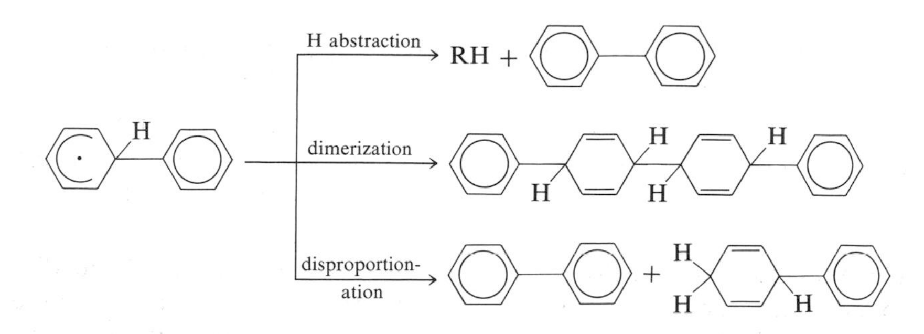

The phenyl radical is not very selective. This lack of discrimination is illustrated in the nearly random product distribution for the phenylation of the monosubstituted benzenes and in the small partial rate factors for phenylation, Table 5-2.

Table 5-2

ISOMER DISTRIBUTIONS AND PARTIAL RATE FACTORS FOR PHENYLATION

Aromatic compound, Y	Isomer distribution			Partial rate factors		
	% *o*-	% *m*-	% *p*-	o_f^Y	m_f^Y	p_f^Y
Benzene, H	40	40	20	1.0	1.0	1.0
Toluene, CH_3	67.3	19.2	13.5	3.5	1.0	1.4
Chlorobenzene, Cl	60.5	25.6	13.9	2.6	1.1	1.2
Benzotrifluoride, CF_3	20.0	40.0	40.0	0.6	1.2	2.4
Nitrobenzene, NO_2	57.7	10.0	32.2	6.9	1.2	7.7

It is evident that the direct phenylation of a monosubstituted benzene would be unsatisfactory for the preparation of one desired substituted biphenyl. Use of the reaction in synthesis requires that the substituent be incorporated in the aromatic amine. Biaryls are obtained in 25–60% yield by this route.

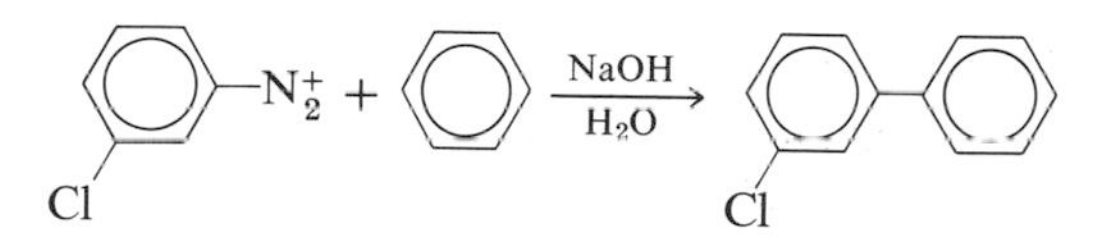

Diazo Coupling: Another important reaction of the benzenediazonium compounds is the coupling reaction that occurs when highly reactive aromatic compounds are treated with diazonium salts. The addition of benzenediazonium chloride to a basic solution of phenol yields *p*-hydroxyazobenzene and the reaction with dimethylaniline yields *p*-dimethylaminoazobenzene.

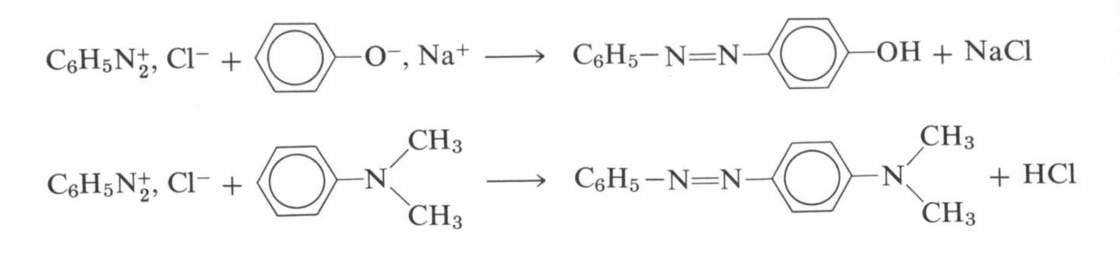

These processes are electrophilic substitution reactions in which the diazonium ion is the electrophilic reagent. The reaction is not general in the sense that highly reactive aromatic compounds are necessary. When the reaction is attempted with less reactive aromatic compounds, the diazonium salts decompose via cation or free radical paths as discussed on p. 82 and 98.

The products of the coupling reactions are highly colored and have been used as dyes since the nineteenth century. One example is Para Red, prepared by the coupling of *p*-nitrobenzenediazonium ion with the anion of 2-hydroxynaphthalene.

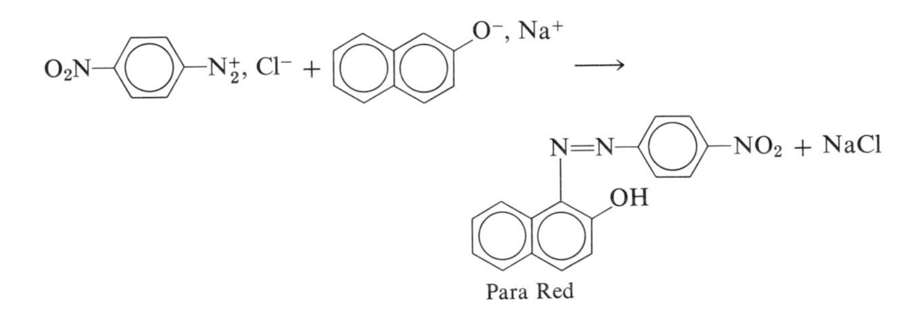

Para Red

PROBLEMS

5.1. Benzenediazonium ion is converted to phenol more rapidly than 4-nitrobenzenediazonium ion is converted to *p*-nitrophenol. In contrast, *p*-nitrochlorobenzene reacts with piperidine to yield N-(*p*-nitrophenyl)piperidine much more rapidly than does chlorobenzene to yield N-phenylpiperidine. Discuss these results in terms of the reaction mechanisms.

5.2. When 1-nitro-2-aminonaphthalene is treated with nitrous acid in aqueous hydrochloric acid, **A** is obtained:

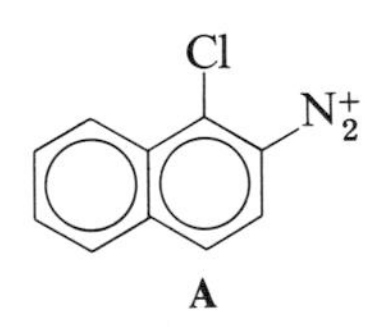

A

Account for the formation of this substance rather than the expected product.

5.3. When *o*- or *m*-chloro (or bromo) anisole is treated with sodium amide, *m*-aminoanisole is obtained as the product. Discuss the factors that might be expected to influence the course of the reaction and that contribute to the essentially exclusive formation of the *meta*-substituted product.

5.4. Outline synthetic methods that are applicable for the preparation of the compounds on the left from the substance on the right.

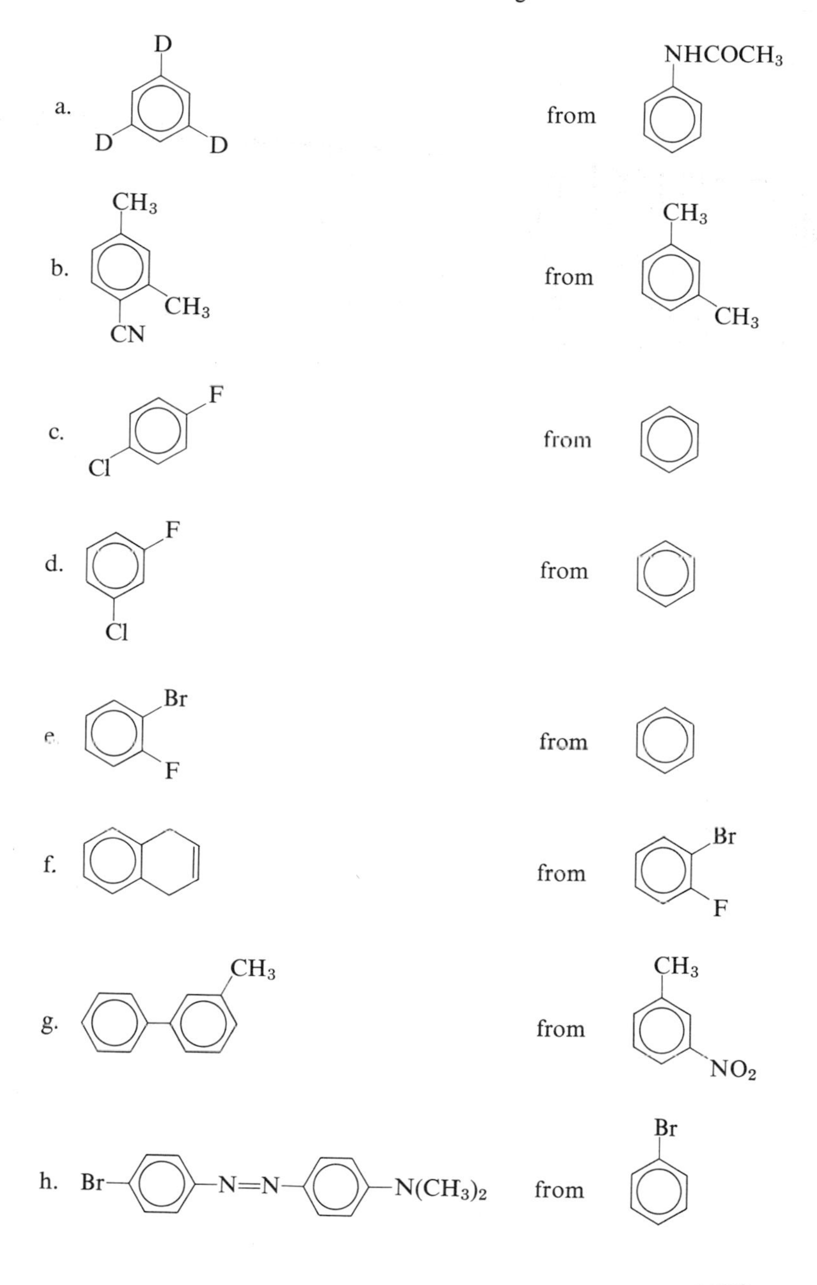

SUGGESTED READING

The mechanism of the aromatic S_N2 reaction is discussed critically by S. D. Ross, *Progress in Physical Organic Chemistry,* S. G. Cohen, A. Streitwieser, and R. W. Taft, editors, Interscience Publishers, New York, 1963, Vol. I.

The chemistry of aromatic (and aliphatic) diazonium compounds is examined in detail by H. Zollinger, *Azo and Diazo Chemistry,* Interscience Publishers, New York, 1961.

6 Rearrangement Reactions

6.1 INTRODUCTION

Certain aromatic molecules undergo rearrangement reactions in which atoms or entire structural fragments are transferred from one site to another site. The formulation of the mechanisms of these processes have intrigued chemists for a considerable period. One of the keys to the definition of the mechanism is the characterization of the reaction as an intramolecular or an intermolecular process. A rearrangement is termed *intramolecular* if the migrating group remains within the same molecule throughout the course of the reaction. Thus, a rearrangement that occurs by the smooth transfer of one atom or group, A, from one site, B, to another site, C, is an intramolecular process.

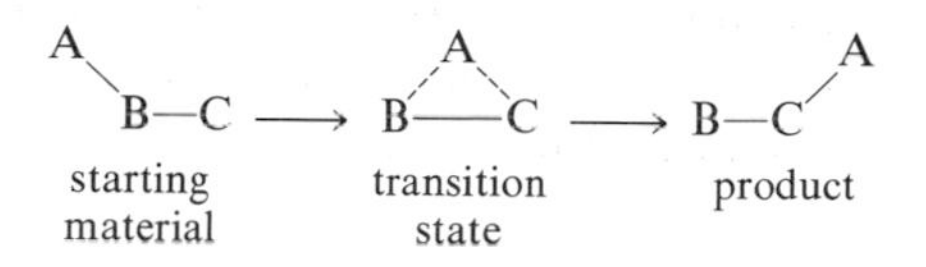

On the other hand, a rearrangement is termed an *intermolecular* process if the migrating group separates from the starting material during the course of the reaction. One intermolecular reaction mechanism that is often observed is the dissociation-recombination sequence.

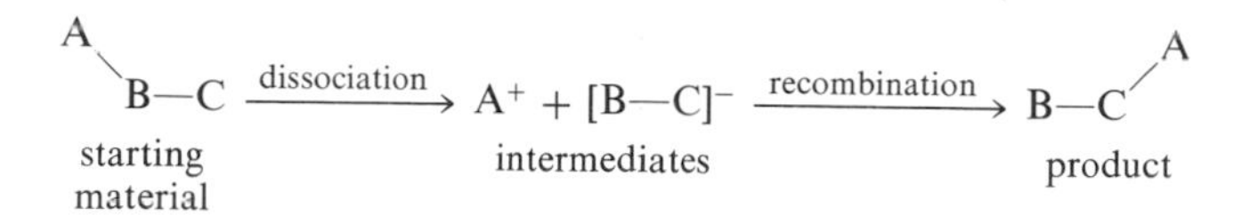

Many clever experiments have been performed to establish the course of the aromatic rearrangement reactions. Some of these experiments and the more important reactions of this kind will be discussed in this chapter.

6.2 INTERMOLECULAR REARRANGEMENTS

The Orton Rearrangement: N-Chloroacetanilide is converted to *o*- and *p*-chloroacetanilide in the presence of hydrogen chloride (or hydrogen bromide).

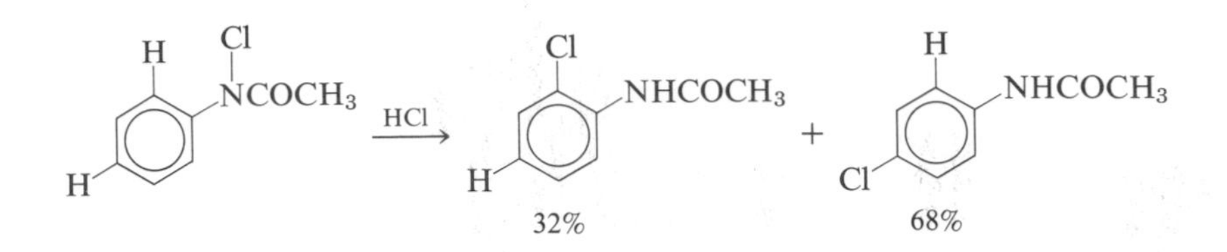

This reaction involving the interchange of chlorine and hydrogen atoms is known as the Orton rearrangement. The hydrogen halides are specific catalysts for the reaction; other acids, such as sulfuric or perchloric acid, do not catalyze the reaction. The intermolecular character of the reaction has been demonstrated in several ways. One convincing discovery is the fact that when ^{36}Cl is incorporated in the hydrogen chloride catalyst, then the label appears in the products. This result reveals that the chlorine atom originally bonded to the nitrogen atom escapes from the anilide prior to its incorporation into the aromatic nucleus. The reaction may be formulated as a three-step process. Protonation occurs in the first step. The second step of the sequence is slow; chloride ion reacts with the protonated anilide to displace acetanilide and form chlorine. The third step is an electrophilic substitution of acetanilide by chlorine containing ^{36}Cl to yield the labeled and unlabeled products.

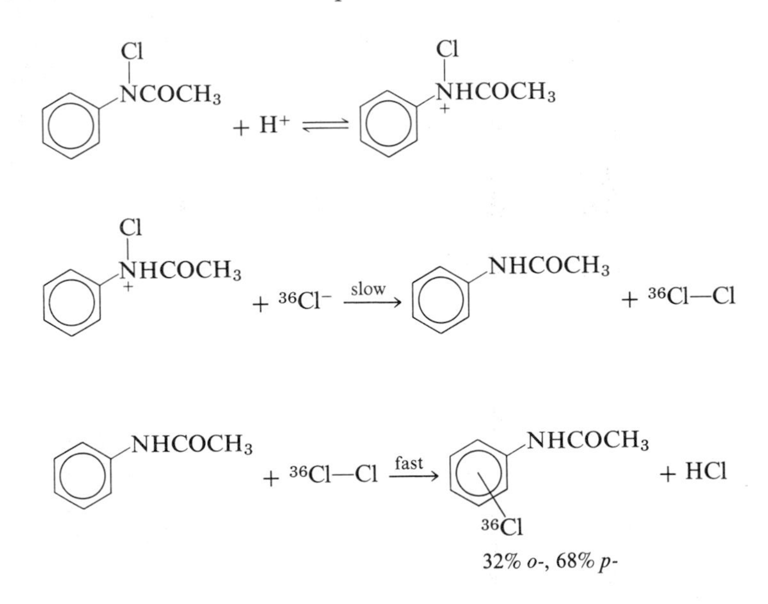

This formulation suggests that molecular chlorine is the actual reagent. This idea is consistent with the observation that acetanilide and chlorine react to produce 32% *o*- and 68% *p*-chloroacetanilide.

Certain other N-substituted derivatives of acetanilide and other aromatic acylamines undergo similar rearrangement reactions.

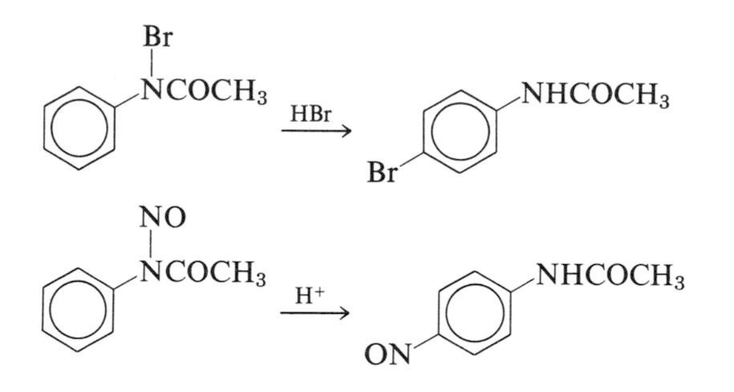

The Fries Rearrangement: Another important rearrangement that occurs at least in part by an intermolecular route is the conversion of phenyl acetate to *o*- and *p*-hydroxyacetophenone in the presence of aluminum chloride.

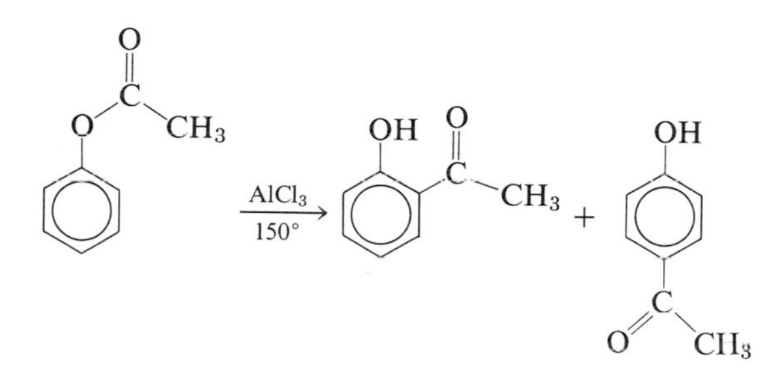

This reaction is known as the Fries rearrangement. The acyl group migrates to the positions that are *ortho* and *para* to the hydroxy group. The isomer distribution, however, is sharply dependent on the reaction temperature. Formation of the *para* isomer is favored at low temperature and the *ortho* isomer at high temperature. Most phenyl esters undergo the rearrangement, and the Fries rearrangement is a convenient synthesis of phenolic ketones. Moreover, the temperature dependence offers a method for the partial control of the isomer distribution.

Although the reaction mechanism is not established with complete confidence, it is known that there is an intermolecular path for the rearrangement. 2-Chloro-4-methylphenyl acetate (**A**) rearranges to 2-chloro-4-methyl-6-acetylphenol (**B**); 4-methylphenyl benzoate (**C**) rearranges to 2-benzoyl-4-methylphenol (**D**).

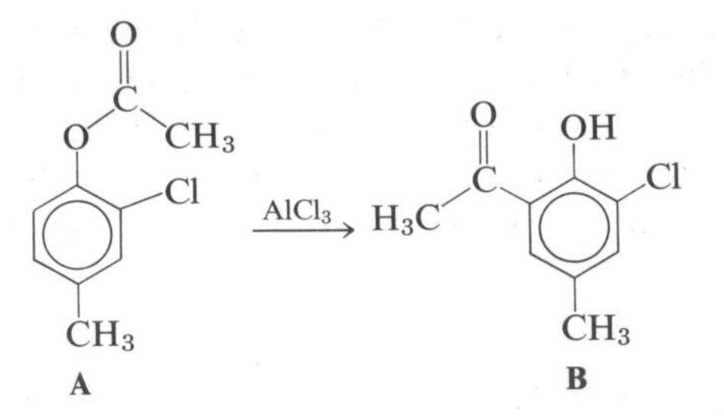

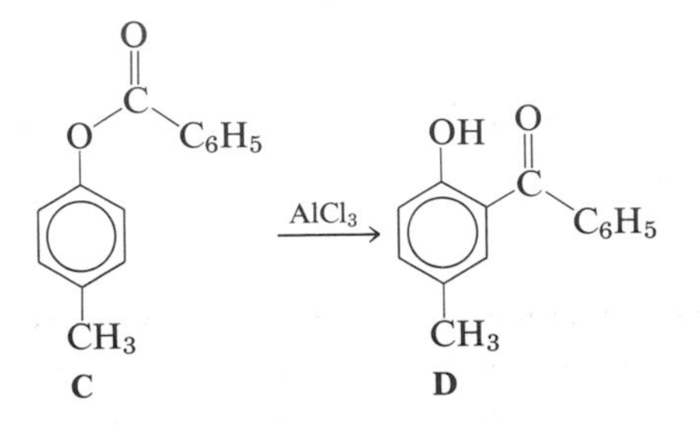

However, when **A** and **C** are rearranged simultaneously in the same solution, two additional products, **E** and **F**, are obtained. The formation of these additional products indicates that the acetyl group of **A** can be transferred to **C** and that the benzoyl group of **C** can be transferred to **A**.

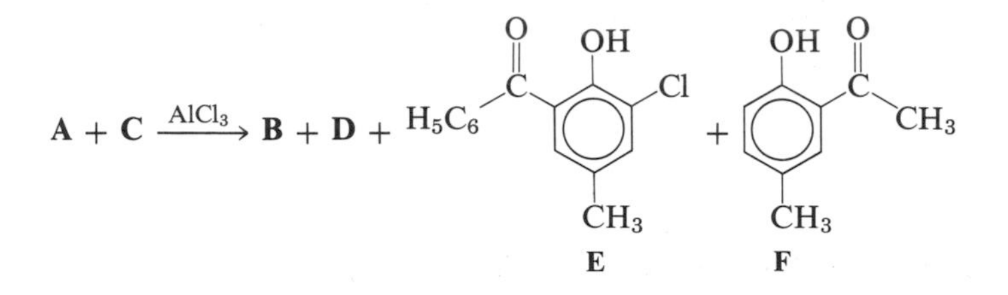

This finding suggests that the Fries rearrangement proceeds by an intermolecular, dissociation-recombination mechanism. One reasonable formulation is illustrated for phenyl acetate.

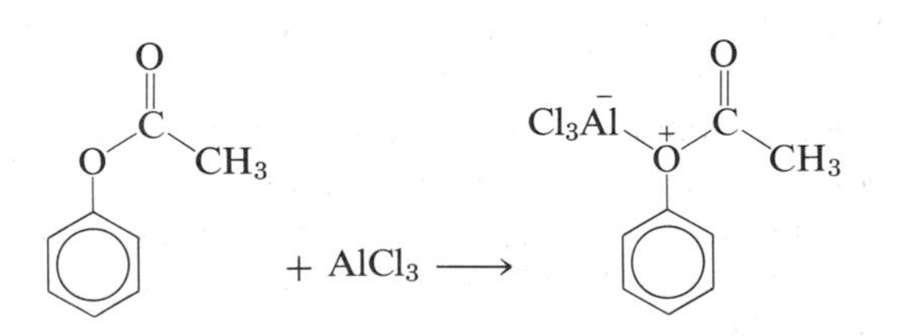

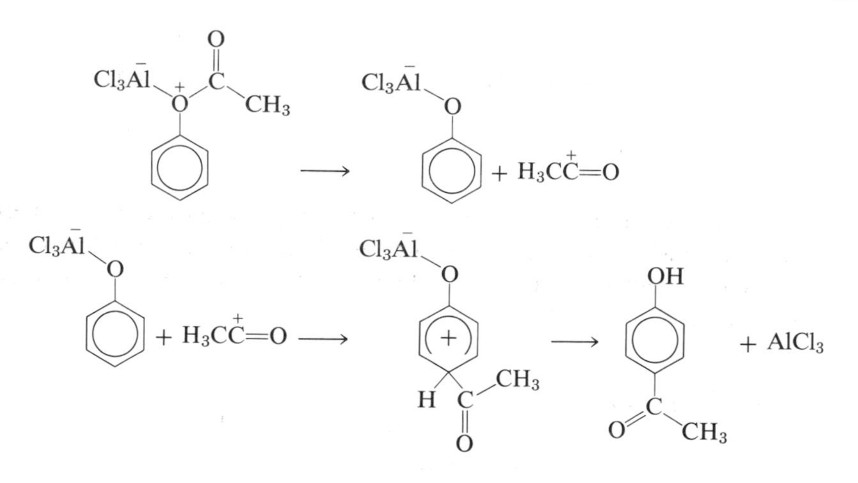

An addition compound between the basic carbonyl group of phenyl acetate and the Lewis acid forms in the first step. This addition compound dissociates in the second step to produce the electrophilic acetylonium ion. Recombination via an electrophilic substitution reaction yields the product. Although intermolecular rearrangement reactions are formally rearrangements, such processes are better regarded as substitution reactions in which the starting material is the source of both the electrophilic reagent and the substrate molecule.

6.3 INTRAMOLECULAR REARRANGEMENTS

The Claisen Rearrangement: The thermal rearrangement of phenyl allyl ether to *o*-allylphenol is known as the Claisen rearrangement.

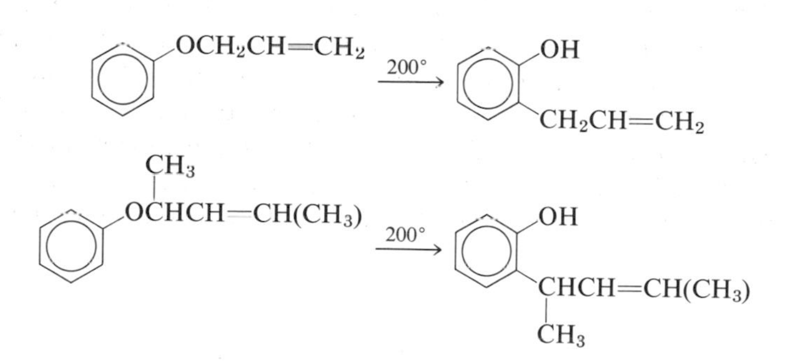

This rearrangement occurs readily with a variety of substituted allyl ethers that are not substituted in both *ortho* positions. When 2,6-dialkylphenyl allyl ethers rearrange, the allyl group migrates to the *para* position.

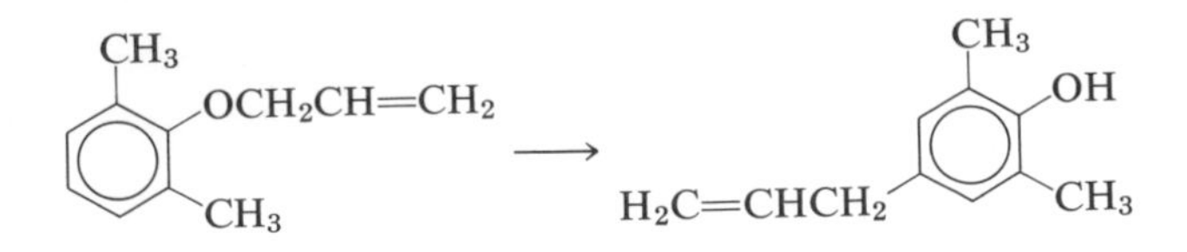

A priori, two quite dissimilar mechanisms require consideration. These mechanisms and one method to distinguish between them are illustrated for the rearrangement of an ether labeled with ^{14}C at the terminal vinyl carbon atom. One formulation

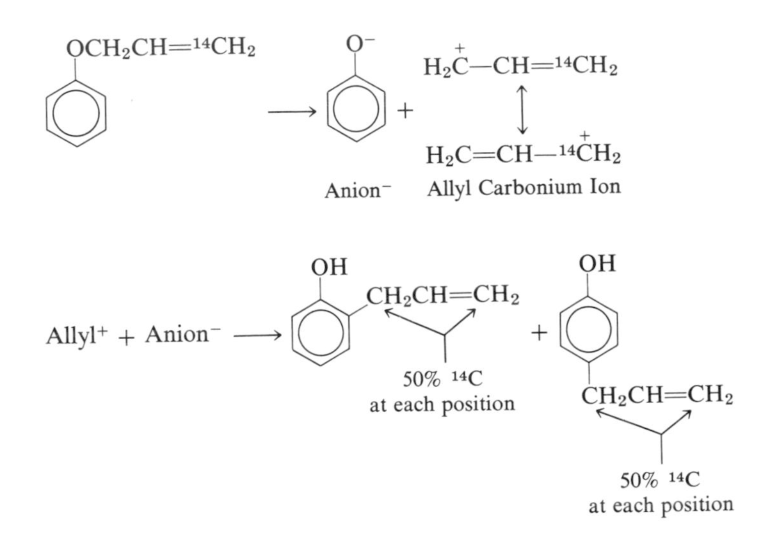

views the reaction as an intermolecular process similar to the mechanism of the Fries rearrangement. Dissociation yields phenoxide ion and allyl carbonium ion. The terminal carbon atoms of the allyl carbonium ion are equivalent as illustrated by the resonance structures. Therefore, the recombination of the ionic fragments by an electrophilic substitution reaction would yield *o*- and *p*-allylphenol with the label distributed equally between the CH_2 units of the allyl group. The alternative formulation views the reaction as an intramolecular rearrangement in which all the

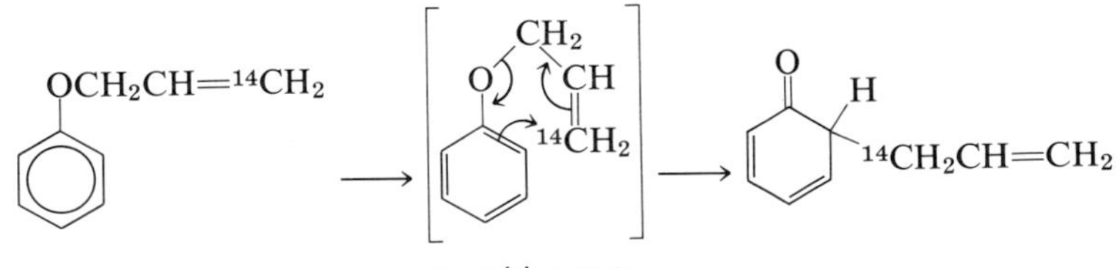

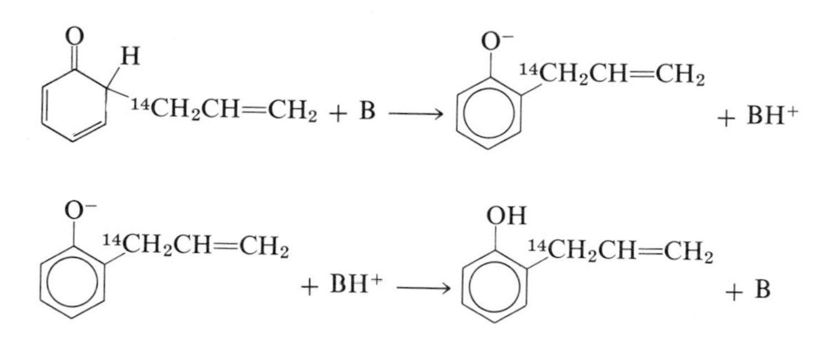

bonds remain partially intact at the transition state. The product of this rearrangement is a dienone (the same dienone would be produced by the electrophilic substitution of phenoxide anion by allyl carbonium ion). The dienone is converted to *o*-allylphenol by tautomerization under the influence of the base (B) in solution. This formulation predicts that the ^{14}C label should appear only at the carbon atom bonded to the aromatic nucleus.

The rearrangement of the labeled ether revealed that the label in *o*-allyphenol was, in fact, located exclusively at the carbon atom bonded to the aromatic ring. This experimental result indicates that the reaction is intramolecular and excludes the intermolecular ionization mechanism.

The *para* Claisen rearrangement is also an intramolecular reaction. When the ^{14}C labeled ether is rearranged, the label is found exclusively at the vinyl position in the product.

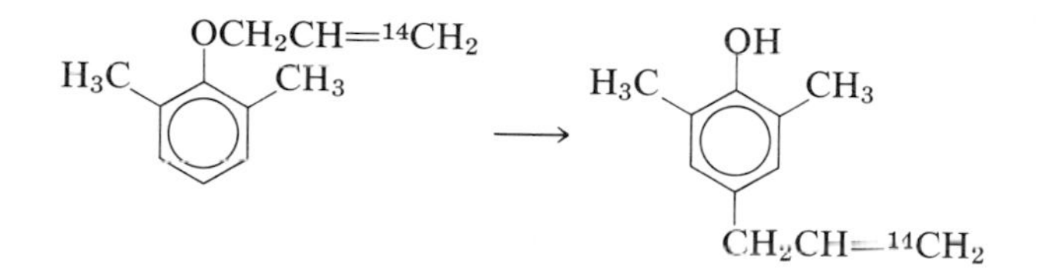

This observation suggests that the *para* rearrangement occurs in two stages,

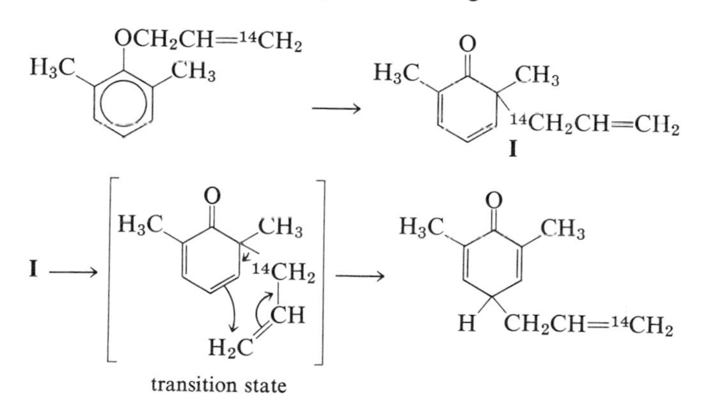

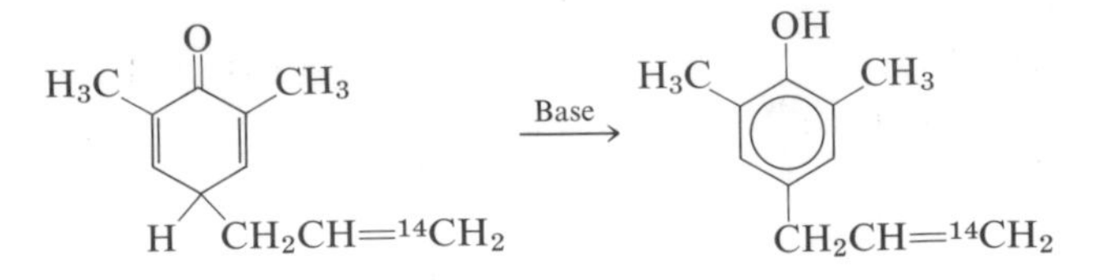

with the allyl group migrating first to the *ortho* position and then to the *para* position. The fate of the label is illustrated in the equations. Both rearrangements proceed through cylic six-membered transition states. This formulation accounts for the position of ^{14}C in the product. In addition the intermediate dienone has been trapped by maleic anhydride in a Diels-Alder reaction.

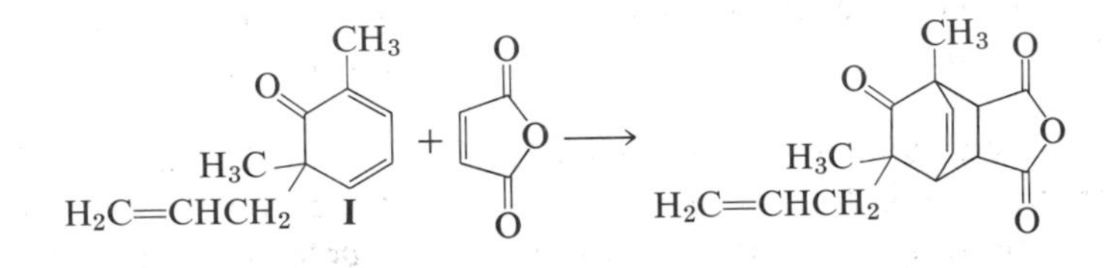

These experiments point to the intramolecular character of the Claisen rearrangement and the existence of a dienone intermediate.

The Benzidine Rearrangement: The acid-catalyzed transformation of diaryl hydrazines to 4,4′-diaminobiaryls is known as the benzidine rearrangement. Hydrazobenzene (1,2-diphenylhydrazine), for example, is readily converted to benzidine (4,4′-diaminobiphenyl) and 2,4′-diaminobiphenyl.

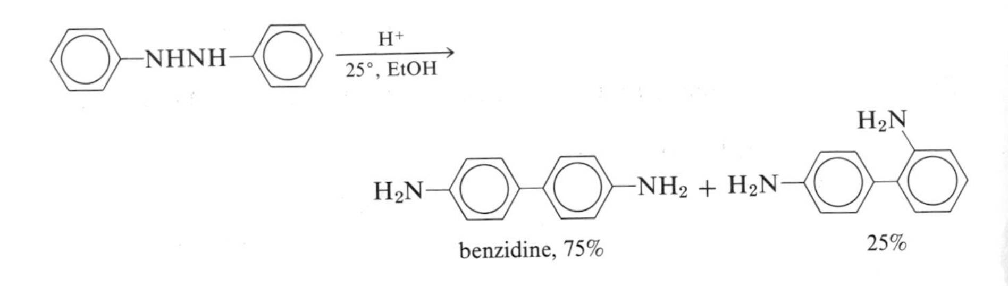

The course of the rearrangement is illustrated by the conversion of 2,2′-dimethylhydrazobenzene to 3,3′-dimethyl-4,4′-diaminobiphenyl.

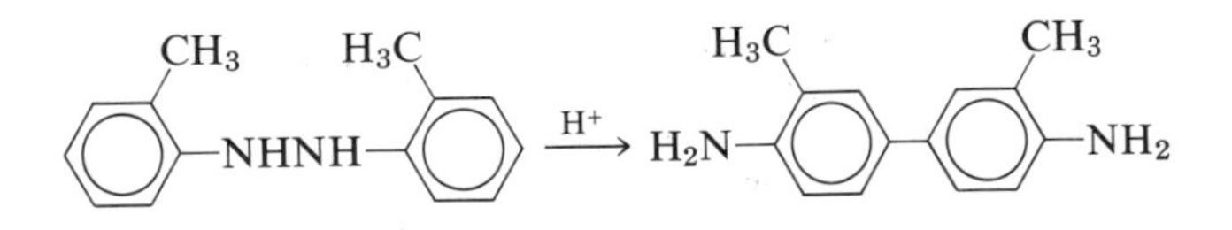

This result illustrates the fact that the carbon atoms originally in the 4,4′-positions are bonded in the product. The intramolecular character of the rearrangement has been demonstrated in several ways. For example, when 2,2′-dimethylhydrazobenzene and 2-methylhydrazobenzene-^{14}C are rearranged simultaneously in the same solution, the product, 3,3′-dimethylbenzidine, is free of ^{14}C. This experiment shows that the hydrazobenzenes do not break up into fragments during the reaction.

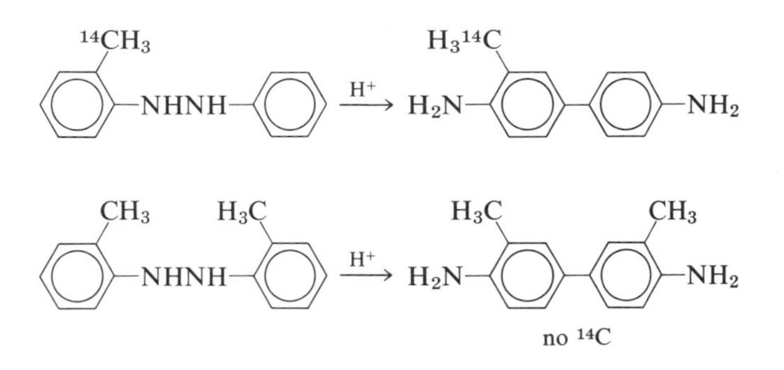

The rate law for the rearrangement of hydrazobenzene is

$$\text{rate} = k[\text{hydrazobenzene}][\text{H}^+]^2$$

Moreover, the rate of rearrangement of 4,4′-dideuteriohydrazobenzene is the same as that for the unlabeled compound. The rate law indicates that two protons are added to hydrazobenzene prior to the rate-determining step. The absence of a kinetic isotope effect indicates that the protons are removed from the 4,4′-positions after the rate-determining step. One reaction path that is compatible with these results is shown:

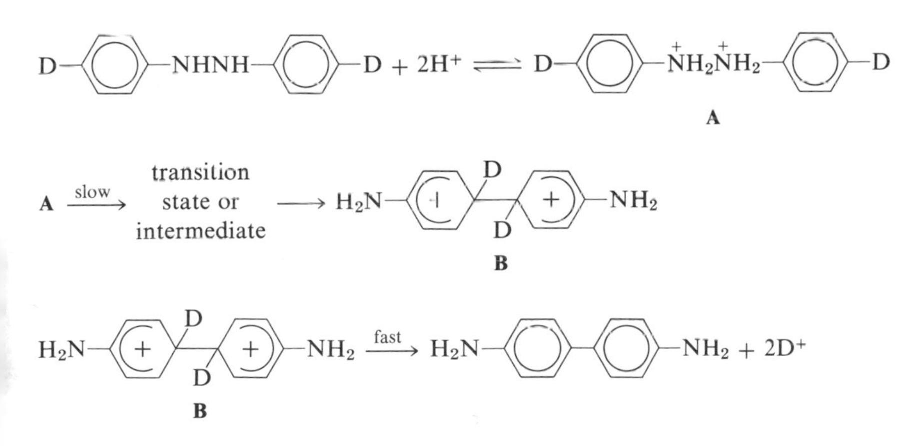

There is some doubt concerning the manner in which **A** is converted to **B**. It seems unlikely that a simple electronic reorganization mechanism such as the one proposed for the Claisen rearrangement is applicable for the benzidine rearrangement. This formulation is objectionable because the benzene ring is thicker, 3.8 Å, than it is long, 2.8 Å; the nitrogen-nitrogen bond must be stretched appreciably, and the new bond between the carbon atoms must be formed at a considerable distance. The energy requirements for the rearrangement seem much too small for a process of this

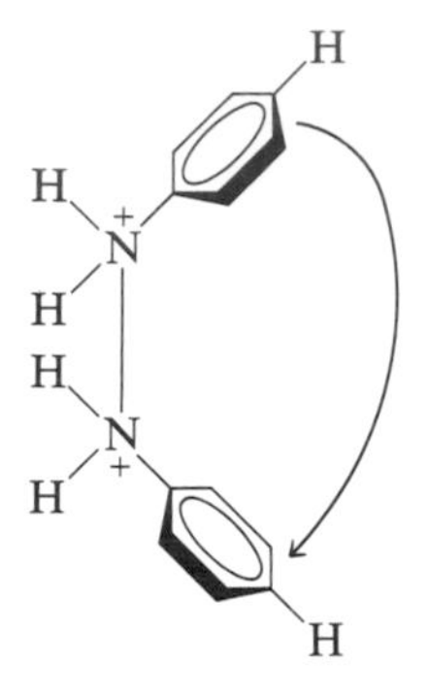

kind. Moreover, this mechanism would not account for the simultaneous formation of 2,4′-diaminobiphenyls. The characterization of the transition state or intermediates other than **A** and **B** remains an unsolved problem. Some possible formulations are discussed in Suggested Reading, p. 117.

6.4 ISOMERIZATION AND DISPROPORTIONATION REACTIONS OF ALKYL BENZENES

The Friedel–Crafts alkylation reaction was examined in Sec. 2.6A. At that time, it was pointed out that the reaction was complex because the alkylating reagents often isomerize under the reaction conditions and that polysubstitution occurs because the products are more reactive than the starting materials. There is a further complication that will now be discussed: the dialkylbenzenes that are formed by the alkylation of an alkylbenzene also rearrange under the conditions of the reaction. Indeed, three quite different isomer distributions may be obtained in these reactions. The isomer distribution that is actually obtained depends on the reaction time and on the quantity of aluminum chloride and hydrogen halide present in the reaction mixture.

The variations in the isomer distribution for the methylation of toluene and the isomerization reactions of the product xylenes illustrate the important features of this rearrangement. When toluene is methylated and the reaction mixture is hydrolyzed to destroy the catalyst after a short reaction time (1 min or less), the isomer distribution is 56% *o*-, 10% *m*-, and 34%

p-xylene. On the other hand, when the same reaction mixture is allowed to stand for several hours before the catalyst is destroyed, then a quite different product distribution (18% *o*-, 60% *m*-, and 22% *p*-xylene) is obtained. This same product distribution results when one pure xylene is treated with a catalytic amount of aluminum chloride (or other Lewis acid) and hydrogen chloride; it is the thermodynamic equilibrium mixture of the three isomeric xylenes.

The different product distributions at short and long reaction times are determined by the relative magnitudes of the rate constants for a number of competing reactions.

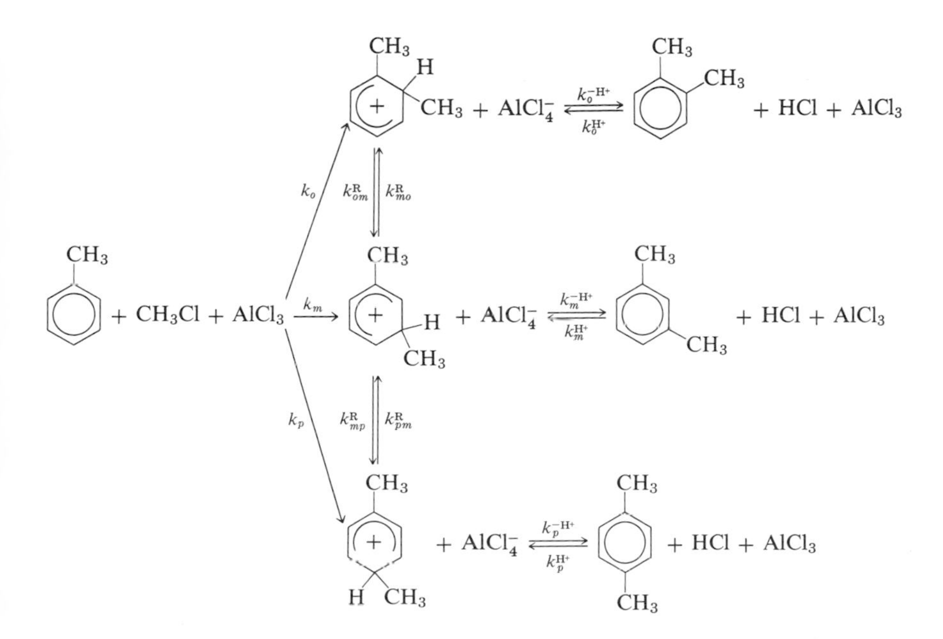

At short reaction times, the product distribution is determined by the relative rates of formation of the benzenonium ions (k_o, k_m, k_p) as discussed in Sec. 3.3. The rate constants for the loss of a proton, k^{-H^+}, are large relative to the rate constants, k^R, for the rearrangement of the benzenonium ions. Thus, at short reaction times the isomer distribution mirrors the stability of the benzenonium ions. The equilibrium product distribution is determined by the thermodynamic stability of the product xylenes. At long reaction times, the product xylenes protonate to reform the benzenonium ions, k^{H^+}. Although the rate constant for the isomerization reaction, k^R, is small relative to the rate constant for deprotonation, k^{-H^+}, a portion of the benzenonium ions rearrange to an isomeric ion via the shift of a methyl group as illustrated in the equation:

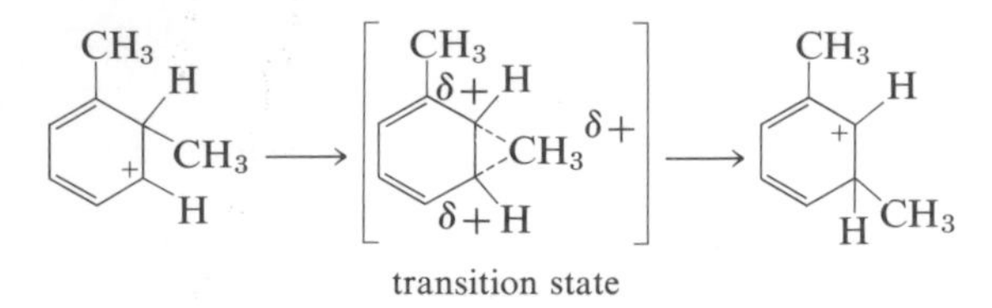

transition state

The product ion then loses a proton to reform a new xylene. The concentration of benzenonium ions is very small when a catalytic quantity of aluminum chloride is used. The final equilibrium composition of the xylene mixture is determined by the relative thermodynamic stability of the isomeric xylenes.

Another product mixture is obtained when a xylene mixture or an individual xylene is treated with a molar equivalent of a proton acid and a Lewis acid. Under these conditions, the xylenes are present in solution as the benzenonium ions and the isomerization reaction proceeds to form the most stable benzenonium ion. Thus 2,4- and 2,6-dimethylbenzenonium ion are each appreciably more stable than the other possible ions. When the reaction mixture is hydrolyzed, *m*-xylene is obtained.

The acid-catalyzed isomerization of the xylenes is an intramolecular reaction; the migrating methyl group is retained in the same molecule. Hydrocarbons with *secondary* and *tertiary* alkyl groups, however, isomerize by both intramolecular and intermolecular paths. The existence of the intermolecular path leads to the disproportionation of dialkylbenzenes to monoalkylbenzenes and trialkylbenzenes. The reaction of cymene (*p*-isopropyltoluene) with a catalytic amount of a proton acid and aluminum chloride illustrates this somewhat more complex process. Protonation may occur at either alkylated carbon atom to yield ions **A** and **B**.

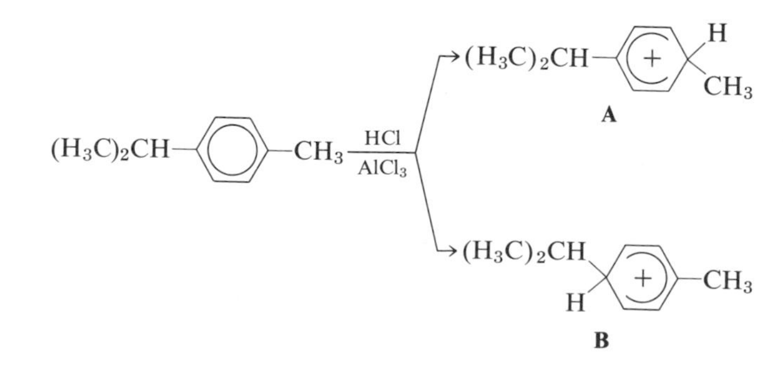

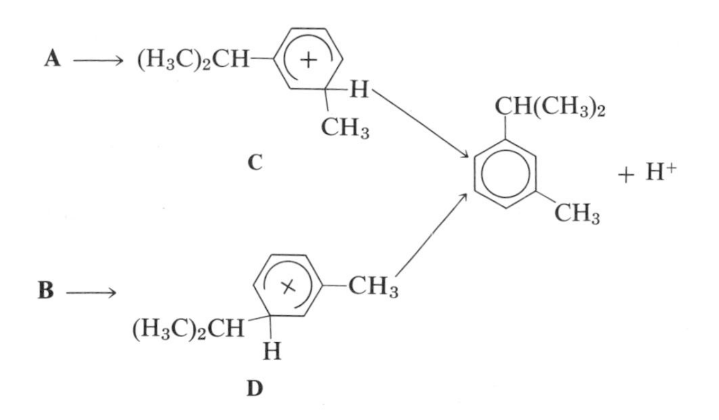

Intramolecular isomerization of the methyl group in **A** or the isopropyl group in **B** leads to ions **C** and **D** and then to *m*-isopropyltoluene. Further migration of the alkyl group in **C** or **D** would lead to *o*-isopropyltoluene. The methyl group migrates only by an intramolecular path. On the other hand, carbon-carbon bond cleavage may occur in ion **B** to produce toluene and isopropyl carbonium ion.

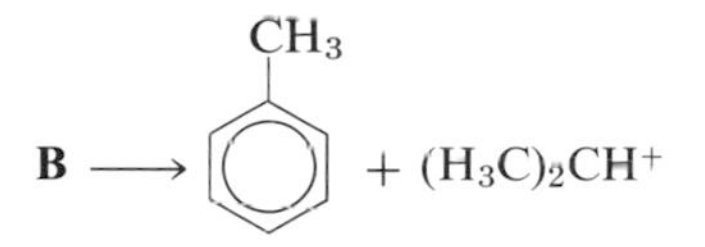

The carbonium ion reacts with the alkylbenzenes that are in solution. Reaction with toluene yields *o*-, *m*- and *p*-isopropyltoluene.

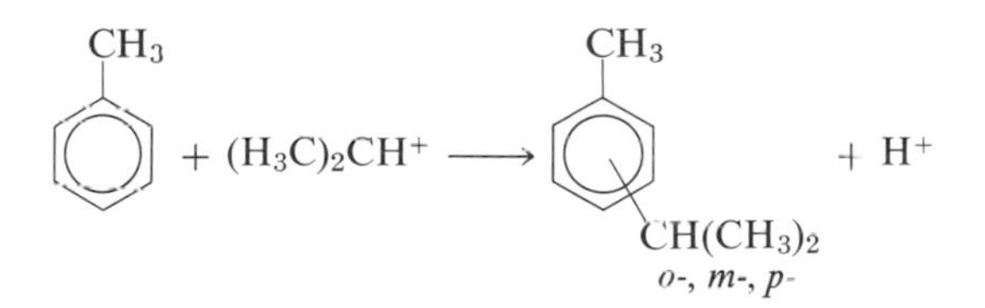

This process constitutes an intermolecular isomerization. The ion also reacts with cymene to yield trialkylbenzenes.

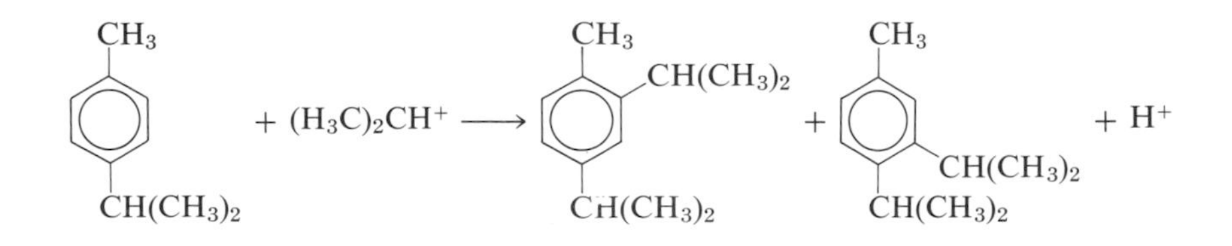

This process constitutes a disproportionation; two molecules of cymene are converted to one molecule of toluene and one molecule of di-isopropyltoluene. These reactions all occur competitively, and complex mixtures of disproportionated and isomerized alkylbenzenes are produced. The reactions by which these complex product mixtures are formed are, however, very simple ones in which one group migrates, a proton is added or lost, or a substitution reaction occurs.

PROBLEMS

6.1. Complete the following equations. State whether the reaction is inter- or intramolecular.

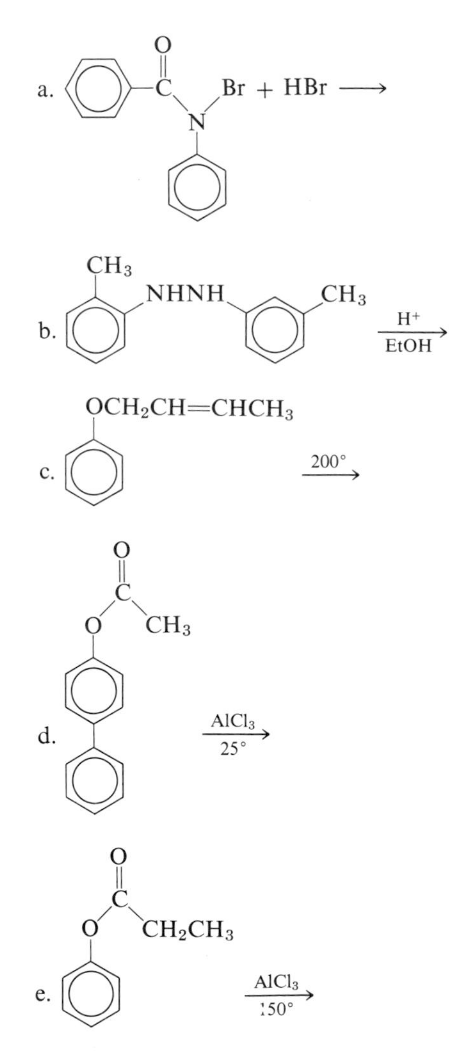

6.2. Estimate the isomer distribution for the ethylation of toluene under the following conditions.

a. Toluene (excess), ethyl bromide (1 mole), aluminum bromide (0.01 mole), 25°, reaction time (1 sec)

b. Toluene (excess), ethyl bromide (1 mole), aluminum bromide (0.01 mole), 25°, reaction time (24 hr)

c. Toluene (excess), ethyl bromide (1 mole), aluminum bromide (1 mole), 25°, reaction time (24 hr)

6.3. **A** rearranges at 200° to produce **B** and **C**. Write a mechanism that accounts for these products.

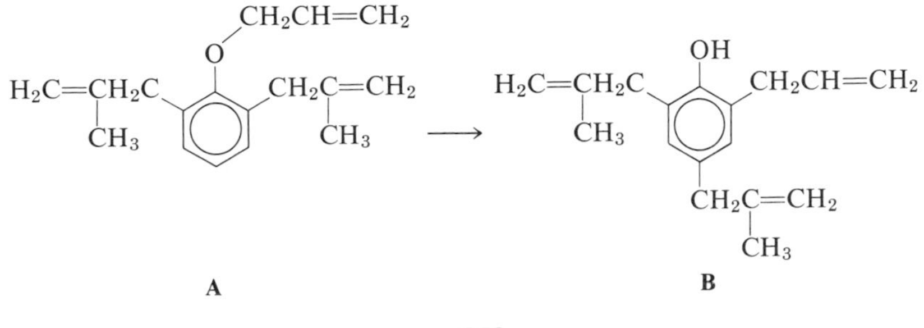

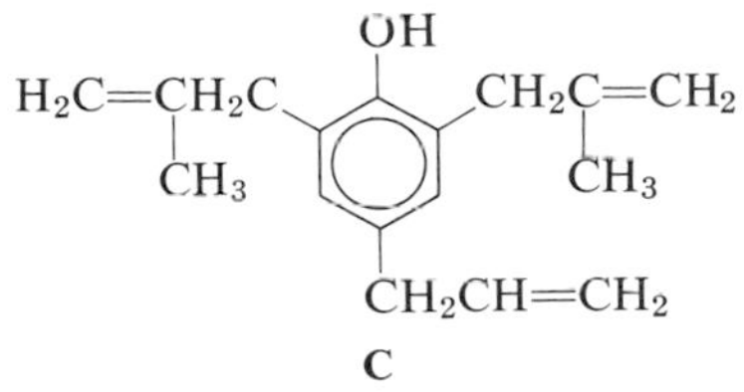

SUGGESTED READING

The Orton, Claisen, Fries, and benzidine rearrangements are discussed in several recent references, including G. W. Wheland, *Advanced Organic Chemistry,* 3rd ed., John Wiley & Sons, Inc., New York, 1960, Chapter 13; M. J. S. Dewar, *Molecular Rearrangements,* P. de Mayo, editor, Interscience Publishers, Inc., New York, 1963, Chapter 5. The mechanism of the benzidine rearrangement has been discussed from two different viewpoints by M. J. S. Dewar and A. P. Marchand, "π-Complexes as Intermediates in Organic Reactions," *Ann. Rev. Phy. Chem.*, **16,** 321 (1965) and C. K. Ingold, *The Transition State,* Special Publication, *Chemical Society, London* (1962), p. 118.

7 The Synthetic Chemistry of Benzene Derivatives

7.1 INTRODUCTION

In the previous chapters, the principal reactions of aromatic molecules have been examined mostly from a theoretical mechanistic viewpoint. Attention is now focused on the preparative aspects of aromatic chemistry. Coal and petroleum are the primary sources for many aromatic hydrocarbons. Benzene, naphthalene and the other polynuclear aromatic hydrocarbons, lesser amounts of toluene, the xylenes, and phenol and its derivatives are obtained as by-products in the conversion of soft coal to coke. In the coking process, soft coal is heated in the absence of air to yield hard coal. Coal gas (largely methane) and coal tar distill under these conditions. The tar, rich in aromatic compounds, is subsequently separated into its components by distillation. During World War II, the amount of toluene that could be produced by this procedure was insufficient to meet demand. A new process for the conversion of the aliphatic hydrocarbons of petroleum to aromatic hydrocarbons, called *hydroformation,* was developed to meet the need for a new source of toluene. This process is now the major industrial method for the preparation of simple aromatic substances. In hydroformation, the aliphatic hydrocarbons of petroleum are dehydrogenated at high temperature over a metal oxide catalyst to yield aromatic compounds. For example, *n*-heptane is converted to toluene and *n*-octane is converted to *o*-xylene. The complex product mixture is separated by distillation to provide benzene, toluene, xylenes, and naphthalene in addition to many other compounds.

Other raw materials such as wood and grain products are less important sources for the simple hydrocarbons. Cumene (isopropylbenzene) and cymene (*p*-isopropyltoluene) are by-products of the manufacture of turpentine from pine tree extracts; some oxygen heterocylic compounds, for example furfural, are obtained by the hydrolysis of waste agricultural

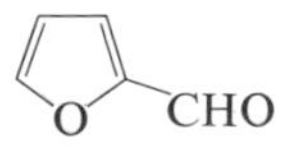

products such as corn stalks. The conversion of these raw materials into other useful intermediates will be discussed in the following sections of this chapter.

7.2 THE ALKYL BENZENES

Benzene, toluene, cumene, and the xylenes are available in abundance from the sources described in Sec. 7.1. A notable omission from this group is ethylbenzene, the precursor of styrene. About 10^9 lb of ethylbenzene are prepared each year by Friedel–Crafts ethylation for conversion to styrene and subsequent polymerization.

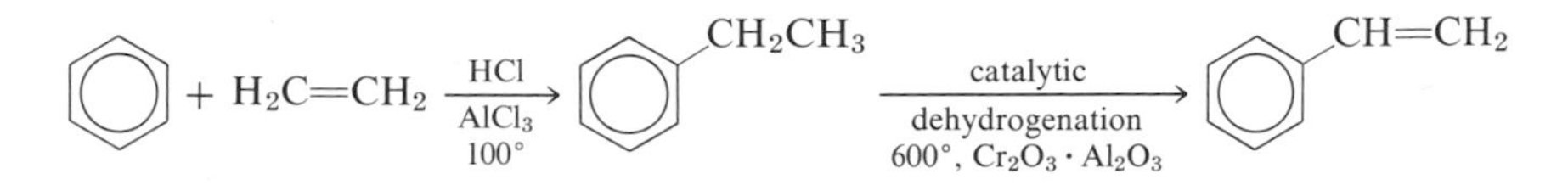

The laboratory method for the synthesis of alkylbenzenes, Friedel–Crafts alkylation, is restricted in its application because polyalkylation and rearrangement reactions occur so readily in the presence of Lewis acids, see Secs. 2.6A and 6.4. The method is, however, useful for the preparation of *t*-alkylbenzenes.

$$C_6H_6 + CH_3CH_2(CH_3)_2CBr \xrightarrow[5^\circ]{AlBr_3} C_6H_5C(CH_2CH_3)(CH_3)_2 + HBr$$

Many of the problems that are associated with the direct alkylation reaction can be avoided by the more circuitous route of Friedel–Crafts acylation and reduction of the ketone to the alkylbenzene. For example, *n*-butylbenzene is prepared by the reaction of *n*-butyryl chloride with benzene and subsequent reduction of phenyl propyl ketone. Two general methods are available for the reduction of carbonyl groups to methylene (CH_2) units—the Clemmensen and Wolff–Kishner reactions.

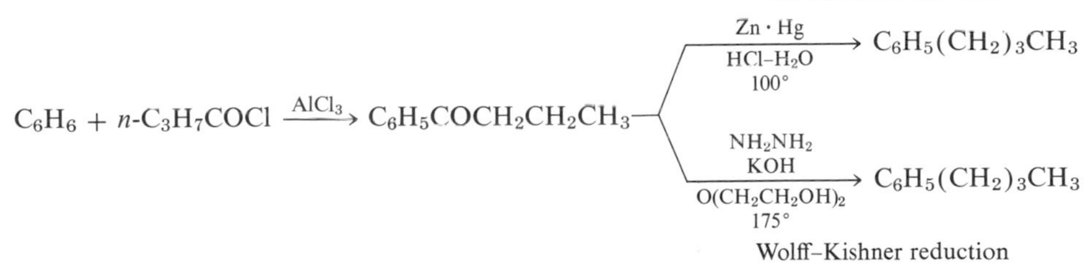

The synthesis of dialkylbenzenes from monoalkylbenzenes is impaired by the unselective character of the alkylation reaction which yields a complex mixture of *o*-, *m*-, and *p*-disubstituted benzenes. The acylation-reduction sequence offers a practical laboratory method for the preparation of *p*-dialkylbenzenes. The acetylation of toluene, for example, yields 90% *p*-methylacetophenone. The ketone may be freed of its isomeric contaminants by the preparation of a solid derivative prior to reduction.

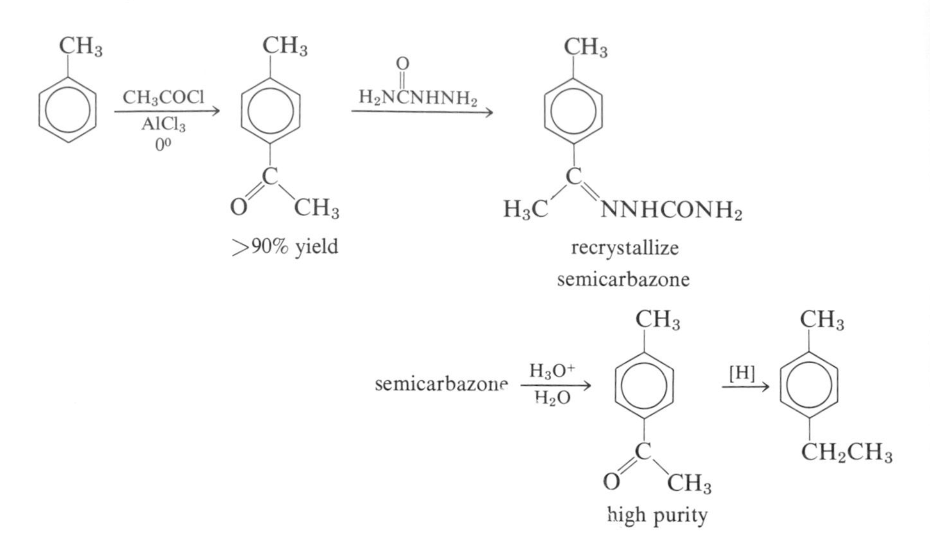

Another method for the synthesis of pure aromatic hydrocarbons utilizes the aryl bromide as the starting material. The bromide is converted to the Grignard reagent and the MgBr group is displaced from the aromatic nucleus by reaction with an electrophilic alkyl halide or sulfate. Allyl- and *n*-propylbenzene may be conveniently prepared by this method.

$$C_6H_5MgBr + H_2C{=}CHCH_2Br \xrightarrow[35^\circ]{\text{ether}} C_6H_5CH_2CH{=}CH_2 \xrightarrow[\text{Pt}]{H_2} C_6H_5(CH_2)_2CH_3$$

Another example is the synthesis of pure 1,2,3,5-tetramethylbenzene from 1,3,5-trimethylbenzene.

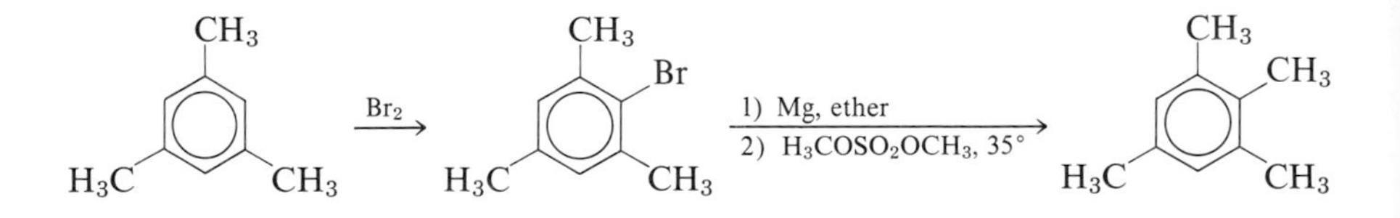

The alkylbenzenes undergo the conventional electrophilic substitution reactions. Many useful materials are produced in these reactions. The explosive TNT is prepared in two steps by the nitration of toluene and the subsequent nitration of the initial reaction product under more vigorous conditions.

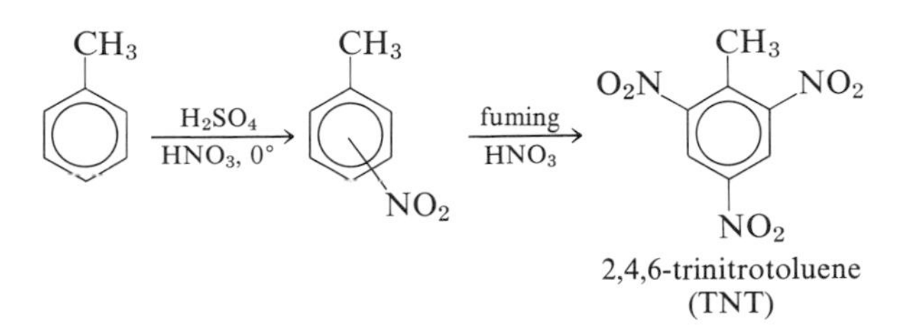

The introduction of a long paraffin chain by alkylation followed by sulfonation and neutralization yields a biodegradable detergent.

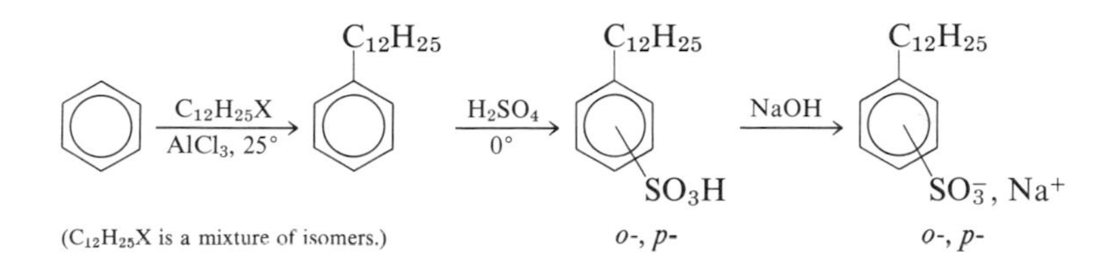

The isomeric toluenesulfonic acids obtained by the sulfonation of toluene are also important intermediates. The *ortho* isomer is converted to saccharin through the reactions outlined.

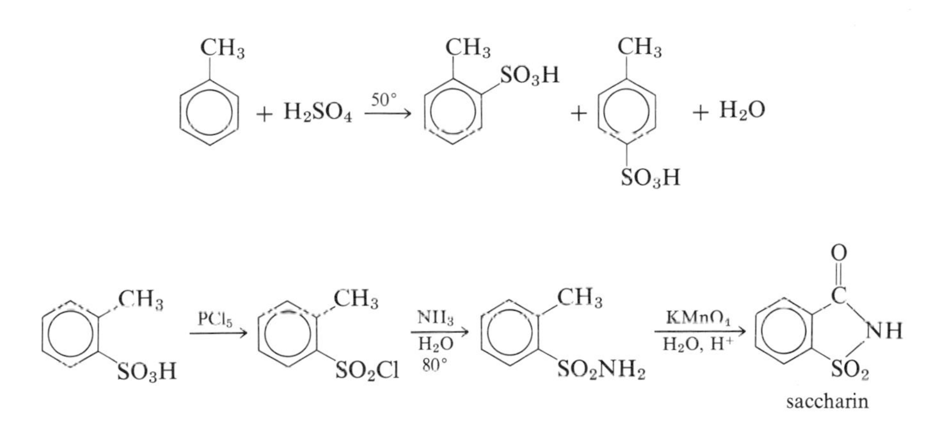

The *para* isomer is a strong acid that is soluble in organic solvents and useful as an acid catalyst in these solvents. This acid can be converted to the sulfonamide by the same reactions used for the preparation of the *ortho* isomer. The sulfonamide in turn may be converted to the N-chloro derivative, which is an antiseptic.

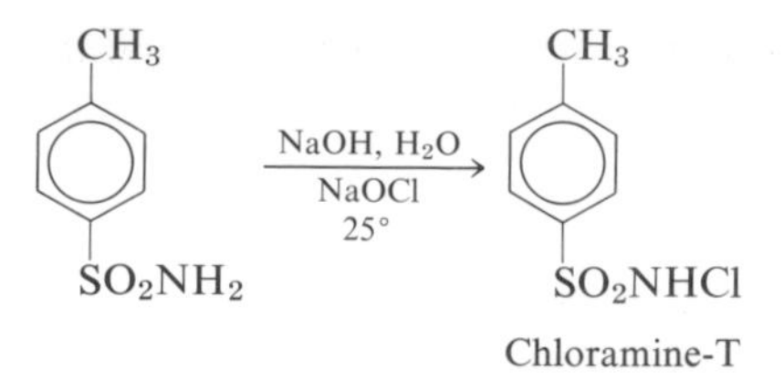

Another less utilitarian product prepared from an alkylbenzene, 2,4,6-trinitro-3-*t*-butyltoluene is a synthetic perfume with a fragrance that Aldous Huxley equates with heaven.

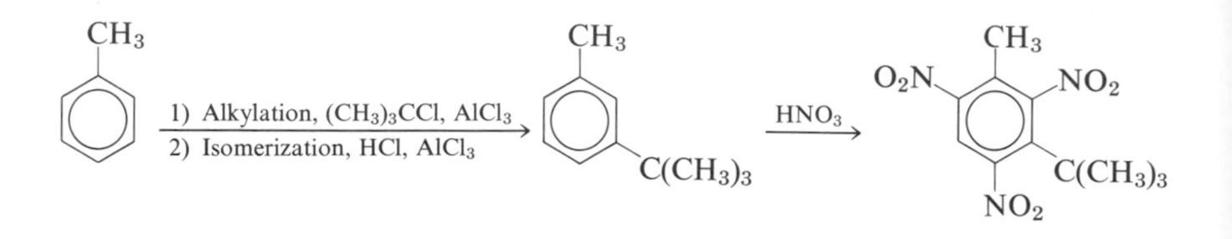

At modest temperatures in the presence of Lewis acids, chlorine and bromine react with toluene to produce *o*- and *p*-halotoluenes. However, the benzylic hydrogen atoms of toluene are easily abstracted in radical reactions because the benzyl radical is stabilized by electron delocalization.

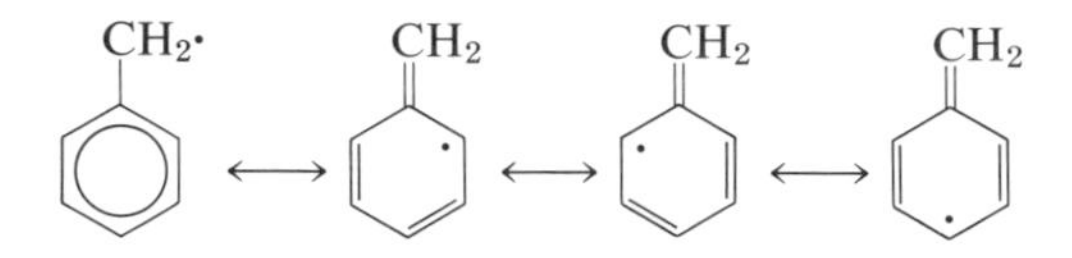

Chlorine or bromine atoms may be selectively introduced at the benzylic position by the adoption of conditions (heat, light, peroxide) that initiate radical reactions. The chlorination reaction, for example, proceeds via a chain mechanism.

Initiation:

$$Cl_2 \xrightarrow{h\nu} 2Cl\cdot$$

Propagation:

$$Cl\cdot + C_6H_5CH_3 \longrightarrow C_6H_5CH_2\cdot + HCl$$

$$C_6H_5CH_2\cdot + Cl_2 \longrightarrow C_6H_5CH_2Cl + Cl\cdot$$

Termination:

$$C_6H_5CH_2\cdot + Cl\cdot \longrightarrow C_6H_5CH_2Cl$$

$$2C_6H_5CH_2\cdot \longrightarrow C_6H_5CH_2CH_2C_6H_5$$

The reaction may be controlled by the adjustment of the chlorine concentration to provide the mono-, di- or trichloro derivative. The names of the products relate to their hydrolysis products.

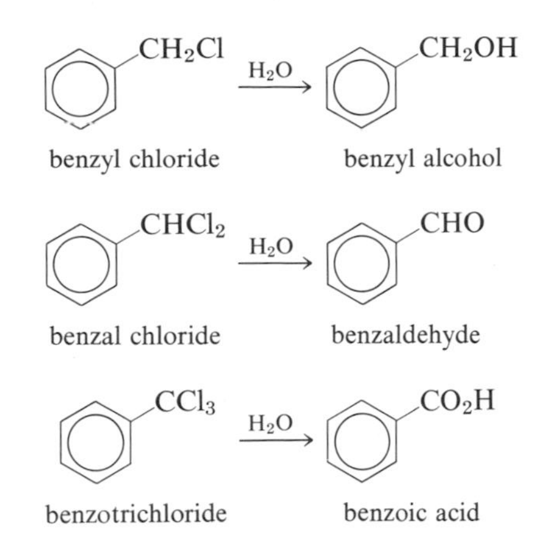

Sulfuryl chloride is an effective laboratory reagent for the synthesis of benzyl chloride. Peroxide radicals decompose sulfuryl chloride,

$$RO\cdot + SO_2Cl_2 \longrightarrow ROCl + SO_2 + Cl\cdot$$

to initiate the chain reaction:

$$C_6H_5CH_3 + Cl\cdot \longrightarrow C_6H_5CH_2\cdot + HCl$$

$$C_6H_5CH_2\cdot + ClSO_2Cl \longrightarrow C_6H_5CH_2Cl + SO_2 + Cl\cdot$$

The alkylbenzenes with one or more benzylic hydrogen atoms may be oxidized by dichromate or permanganate to benzoic acid.

$$C_6H_5R + K_2Cr_2O_7 + H_2SO_4 \xrightarrow[100^\circ]{H_2O} C_6H_5CO_2H + K_2SO_4 + Cr_2(SO_4)_3$$

($R{=}CH_3$, C_2H_5, $CH(CH_3)_2$)

In contrast, *t*-butylbenzene is unreactive; *p*-*t*-butylbenzoic acid is the only product in the dichromate oxidation of *p*-*t*-butyltoluene. The oxidation reactions of substituted alkylbenzenes offer convenient methods for the synthesis of substituted benzoic acids. Halogen and nitro groups are retained in these oxidations. However, hydroxy or amino groups make the aromatic nucleus more susceptible to oxidation than the alkyl side-chain. Fragmentation products or quinones are obtained under the rather vigorous conditions necessary for the oxidation of the alkyl group.

7.3 STYRENE, STILBENE, AND PHENYLACETYLENE

The chemistry of styrene (vinylbenzene), *cis*- and *trans*-stilbene (1,2-diphenylethylene) and phenylacetylene is typical of the chemistry of other

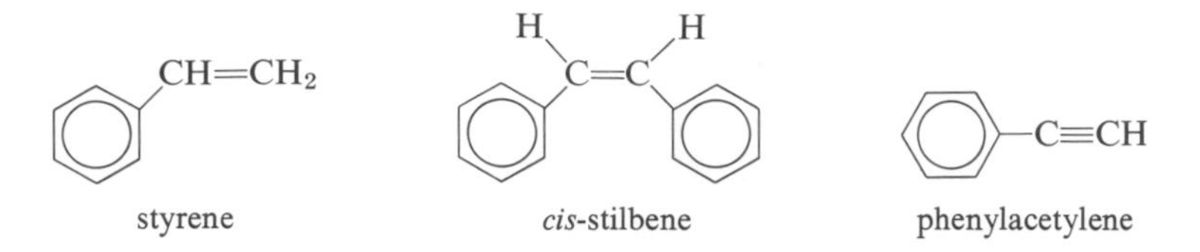

phenyl-substituted unsaturated compounds. Most methods for the laboratory synthesis of these compounds differ only negligibly from the routes used for the preparation of unsaturated aliphatic compounds. Typical methods are the dehydration of an alcohol or the dehydrohalogenation of a halide.

$$C_6H_5CH(OH)CH_3 + H_2SO_4 \xrightarrow[\text{product}]{\text{distill}} C_6H_5CH{=}CH_2$$

$$C_6H_5CH_2CH_3 + SO_2Cl_2 \xrightarrow[80^\circ]{\text{peroxide}} C_6H_5CH(Cl)CH_3 \xrightarrow{H^+} C_6H_5CH{=}CH_2$$

$$C_6H_5CH{=}CH_2 \xrightarrow{Br_2} C_6H_5CHBrCH_2Br \xrightarrow{KOH} C_6H_5C{\equiv}CH$$

A convenient synthesis of *trans*-stilbene is the Clemmensen reduction of benzoin followed by dehydration of the alcohol.

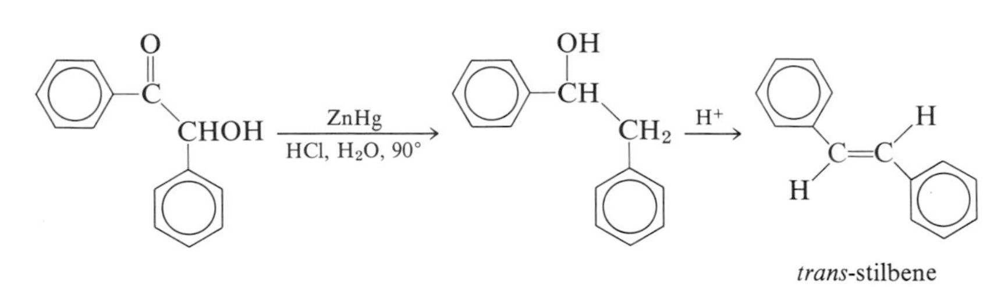

The reaction yields only the thermodynamically stable *trans* isomer. The *cis* isomer may be prepared from the *trans* isomer by photochemical isomerization.

$$trans\text{-stilbene} \xrightarrow{h\nu} cis\text{-stilbene}$$

Styrene, the stilbenes, and phenylacetylene react with electrophilic reagents to yield side-chain addition products rather than aromatic ring substitution products. Accordingly, the chemistry of these unsaturated compounds is best discussed from the viewpoint of aliphatic ionic reactions.

7.4 BIPHENYL AND THE PHENYL ALKANES

Biphenyl is prepared on a commercial scale by the dehydrogenation of benzene.

$$2C_6H_6 \xrightarrow{600^\circ} C_6H_5{-}C_6H_5 + H_2$$

In addition, there are two general laboratory methods for the preparation of biphenyl. The synthesis of *p*-terphenyl illustrates the useful free radical phenylation reaction discussed in Sec. 5.5.

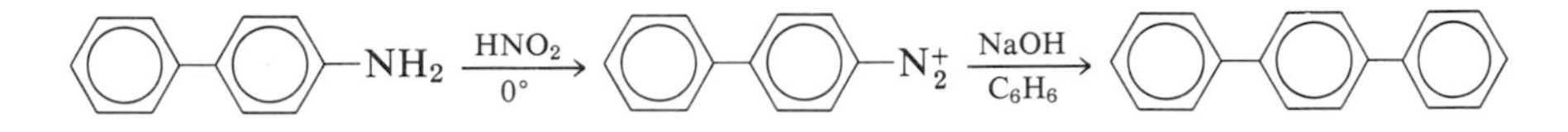

A second method for the preparation of biaryls is the Ullman reaction. In this reaction, two aromatic nuclei are coupled by the decomposition of an aryl iodide in the presence of copper.

$$2\,C_6H_5I + Cu \xrightarrow{230^\circ} C_6H_5{-}C_6H_5 + CuI$$

This reaction is not, in general, as useful as free radical phenylation.

Friedel–Crafts methods offer the most direct route to di- and triphenylmethane. Thus, diphenylmethane is prepared by the benzylation of benzene.

$$C_6H_5CH_2Cl + C_6H_6 \xrightarrow[0^\circ]{AlCl_3} C_6H_5CH_2C_6H_5 + HCl$$

Benzylation is not a selective reaction and complex mixtures of isomers are formed in the benzylation of monosubstituted benzenes. Substituted diphenylmethanes are most conveniently prepared via substituted benzyl chlorides.

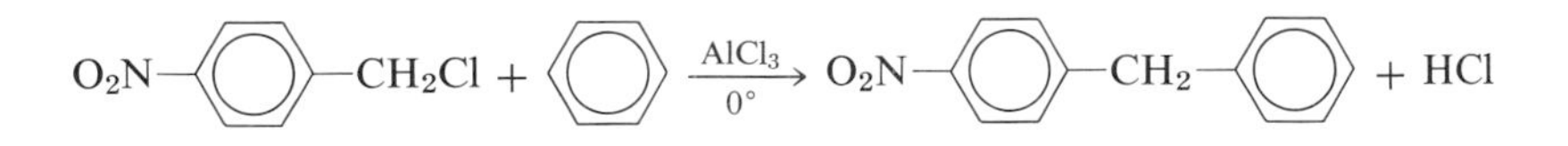

Triphenylmethane is prepared by the reaction of benzene and carbon tetrachloride.

$$3C_6H_6 + CCl_4 \xrightarrow[0^\circ]{AlCl_3} (C_6H_5)_3CCl + 3HCl$$

The desired hydrocarbon may be obtained by the reduction of the chloride. Several methods are available. The reduction of the halide with triphenyltin hydride is one general method.

$$(C_6H_5)_3CCl + (C_6H_5)_3SnH \longrightarrow (C_6H_5)_3CH + (C_6H_5)_3SnCl$$

Tetraphenylmethane and its derivatives are obtained by the alkylation of aniline with triphenylmethyl alcohol. The alcohol is, of course, the hydrolysis product of triphenylmethyl chloride. The intermediate **A** is converted to tetraphenylmethane via the diazonium route.

$$(C_6H_5)_3COH + C_6H_5NH_2 \xrightarrow{HCl} \underset{\mathbf{A}}{(C_6H_5)_3C{-}C_6H_4{-}NH_2} \xrightarrow[2)\ H_3PO_2]{1)\ HNO_2,\ 0^\circ} (C_6H_5)_4C$$

7.5 THE ARYL HALIDES

The preparative chemistry and reaction chemistry of the aryl halides was outlined in Chapters 3 and 5. Only a few additional illustrations will be presented here. Many of the *p*-dihalobenzenes may be prepared by catalytic halogenation.

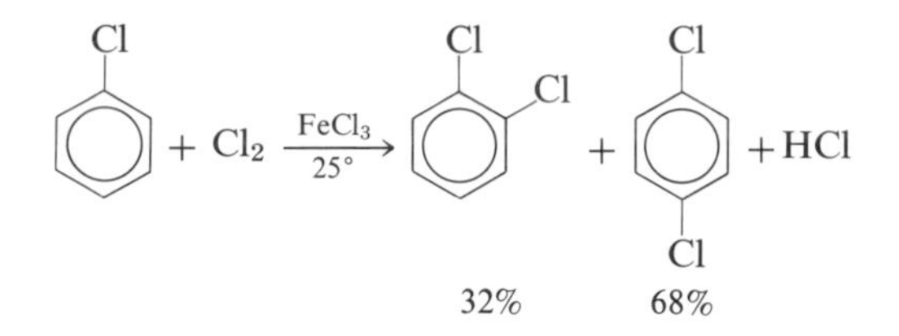

This procedure is satisfactory because the *para* isomer is a solid that may be separated and purified by crystallization. *p*-Dichlorobenzene, a useful mothicide, is prepared in this way. The *ortho* isomer obtained as a by-product is purified by fractionation of the liquid residue. The diazonium route is, however, the method of choice for the preparation of pure samples of the *ortho* and *meta* isomers of the dihalobenzenes.

Another insecticide, DDT, is produced from chlorobenzene and chloral hydrate.

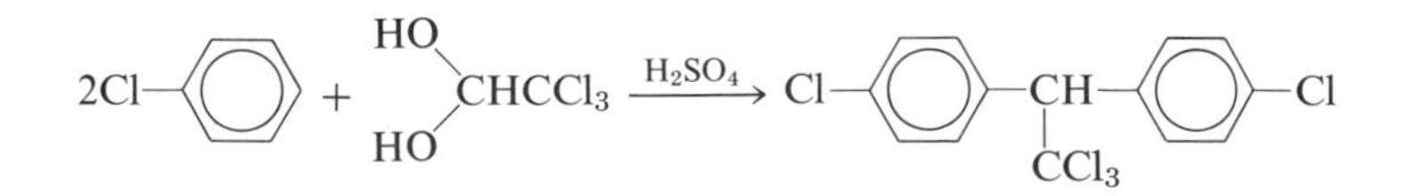

This reaction is another of the Friedel–Crafts series proceeding via carbonium ion intermediates.

Iodobenzene and its derivatives frequently do not react in the conventional way. One problem is that I^+ is a quite stable cation and the iodine atom rather than a hydrogen atom may be replaced by the cationic reagent.

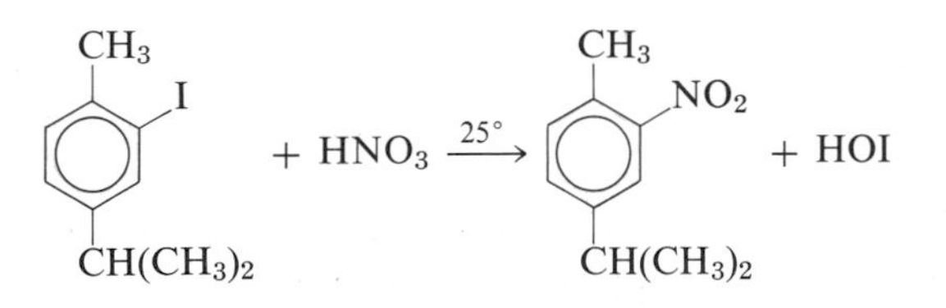

A second problem encountered with iodobenzene is that the reagent may react with the iodine atom. For example, iodobenzene dichloride is produced when iodobenzene reacts with chlorine.

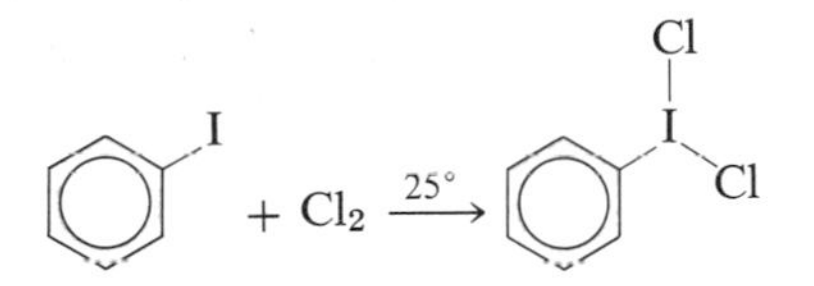

Organometallic reagents prepared from haloaromatic compounds provide a convenient route for the synthesis of other derivatives. Magnesium and lithium compounds are easily formed from aryl bromides and iodides.

$$C_6H_5Br + Mg \xrightarrow[35^\circ]{\text{ether}} C_6H_5MgBr$$

$$C_6H_5I + 2Li \xrightarrow[35^\circ]{\text{ether}} C_6H_5Li + LiI$$

These reagents enable the introduction of the phenyl group into a variety of compounds that are useful for the preparation of side-chain derivatives.

$$C_6H_5MgBr + H_3C\overset{\overset{\displaystyle O}{\|}}{C}CH_3 \xrightarrow[35^\circ]{\text{ether}} C_6H_5\overset{\overset{\displaystyle OH}{|}}{C}(CH_3)_2$$

$$C_6H_5Li + H_3CCH_2CHO \xrightarrow[35^\circ]{\text{ether}} C_6H_5\overset{\overset{\displaystyle OH}{|}}{C}HCH_2CH_3$$

$$2C_6H_5MgBr + H_3CCO_2C_2H_5 \xrightarrow[35^\circ]{\text{ether}} (C_6H_5)_2\overset{\overset{\displaystyle OH}{|}}{C}CH_3$$

7.6 AROMATIC AMINES AND NITRO COMPOUNDS

These compounds occupy a central position in the synthetic chemistry of benzene. The importance of the nitro derivatives stems from their ease of preparation and purification, their activating influence on nucleophilic substitution reactions, and their convenient reduction to amines. The aromatic amines, in turn, are readily converted to diazonium compounds providing an important method for the introduction of other substituents. Moreover, these amines exhibit a versatile chemistry originating in the basic and nucleophilic properties of the amino group and the highly activated aromatic nucleus.

Electrophilic nitration is the most direct and generally most useful method for the introduction of the nitro group. Even when isomeric products form, nitration offers a practical synthetic method because the products are usually solids that may be purified by crystallization. A mixture of nitric and sulfuric acids is the conventional reagent for the nitration of benzene derivatives of intermediate reactivity, the halobenzenes, the alkylbenzenes, and similar compounds. A mixture of fuming nitric acid and sulfuric acid is necessary for the nitration of less reactive compounds such as nitrobenzene.

$$C_6H_5NO_2 + \underset{\text{(fuming)}}{HNO_3} \xrightarrow[95^\circ]{H_2SO_4} \underset{80\%}{C_6H_4(NO_2)_2} + H_2O$$

The nitration of phenol and aniline present some special problems. Precautions are necessary to avoid the nitric acid oxidation of these aromatic nuclei. Phenol is nitrated by dilute nitric acid to yield both the *ortho* and *para* isomers.

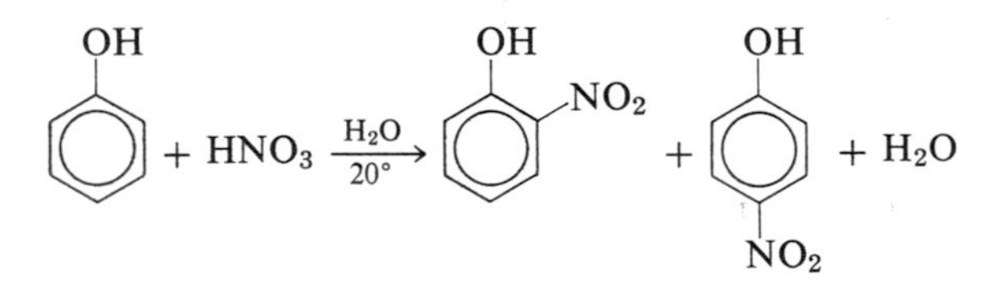

The mononitrophenols can be separated and purified by steam distillation of the reaction mixture. The *ortho* isomer is quite volatile because a strong intramolecular hydrogen bond forms.

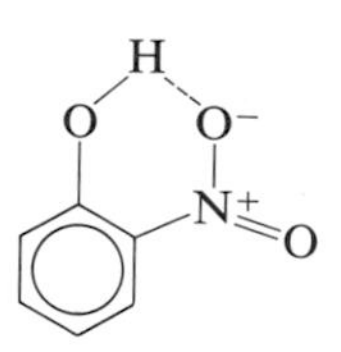

The *para* isomer is much less volatile and remains in the distillation flask because the hydrogen bond forms intermolecularly.

The basic amino group of aniline is protonated in the mixed acid. The rate of nitration of the anilinium ion is quite slow and the three isomeric compounds are formed.

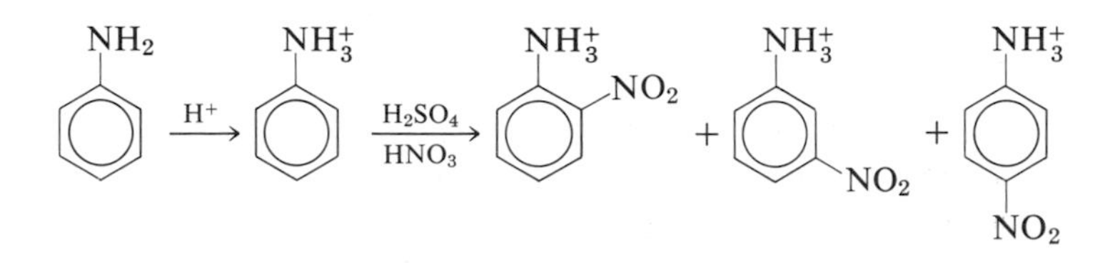

The conversion of aniline to acetanilide avoids this problem. It yields the *ortho* and *para* derivatives. The free amines are readily obtained by the hydrolysis of the nitroacetanilides.

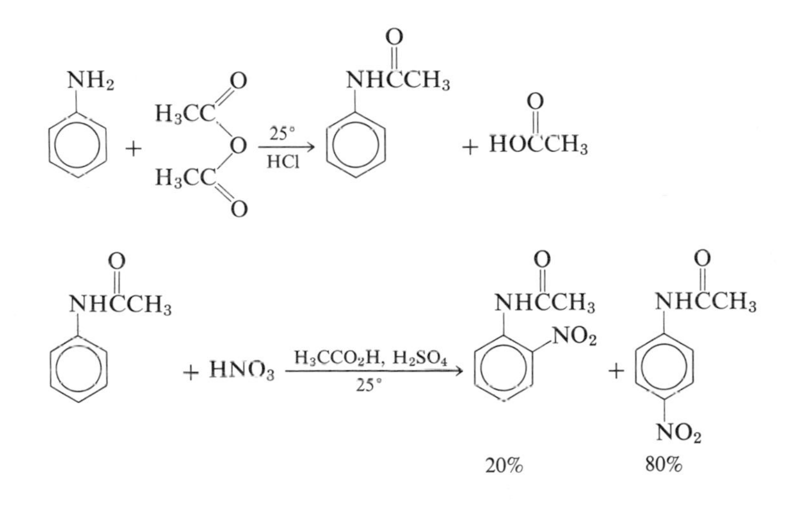

Nitro compounds that are not available through direct substitution reactions often may be prepared by the diazonium route; for example, *o*- and *p*-dinitrobenzene are synthesized from *o*- and *p*-nitroaniline by this method, Sec. 5.5. These same dinitro compounds may be prepared by a highly specific oxidation reaction with peroxytrifluoroacetic acid.

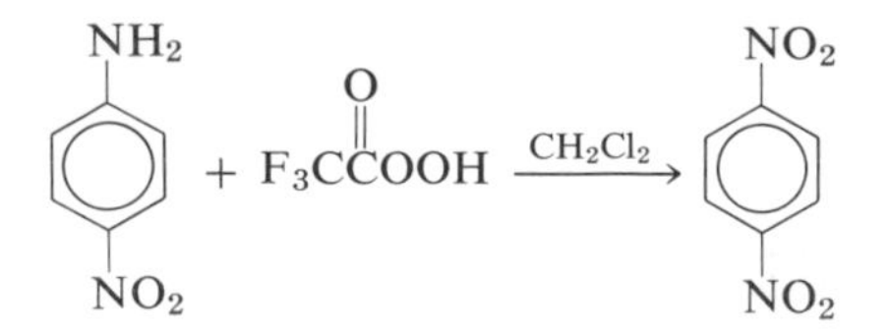

Aromatic nitro compounds are easily reduced to the corresponding anilines. Typical reagents are illustrated in the equation.

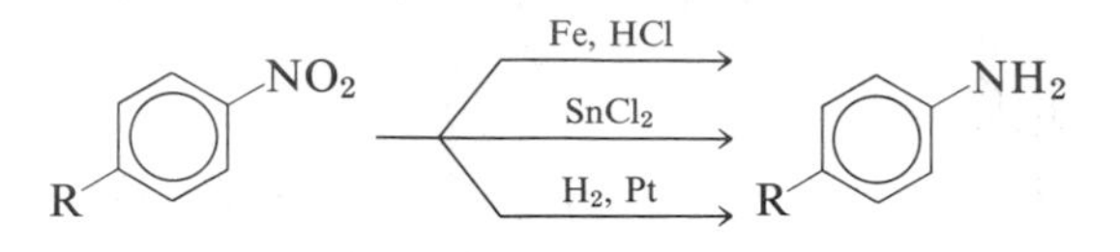

There are several intermediate oxidation states between nitrobenzene and aniline. The compounds corresponding to these oxidation states are prepared by specific methods as shown in Table 7.1. Each of these substances exhibits a rich chemistry. The double bond in azobenzene, for

Table 7-1

REDUCTION PRODUCTS OF NITROBENZENE

Reduction product	Structure	Preparation
Nitrosobenzene	N=O:	PhNHOH + $Na_2Cr_2O_7$, H_2SO_4
Phenylhydroxylamine	NHOH	$PhNO_2$ + Zn, NH_4Cl, H_2O
Azoxybenzene	N=N⁺–O⁻	$PhNO_2$ + glucose, NaOH, H_2O
Azobenzene	N=N	$PhNO_2$ + $LiAlH_4$
Hydrazobenzene	NHNH	$PhNO_2$ + Zn, NaOH, ROH

example, restricts rotation; *cis*- and *trans*-azobenzene are known. The *trans* isomer is, like *trans*-stilbene, thermodynamically more stable. The *cis* isomer may be prepared by photochemical isomerization.

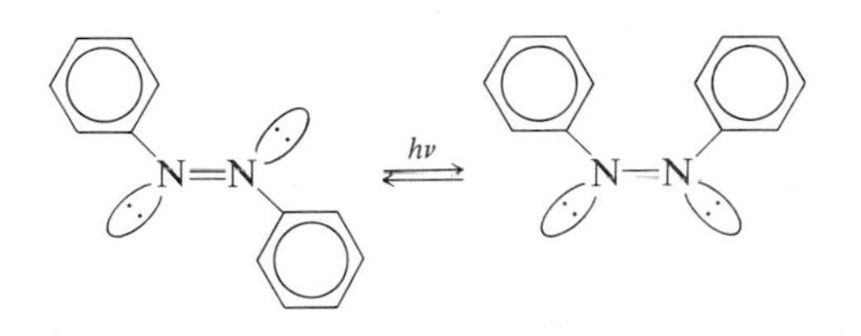

The *cis* isomer spontaneously converts to the *trans* isomer in solution. The interesting rearrangement of hydrazobenzene was discussed in Sec. 6.3.

The direct introduction of the amino group via an electrophilic reaction is not, as yet, a practical synthetic method. Anilines are usually prepared by reduction of nitro compounds as noted above. Some selective reduction reactions are known. One very useful example is the formation of *m*-nitroaniline from *m*-dinitrobenzene.

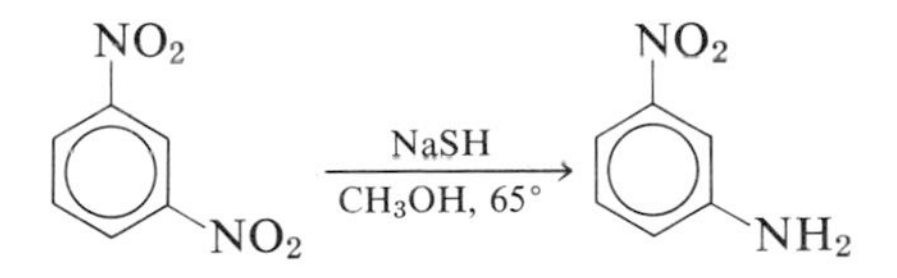

Alternative methods are sometimes quite useful, for example, the aromatic S_N2 reaction of activated halides.

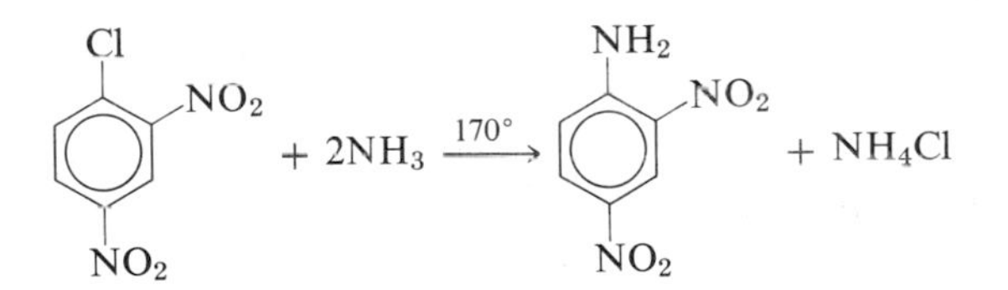

The Hofmann and Beckmann rearrangement reactions also provide the amines. These synthetic methods enable the preparation of a host of different aromatic amines. Subsequent replacement reactions via the diazonium compounds permit the synthesis of virtually any substituted benzene.

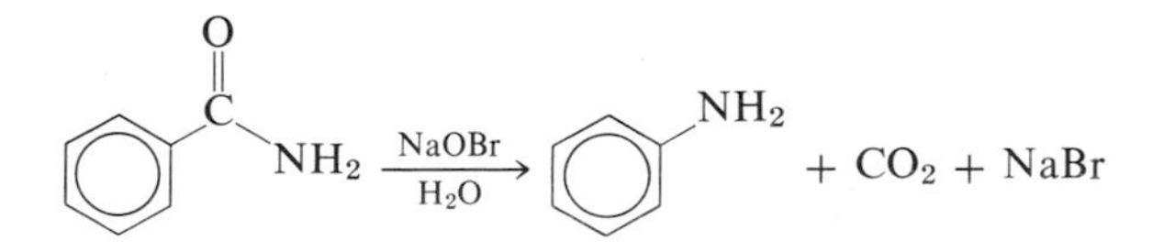

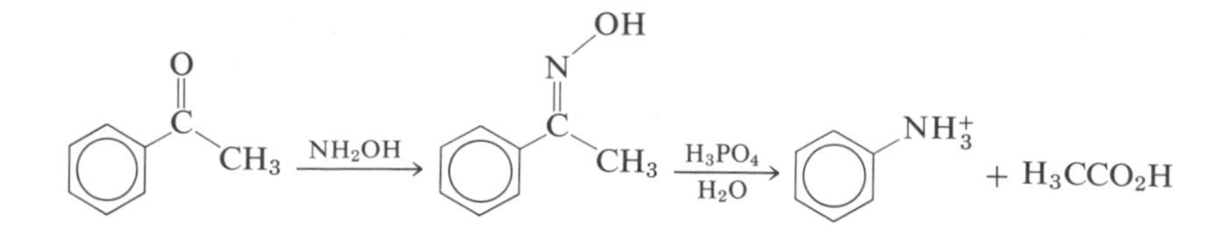

The aryl amines are both basic and nucleophilic. Accordingly, these compounds form salts and may be used as nucleophiles to displace groups from saturated carbon atoms,

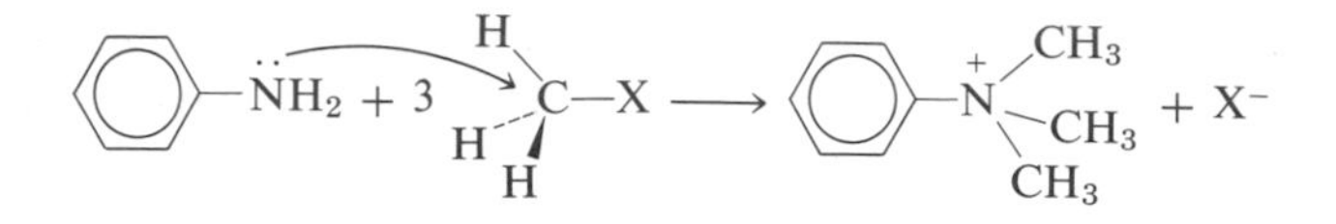

and to add to carbonyl carbon atoms,

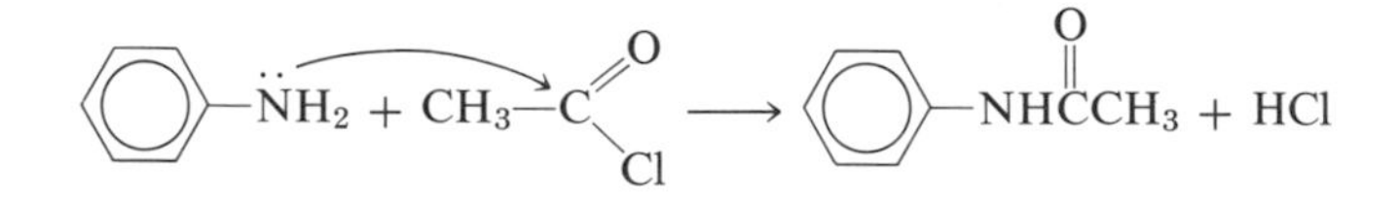

These aspects of the chemistry of the aryl amines are discussed by W. H. Saunders, *Ionic Aliphatic Reactions,* and C. D. Gutsche, *Chemistry of Carbonyl Compounds* (both books this series).

7.7 PHENOL AND ITS DERIVATIVES

Phenol is a weakly acidic ($pK_A = 9.95$), highly reactive compound. The importance of phenol as an intermediate has led to the development of several commercial methods for its preparation. The aromatic S_N2 reaction of hydroxide ion with chlorobenzene (Sec. 5.3) is one route. A side reaction in this process, the S_N2 displacement of the product (phenoxide ion) on chlorobenzene, yields diphenyl ether. This ether and its chlorinated derivatives are useful heat transfer agents.

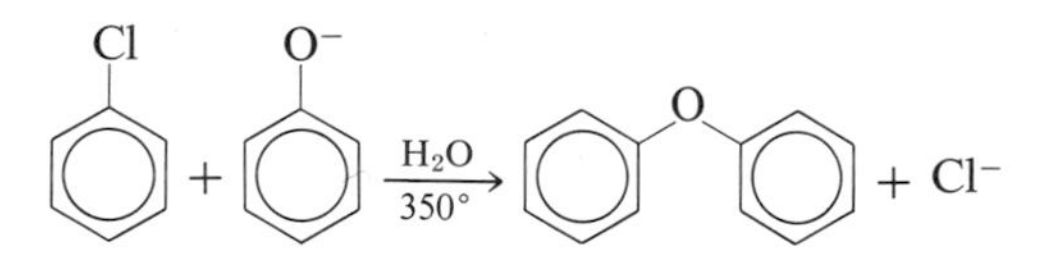

The oxidation of cumene is another commercial method for the synthesis of phenol. This process takes advantage of the high reactivity of the *tertiary,* benzylic hydrogen atom of cumene. Cumene is oxidized to the hydroperoxide in a free radical process.

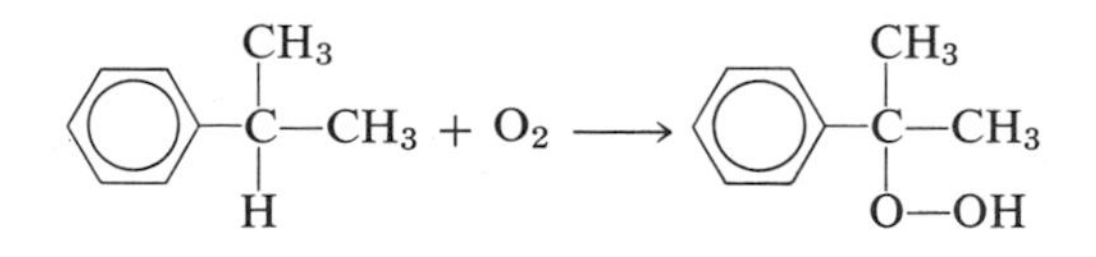

The hydroperoxide is transformed to phenol and acetone via an acid-catalyzed rearrangement reaction in which the phenyl group migrates to the formally electron deficient oxygen atom to yield the resonance stabilized ion.

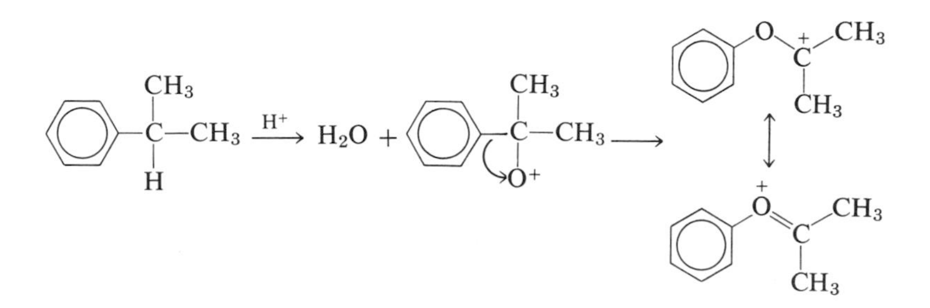

Hydrolysis of the ion yields phenol and acetone.

$$C_6H_5\text{—}O\text{—}\overset{+}{C}(CH_3)_2 + H_2O \longrightarrow C_6H_5OH + H^+ + O{=}C(CH_3)_2$$

Several laboratory methods for the preparation of phenol were discussed in Chapter 5. These nucleophilic substitution reactions involve the fusion of the sodium salt of a benzenesulfonic acid with sodium hydroxide, the displacement of a halide ion from a halobenzene derivative, or the decomposition of a diazonium salt in acid solution. Many phenolic compounds may be prepared in reactions of this kind.

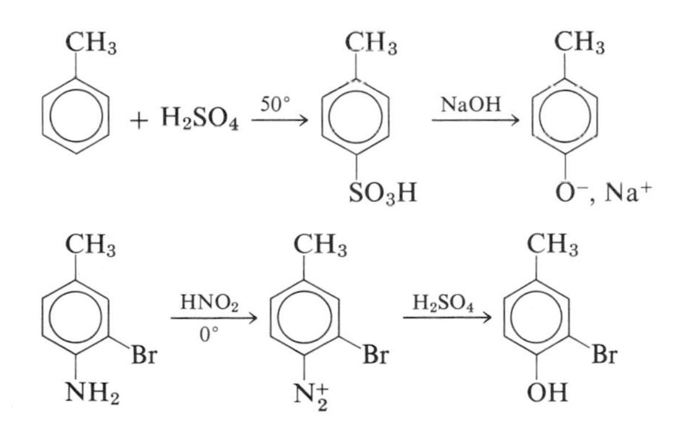

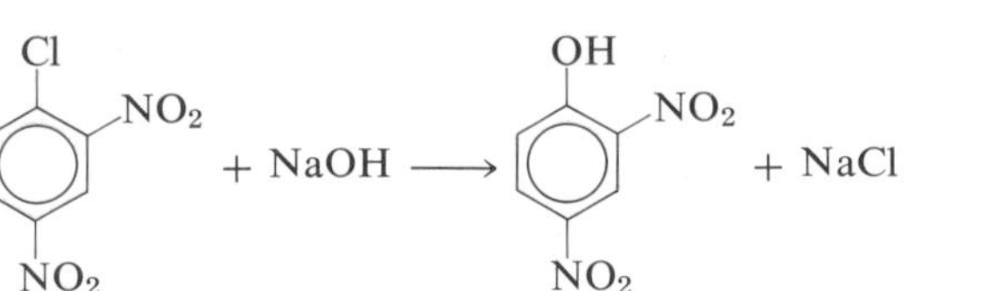

The high reactivity of phenol and its facile oxidation make electrophilic substitution reactions both easy and difficult. Under mild conditions, one halogen atom may be introduced via an electrophilic substitution reaction.

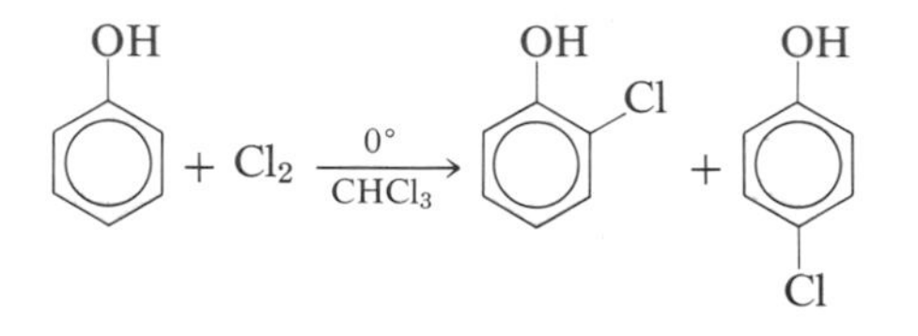

However, the use of excess reagent leads rapidly to the trihalo derivative, as illustrated for the bromination reaction.

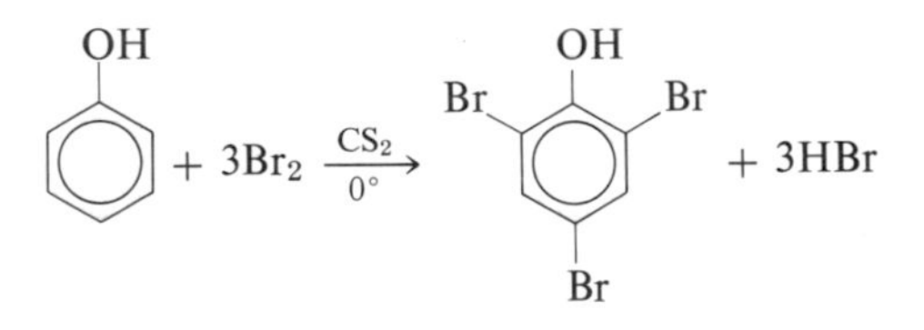

The nitration reaction was discussed on p. 128, there is an alternative route for the preparation of *p*-nitrophenol that avoids both the concomitant formation of *o*-nitrophenol and the oxidation of phenol. Phenol is nitrosated and *p*-nitrosophenol is then oxidized under mild conditions.

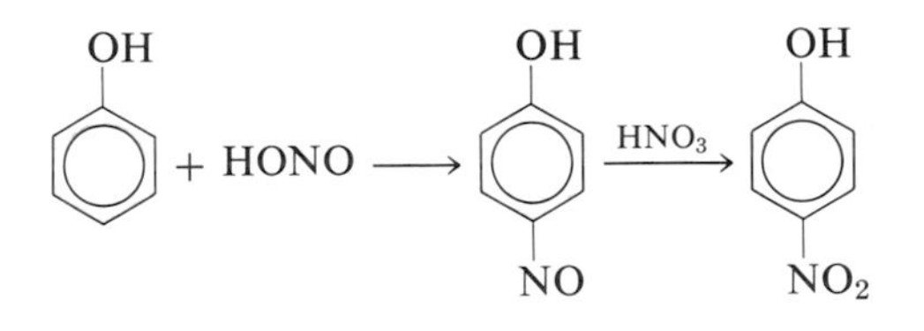

The successful nitrosation reaction involving a feebly electrophilic reagent reflects the ease with which phenol undergoes electrophilic substitution reactions. Phenol may also be alkylated; but the reaction is not always successful. One process that is important is the *t*-butylation of phenol or *p*-methylphenol to 2,6-di-*t*-butyl derivatives.

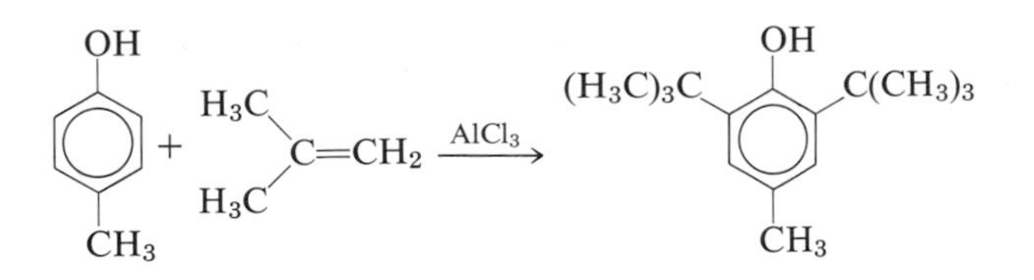

These compounds exhibit the important property of inhibiting oxidation reactions and are often added to stabilize compounds that are easily oxidized in air. The Friedel–Crafts acetylation of phenol is rarely attempted because the Fries rearrangement, Sec. 6.2, provides a convenient approach for the synthesis of the ketones. Phenol reacts with formaldehyde to yield the Bakelite polymers in another reaction of the Friedel–Crafts type. Protonation of the aldehyde yields the carbonium ion that alkylates phenol to yield *o*- and *p*-hydroxymethylphenols. The acid-catalyzed ionization of the benzyl alcohol derivative yields a new carbonium ion which in turn alkylates phenol. With excess formaldehyde, this product is alkylated further to yield a highly cross-linked polymer of high molecular weight. The polymer is known as a phenol-formaldehyde resin or Bakelite.

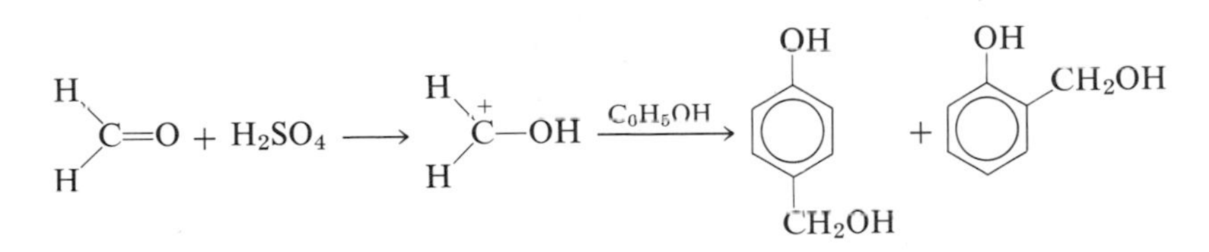

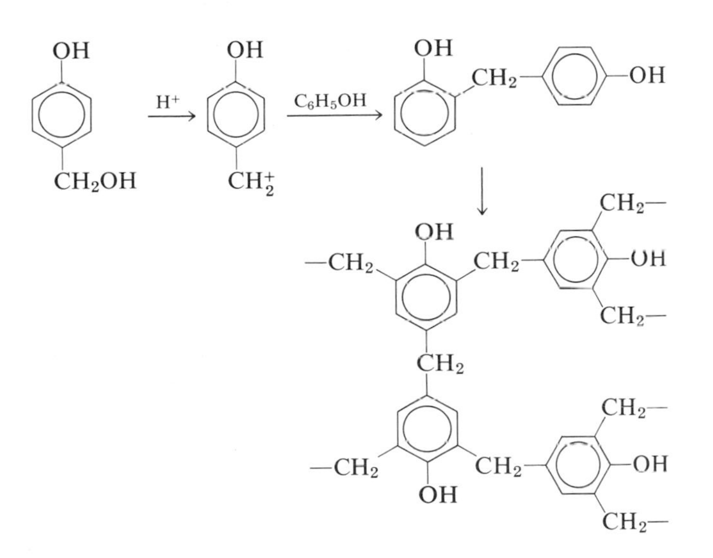

The stabilization of the benzenonium ion intermediate by the hydroxy group greatly facilitates these electrophilic substitution reactions. The phenoxide ion is, of course, even more reactive in electrophilic reactions since a neutral molecule is produced in the reaction.

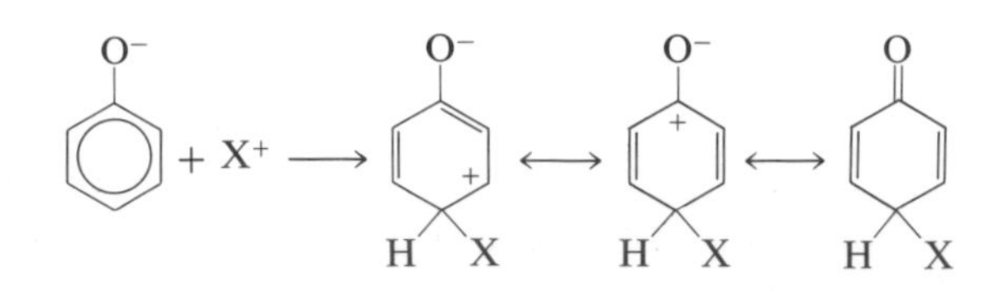

Two other reactions depend on this characteristic. Thus, the sodium salt of phenol reacts with carbon dioxide to yield sodium salicylate.

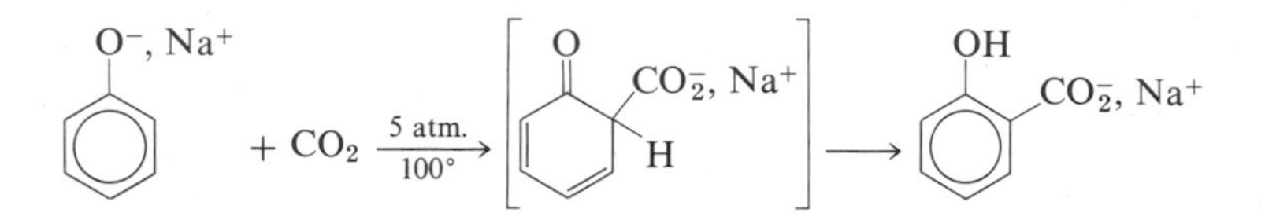

This method for the synthesis of phenolic acids is known as the Kolbe reaction. In another process, the Reimer—Tiemann reaction, the sodium salt reacts with the weakly electrophilic dichlorocarbene to form 30% *o*- and 70% *p*-hydroxybenzaldehyde.

$$HCCl_3 + NaOH \longrightarrow NaCl + H_2O + :CCl_2$$

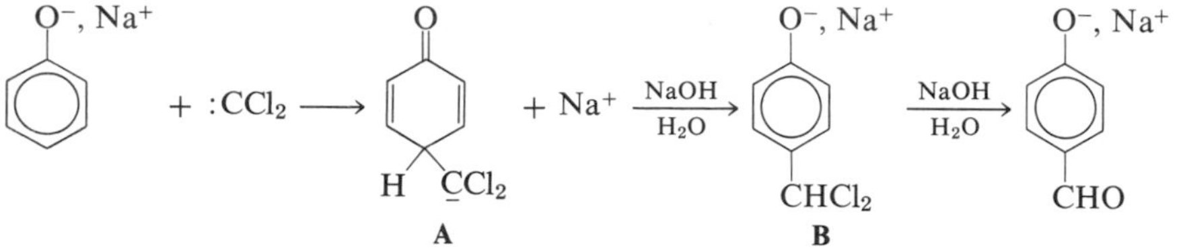

$$C_6H_5O^-, Na^+ + :CCl_2 \longrightarrow \underset{\mathbf{A}}{\text{(O=C}_6\text{H}_4\text{(H)CCl}_2)} + Na^+ \xrightarrow[H_2O]{NaOH} \underset{\mathbf{B}}{p\text{-}(O^-, Na^+)C_6H_4CHCl_2} \xrightarrow[H_2O]{NaOH} p\text{-}(O^-, Na^+)C_6H_4CHO$$

The carbene is generated from chloroform and substitutes the reactive phenoxide anion to form dieneone **A**. **A** spontaneously converts to **B**, and **B** hydrolyzes to form the aldehyde under the conditions of the reaction.

The oxygen atom of phenol with two unshared electron pairs is nucleophilic. Accordingly, ethers are produced by nucleophilic substitution reactions. Anisole, for example, is prepared from sodium phenoxide and dimethyl sulfate or methyl iodide.

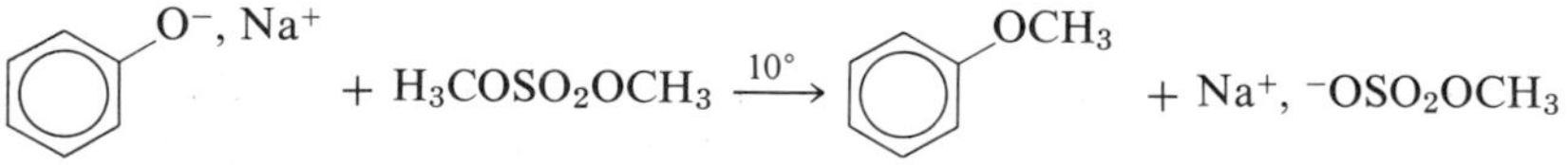

$$C_6H_5O^-, Na^+ + H_3COSO_2OCH_3 \xrightarrow{10^\circ} C_6H_5OCH_3 + Na^+, {}^-OSO_2OCH_3$$

The broad-leafed weed killer, 2,4-D, is prepared in a similar nucleophilic substitution reaction.

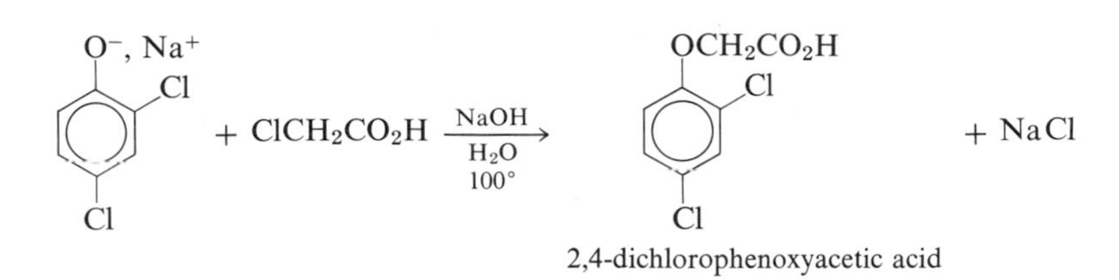

The phenolic hydroxy group also reacts with carbonyl compounds. Aspirin is produced by the acetylation of salicyclic acid with acetic anhydride.

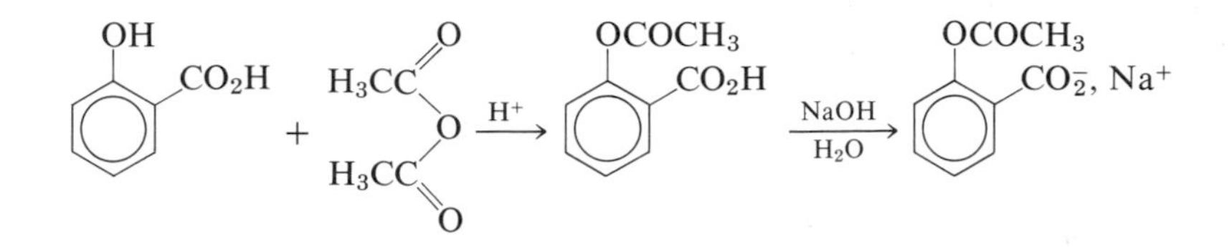

These reactions illustrate the fact that there are no important differences in the reactions of the phenolic hydroxyl group and the reactions of aliphatic alcohols.

The three dihydroxybenzenes are synthesized by methods that are similar to the techniques useful for the preparation of phenol. Catechol, the *ortho* isomer, is obtained by the aromatic S_N2 reaction of hydroxide ion with either *o*-dichlorobenzene or *o*-chlorophenol.

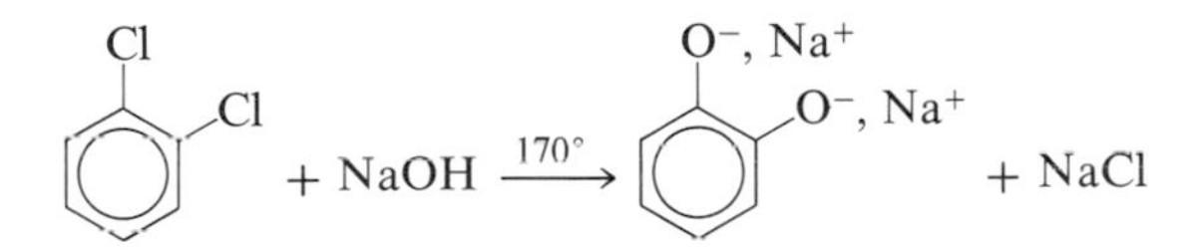

Resorcinol, the *meta* isomer, is conveniently prepared by the disulfonation of benzene and subsequent fusion of the *m*-disulfonic acid with sodium hydroxide.

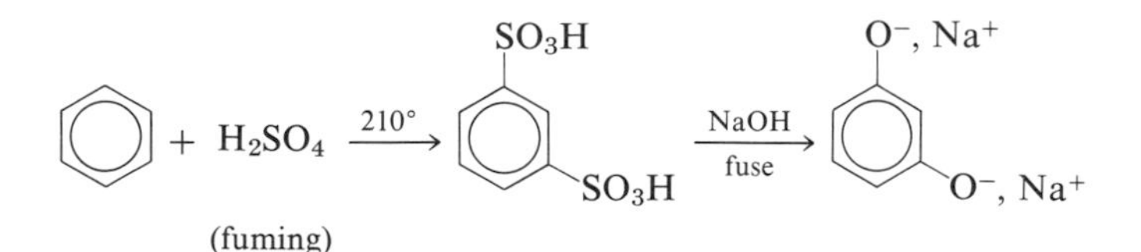

The hydroxy compounds are liberated by treatment of these sodium salts with acid. The *para* isomer, hydroquinone, is produced by the oxidation of aniline in acidic solution. The oxidation yields quinone, which is reduced to the dihydroxy compound with sulfur dioxide.

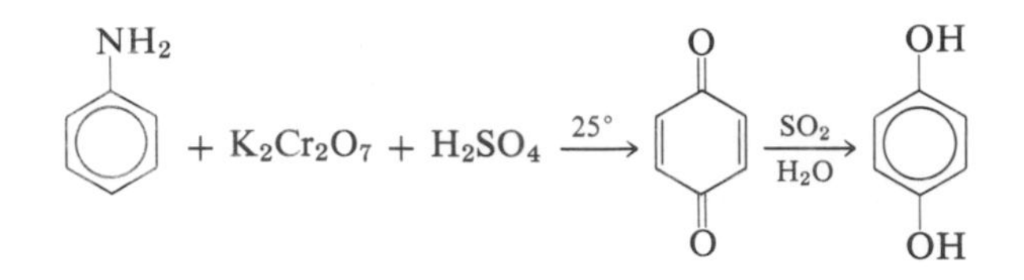

These dihydroxybenzenes are easily substituted in electrophilic reactions. Resorcinol, for example, reacts with caproic acid (rather than the acid chloride) to yield 2,4-dihydroxyphenyl *n*-pentyl ketone in the presence of the mild Lewis acid, zinc chloride. Reduction of the carbonyl compound gives 4-*n*-hexylresorcinol, a disinfectant.

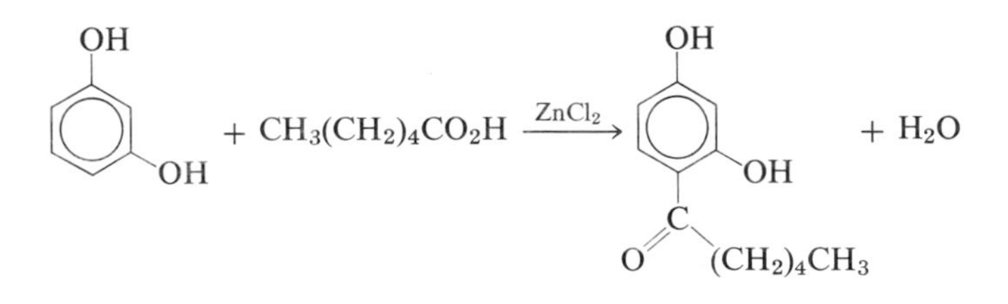

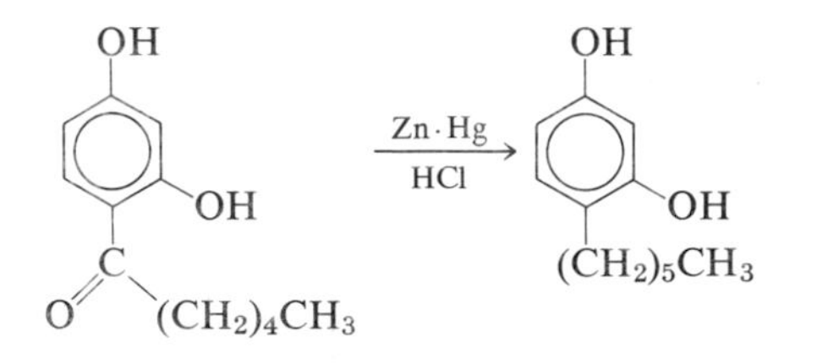

The monomethylation of catechol yields guaiacol, which may also be obtained from natural sources. Vanillin, the principal of the vanilla bean, is obtained from the ether through the Reimer–Tiemann reaction.

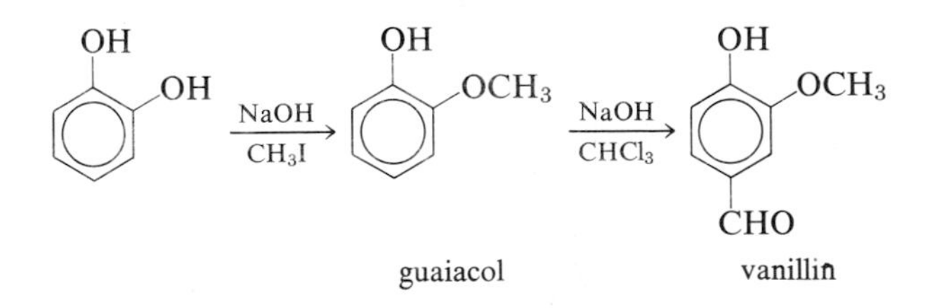

Other derivatives of catechol are found in important natural products.

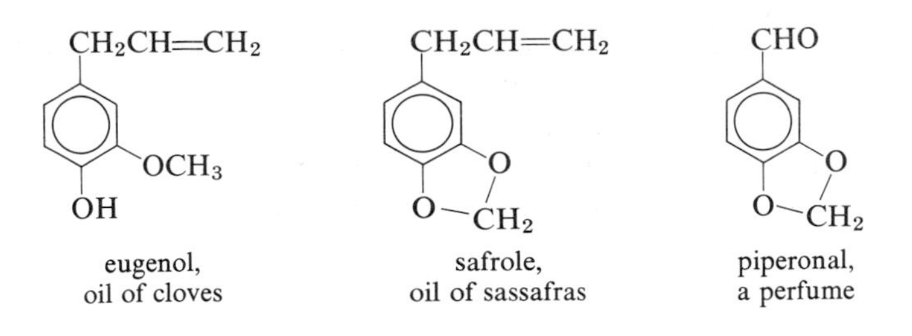

eugenol, oil of cloves — safrole, oil of sassafras — piperonal, a perfume

7.8 AROMATIC CARBOXYLIC ACIDS, ALDEHYDES, AND KETONES

Aromatic compounds with a carbonyl group bonded to the aromatic nucleus are key intermediates for the preparation of other side-chain derivatives. The reaction chemistry of these acids, aldehydes, and ketones does not differ from the reaction chemistry of other aliphatic compounds of the same functional type; this aspect of their chemistry is discussed by C. D. Gutsche in *The Chemistry of Carbonyl Compounds* (this series). In this section, attention will be focused on the methods that are available for the synthesis of these benzene derivatives.

Benzoic acid and its derivatives may be prepared from aryl halides via Grignard or lithium reagents, p. 127; by the hydrolysis of aryl cyanides, p. 96; by the hydrolysis of benzotrichloride, p. 123; by oxidation of an alkylbenzene, p. 123; or by the haloform reaction of an alkyl aryl ketone. These diverse methods enable the preparation of virtually any derivative of benzoic acid. Four examples are presented to illustrate these methods.

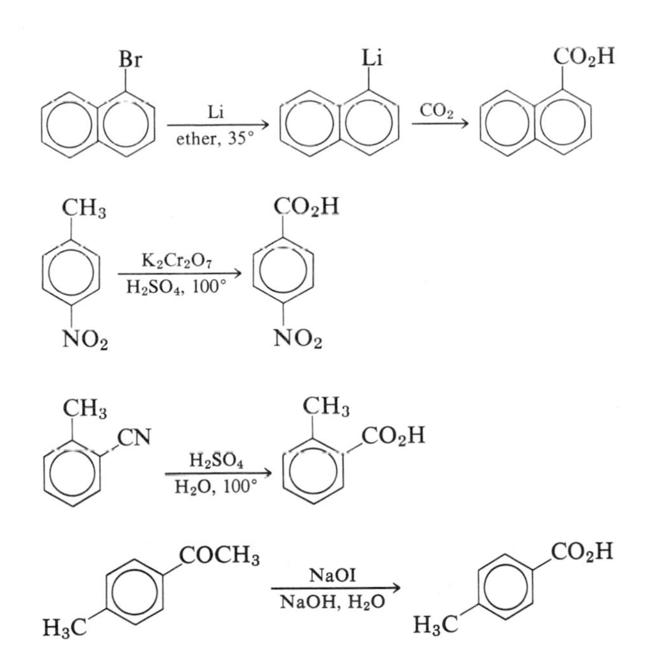

In addition, certain *meta*-substituted benzoic acids may be prepared by electrophilic substitution reactions. Vigorous conditions are necessary for these reactions because the carbonyl group destabilizes the benzenonium ion. Nitration occurs with fuming nitric acid and halogenation occurs with a halogen and silver sulfate in sulfuric acid solution.

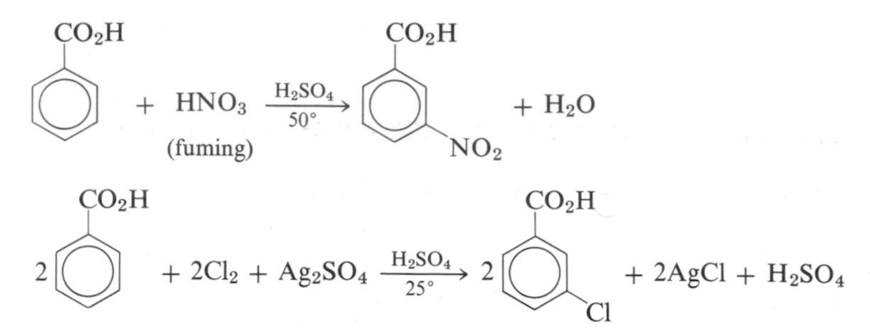

The dicarboxylic acids, phthalic acid and terephthalic acid, are important intermediates in the synthetic polymer industry. Both are prepared on a large scale by the oxidation of simple aromatic hydrocarbons. Phthalic acid is produced by the catalytic air oxidation of either *o*-xylene or naphthalene.

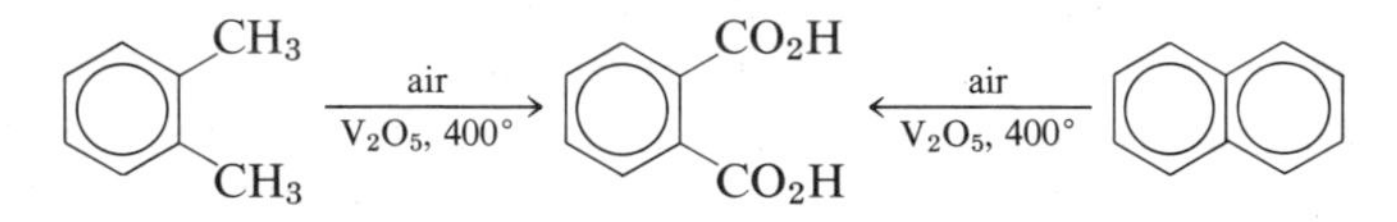

p-Xylene is converted to terephthalic acid by oxidation in the presence of a copper bromide catalyst.

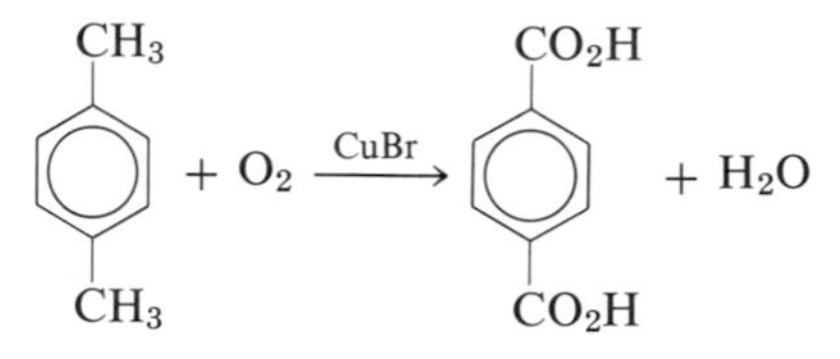

The polymer, Dacron, is a derivative of terephthalic acid.

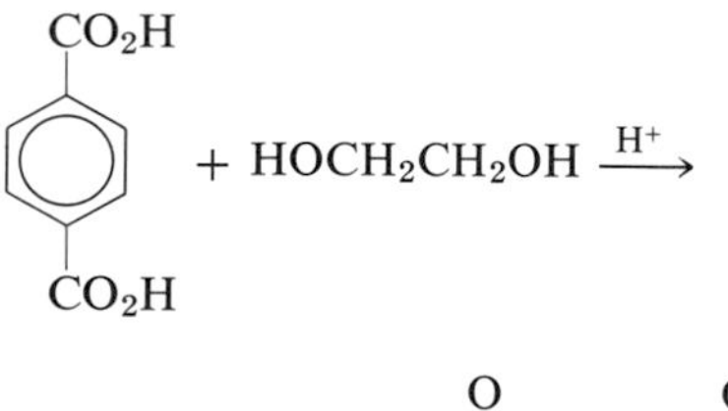

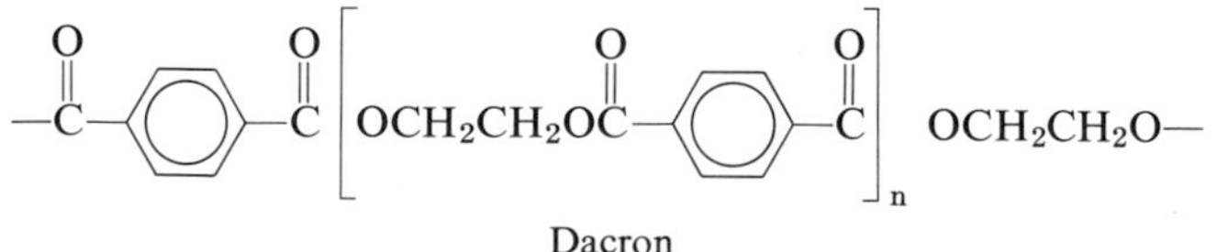

Dacron

Phthalic acid is used for the preparation of several other useful polymers. This acid is also a useful intermediate for the preparation of polynuclear aromatic compounds. The Friedel–Crafts acylation reaction between the acid and benzene leads first to *o*-benzoylbenzoic acid and then to anthraquinone. Other quinones may be prepared in similar reactions.

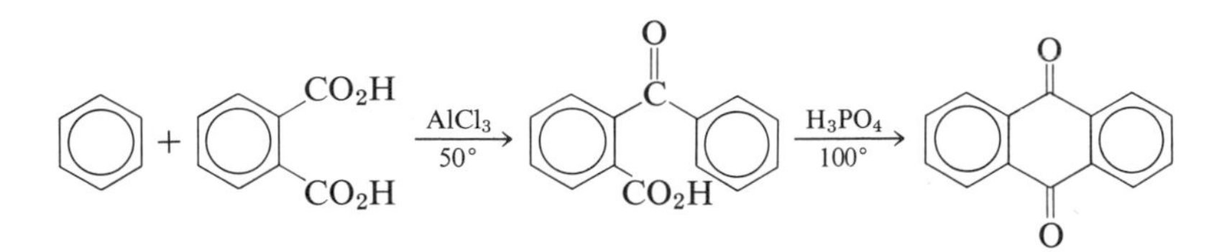

Reduction of these quinones yields the polynuclear aromatic hydrocarbons.

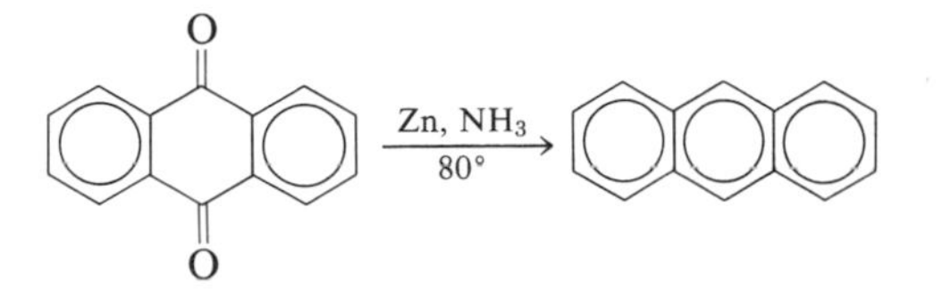

Benzaldehyde and the other aryl aldehydes may be prepared in a variety of different ways. These aldehydes are extremely useful synthetically because they are readily converted to alcohols by reduction and to acids by oxidation; and they possess a highly reactive carbonyl group that undergoes nucleophilic addition reactions. Toluene is the starting material in the principal industrial method that proceeds through the hydrolysis of benzal chloride, p. 123. The direct Friedel–Crafts formylation reaction employing carbon monoxide and hydrogen chloride provides the aldehyde in low yield, Sec. 2.7. There are several variations of this approach that employ reagents of the proper oxidation state that may eventually be hydrolyzed to the aldehyde. For example, the aluminum chloride-catalyzed reaction of hydrogen cyanide with benzene yields the aldehyde after hydrolysis.

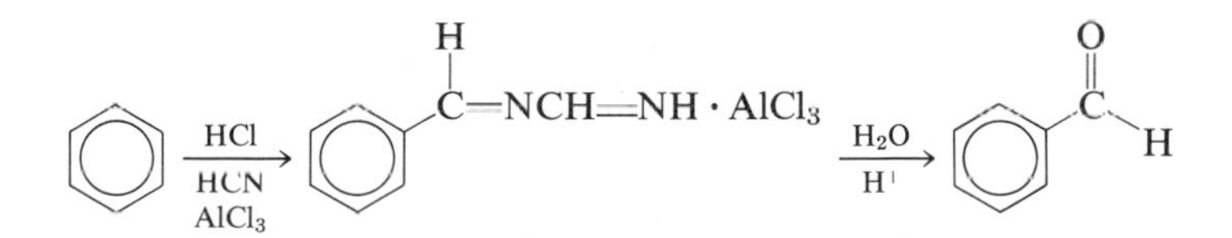

In addition, this aldehyde and its derivatives may be prepared by many of the methods that are useful in the synthesis of aliphatic aldehydes. One most useful approach is by the oxidation of benzyl tosylate (the *p*-methylbenzenesulfonate group) with dimethyl sulfoxide in the presence of base.

The conversion of benzyl tosylate to benzaldehyde illustrates this method. Benzyl alcohol and *p*-toluenesulfonyl chloride react to yield the necessary tosylate. Benzylic alcohols are conveniently prepared by the hydrolysis of benzyl chloride or by the reaction of the phenyl Grignard reagent with formaldehyde.

$$C_6H_5CH_2Cl \xrightarrow{H^+,\ H_2O} C_6H_5CH_2OH$$

$$C_6H_5Br \xrightarrow[2)\ H_2C=O]{1)\ Mg} C_6H_5CH_2OH$$

$$C_6H_5CH_2OH \xrightarrow{C_6H_5SO_2Cl} \underset{\mathbf{A}}{C_6H_5CH_2OSO_2C_6H_4CH_3}$$

When the tosylate is heated in dimethyl sulfoxide, dimethyl sulfoxide displaces the *p*-toluenesulfonate group.

$$\mathbf{A} + (H_3C)_2\overset{+}{S}-\overset{-}{O} \longrightarrow \underset{\mathbf{C}}{C_6H_5CH_2O-\overset{+}{S}(CH_3)_2} + {}^-OSO_2C_6H_4CH_3$$

The base, **B**, in the solution extracts a benzylic proton to produce the oxidation product (the aldehyde) and the reduction product (dimethyl sulfide).

$$\mathbf{C} + \mathbf{B} \longrightarrow \left[C_6H_5\underset{H\cdots\mathbf{B}}{\overset{H}{C}}-O-\overset{+}{S}(CH_3)_2 \right] \longrightarrow C_6H_5CHO + S(CH_3)_2 + \mathbf{BH}^+$$

transition state

The aldehyde may also be obtained through selective reduction reactions as illustrated in the equations.

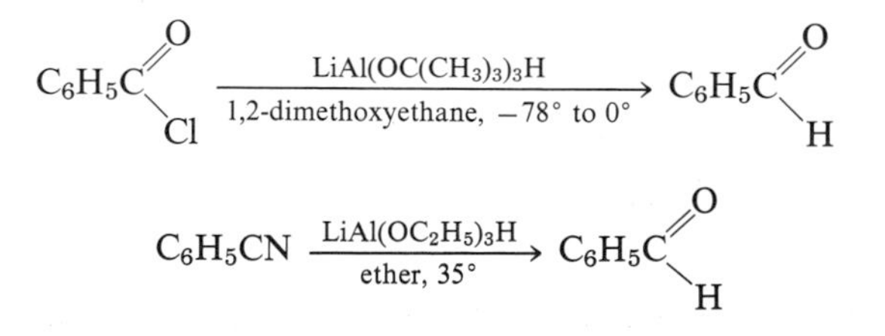

$$C_6H_5COCl \xrightarrow[1,2\text{-dimethoxyethane},\ -78^\circ \text{ to } 0^\circ]{LiAl(OC(CH_3)_3)_3H} C_6H_5CHO$$

$$C_6H_5CN \xrightarrow[\text{ether, } 35^\circ]{LiAl(OC_2H_5)_3H} C_6H_5CHO$$

These new methods permit the synthesis of most aryl aldehydes. Occasionally, it is necessary to carry out a direct substitution reaction. Nitration with fuming acid yields 3-nitrobenzaldehyde. Lewis acid-catalyzed halogenation is ineffective because the catalyst is removed by interaction with the basic carbonyl oxygen atom.

$$C_6H_5C(=O)H + AlCl_3 \longrightarrow C_6H_5C(=\overset{+}{O}-\overset{-}{Al}Cl_3)H$$

Halogenation may be accomplished, however, by a swamping catalyst technique in which a large excess of aluminum chloride is used. Under these conditions the aldehyde is completely converted to the oxonium compound but a sufficient amount of the Lewis acid is available to catalyze the halogenation reaction.

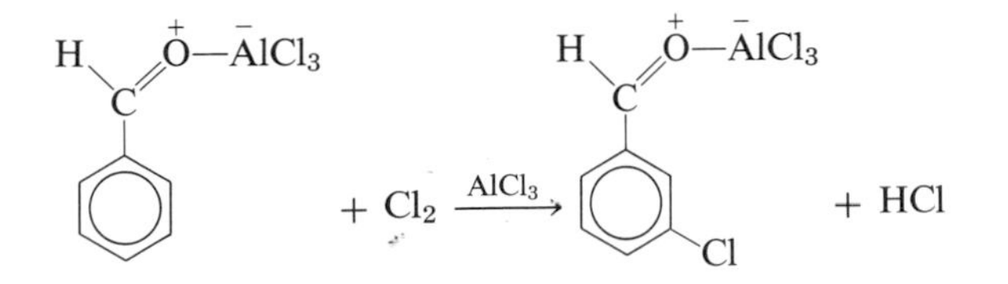

The Friedel–Crafts acylation reaction, Sec. 2.6, is the principal method for the synthesis of phenyl ketones. This reaction is useful for the introduction of acyl groups into benzene and substituted benzenes that are as reactive as the halobenzenes. Thus, monosubstituted benzenes bearing *ortho-para*-directing groups may be acylated. The *para* isomer is usually obtained in high yield.

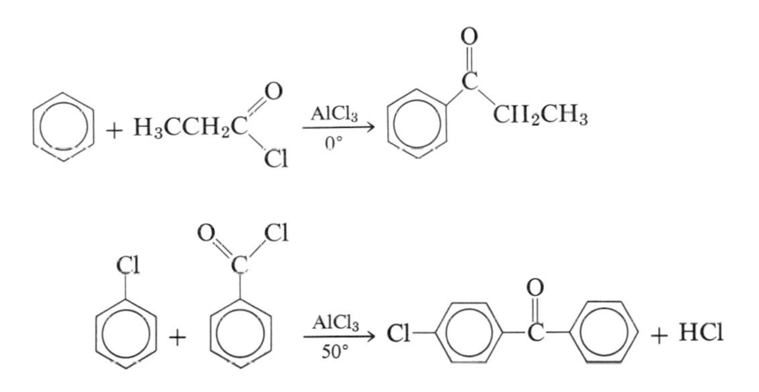

The *ortho* and *meta* derivatives must be prepared in other ways. These compounds are usually obtained by the monoalkylation of benzoic acid derivatives or by the selective oxidation of *secondary* alcohols, as illustrated for *m*- and *p*-chloroacetophenone.

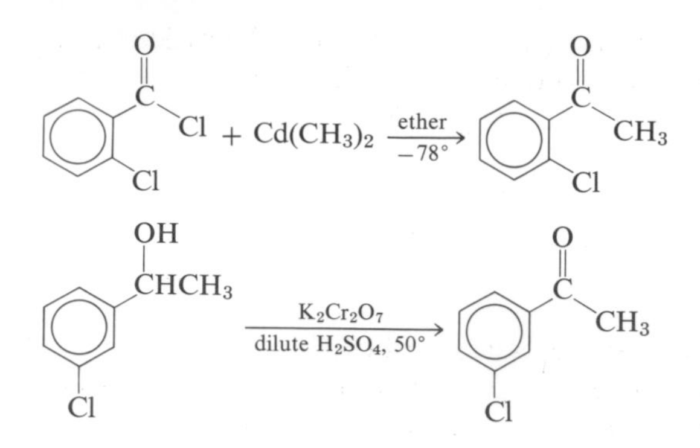

The electrophilic substitution reactions of acetophenone and the other aryl alkyl ketones are complicated by the reactivity of the active hydrogen atoms of the methyl group.

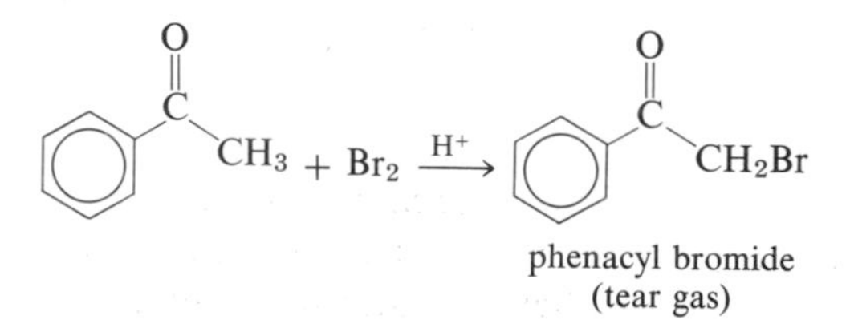

However, the swamping catalyst technique successfully blocks the reaction at the methyl group and permits the synthesis of *m*-bromoacetophenone.

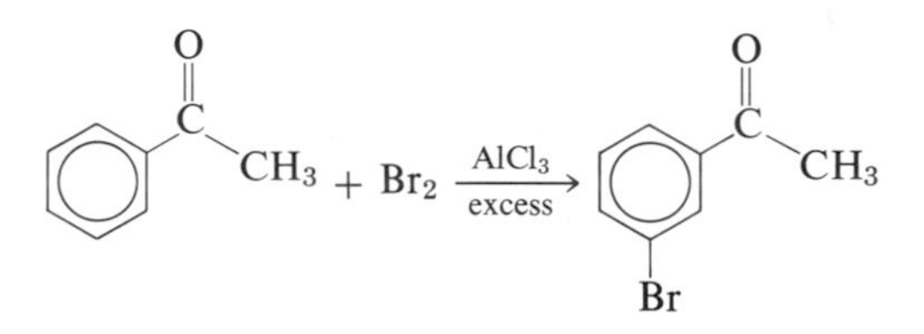

As noted, there are no major differences in the reactions of aromatic aldehydes and ketones and the reactions of aliphatic compounds. The absence of an α-hydrogen atom in the aromatic aldehydes precludes the aldol condensation reaction and the related reactions that require the abstraction of an α-hydrogen atom. Other processes, such as the Cannizzaro reaction or the benzoin condensation, that require the absence of α-hydrogen atoms proceed normally.

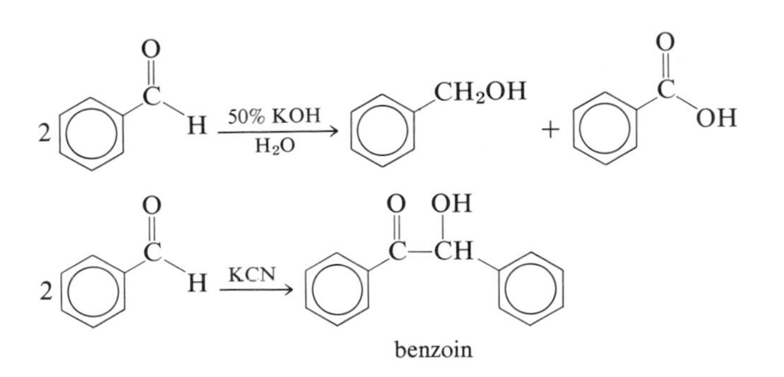

In addition, the reactive carbonyl groups of the aromatic aldehydes and ketones undergo the conventional series of nucleophilic addition reactions. Complex side-chain derivatives may be synthesized through these reactions.

PROBLEMS

7.1. Suggest methods for the synthesis of the following compounds from the starting materials that are indicated. Other inorganic and aliphatic reagents are presumed to be readily available.

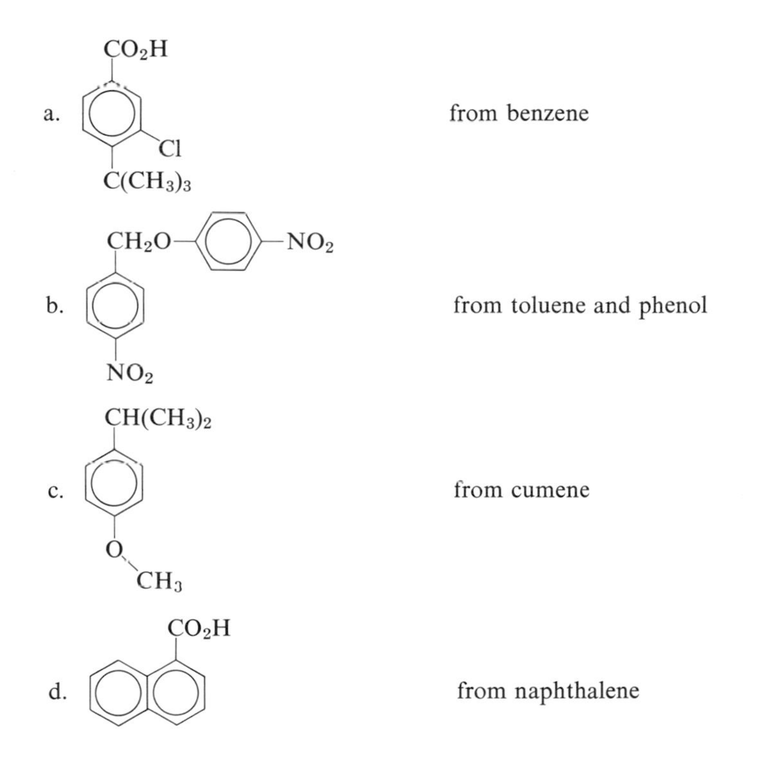

e. 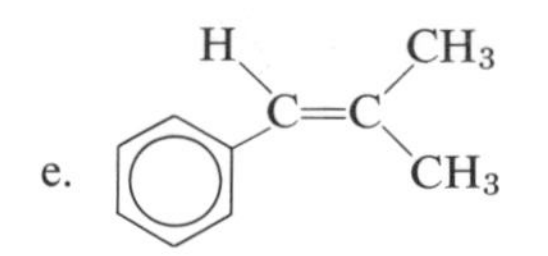

from benzene

f. 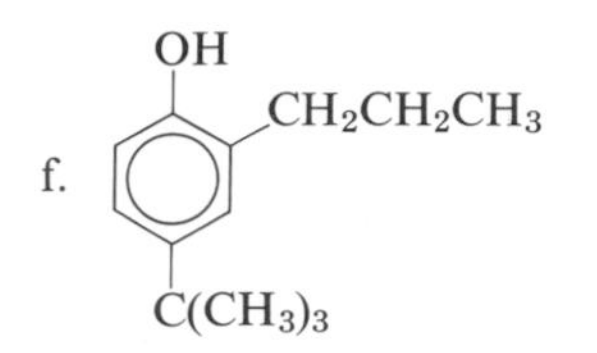

from *t*-butylbenzene

g. 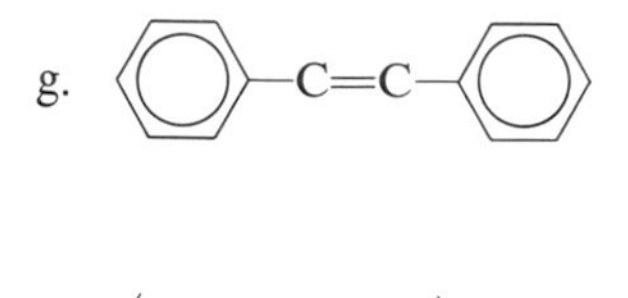

from benzaldehyde

h. 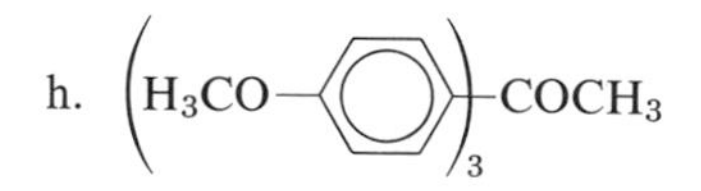

from phenol

i. 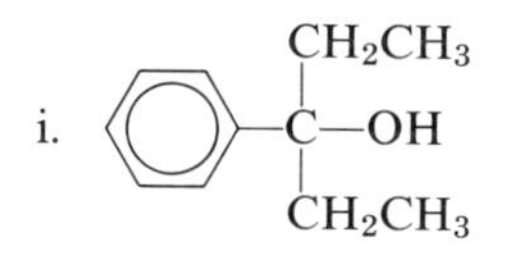

from bromobenzene

j. 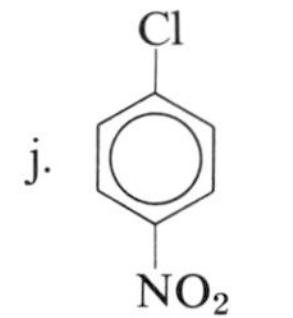

from aniline

k. NO_2, CN from nitrobenzene

l. 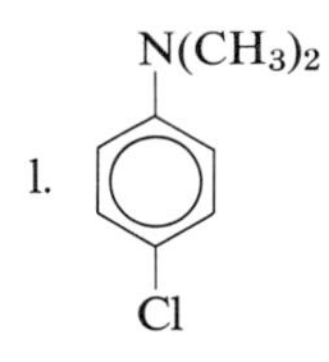

from *p*-chloronitrobenzene

m. 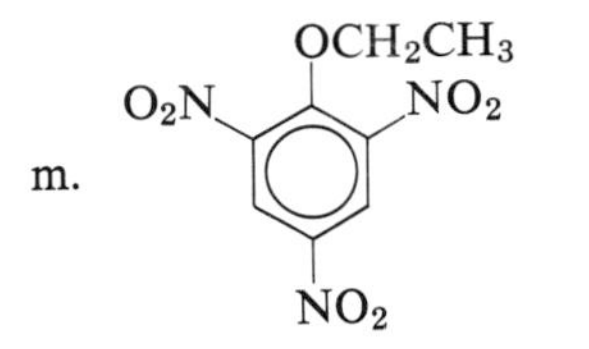

from chlorobenzene

n. 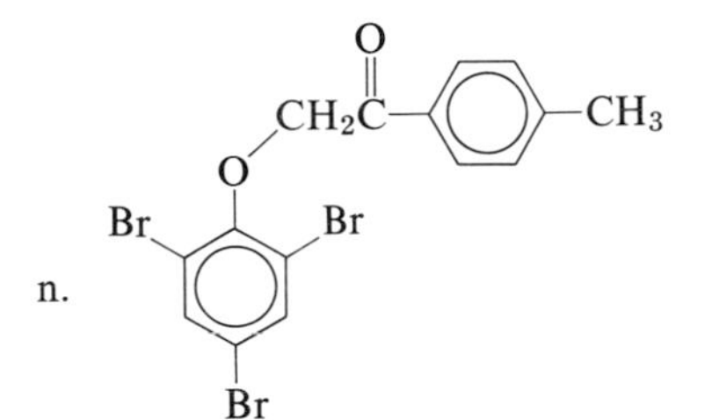

from phenol and toluene

Index†

†For pedagogical reasons, the *o*-, *m*-, *p*-, and the 2-, 3-, 4- nomenclature systems are used interchangeably in the text. However, only the numerical system is used in this index. Thus, *para*-nitrophenol is entered as 4-nitrophenol and *m*-xylene is entered as 1,3-dimethylbenzene.